Introduction to
RIEMANN SURFACES

ADDISON–WESLEY MATHEMATICS SERIES

Eric Reissner, *Consulting Editor*

Apostol—Mathematical Analysis, A Modern Approach to Advanced Calculus

Bardell and Spitzbart—College Algebra

Dadourian—Plane Trigonometry

Davis—Modern College Geometry

Davis—The Teaching of Mathematics

Fuller—Analytic Geometry

Gnedenko and Kolmogorov—Limit Distributions for Sums of Independent Random Variables

Kaplan—Advanced Calculus

Kaplan—A First Course in Functions of a Complex Variable

LeVeque—Topics in Number Theory, Vols. I and II

Martin and Reissner—Elementary Differential Equations

Meserve—Fundamental Concepts of Algebra

Meserve—Fundamental Concepts of Geometry

Munroe—Introduction to Measure and Integration

Perlis—Theory of Matrices

Spitzbart and Bardell—College Algebra and Plane Trigonometry

Spitzbart and Bardell—Plane Trigonometry

Springer—Introduction to Riemann Surfaces

Stabler—An Introduction to Mathematical Thought

Struik—Differential Geometry

Struik—Elementary Analytic and Projective Geometry

Thomas—Calculus

Thomas—Calculus and Analytic Geometry

Vance—Trigonometry

Vance—Unified Algebra and Trigonometry

Wade—The Algebra of Vectors and Matrices

Wilkes, Wheeler, and Gill—The Preparation of Programs for an Electronic Digital Computer

Introduction to
RIEMANN SURFACES

by

GEORGE SPRINGER

Department of Mathematics
University of Kansas

ADDISON-WESLEY PUBLISHING COMPANY, INC.

READING, MASSACHUSETTS, U.S.A.

PREFACE

The reawakening of interest in the subject of Riemann surfaces has brought with it the need for a textbook in English offering an introduction to the field. This book presents a self-contained, modern treatment of the fundamental concepts and basic theorems concerning Riemann surfaces. We assume that the reader is familiar with elementary complex function theory and with some real variables and algebra. Because we shall have to draw heavily from topology and Hilbert space theory, the reader will also find in this book an introduction to these fields, so that no previous knowledge of these subjects is required. This book is not meant to be a survey of the current work being done in the realm of Riemann surfaces, but rather is a modern presentation of the classical theory which will prepare the reader for further study in this and related fields.

Anyone writing a book on Riemann surface theory would certainly be influenced by the magnificient work of Professor Hermann Weyl in his *Idee der Riemannschen Fläche*, which laid the foundations for the theory of abstract Riemann surfaces. I am particularly indebted to this work, for it was there that I had my own introduction to the subject. I have also been very strongly influenced by the lectures on Riemann surfaces delivered by Professor Lars V. Ahlfors at Harvard University in 1948.

The original idea of writing this book came from Dr. L. Geller, who helped lay out the general plan and collaborated in writing Chapters 6 and 7. I am deeply indebted to him both for his help and for his enthusiasm. I wish to express my gratitude to Professor Maxwell Rosenlicht, who contributed numerous suggestions for making the proofs of many theorems more elegant, especially in the chapters on combinatorial topology and abelian integrals. My sincere thanks also go to the many other people who read the manuscript and offered constructive suggestions for improving it.

To find time to write such a book is always a difficult problem, and I am grateful for the C. L. E. Moore Instructorship at the Massachusetts Institute of Technology from 1949 to 1951 and to the Summer scholarship at Northwestern University in 1952 which gave me the opportunity to devote myself to this task. I also received many valuable suggestions from the 1956 Summer Seminar Group sponsored by the National Science Foundation at the University of Kansas. I wish to thank Miss Vera Fisher for the excellent job of typing the manuscript, and Addison-Wesley Publishing Company for their friendly cooperation in the publication of the final work.

January 1957

G. S.

v

CONTENTS

CHAPTER 1

INTRODUCTION

1-1 Algebraic functions and Riemann surfaces. A student in the theory of functions of a complex variable usually first encounters the notion of a Riemann surface in connection with the multiple-valued behavior of the function $w = \sqrt{z}$. In this book, we shall first regard a Riemann surface from a more abstract point of view. The aims of this introduction are to lead the reader over the bridge from the notion of several sheets covering the z-plane to the abstract definition, and to point out the goals of our study of Riemann surfaces and the routes we follow to attain these goals. The definitions made in the introduction will necessarily be vague and the arguments heuristic, but these will be set on a firm foundation in the later chapters.

An important part of the theory of functions of a complex variable is devoted to the study of algebraic functions and their integrals. An analytic function $w = w(z)$ is called an *algebraic function* if it satisfies a functional equation

$$a_0(z)w^n + a_1(z)w^{n-1} + \cdots + a_n(z) = 0, \qquad a_0(z) \not\equiv 0,$$

in which the $a_i(z)$ are polynomials in z with complex numbers as coefficients. From this algebraic equation in w, we note that each value of z determines several values of w, so that w is a multiple-valued function of z. How the different values vary to form the continuous branches of $w(z)$ is one object of our investigation.

Moreover, a rational function of z and w is of the form

$$R(z, w) = \frac{b_0(z)w^m + b_1(z)w^{m-1} + \cdots + b_m(z)}{c_0(z)w^k + c_1(z)w^{k-1} + \cdots + c_k(z)}$$

where the $b_j(z)$ and $c_j(z)$ are polynomials in z with constant complex coefficients, and the denominator is not identically zero. We shall be interested in studying the function $F(z)$ defined by selecting one branch of an algebraic function $w(z)$ at z_0, a path from z_0 to z, and setting

$$F(z) = \int_{z_0}^{z} R(z, w(z))\, dz,$$

1

where the value of $w(z)$ is determined by analytic continuation along the path of integration from the fixed branch at z_0. In general, $F(z)$ is also a multiple-valued function of z. We shall find a system of canonical forms for these integrals so that any integral of this type can be transformed into a canonical form by a suitable change of variables. Then we shall study the canonical forms to learn more about the nature of these integrals.

Starting from a single function element of an algebraic function $w(z)$, we could use analytic continuation to piece together the whole function and in this way study its multiple-valuedness. In this book, however, we shall use Riemann's approach, in which one looks for a new surface (instead of the z-plane) on which to consider the algebraic function defined, and on which it is an ordinary single-valued function. It is this surface that we call a *Riemann surface*.

The simplest algebraic functions are those defined by an equation of the form $a_0(z)w + a_1(z) = 0$, where a_0 and a_1 are polynomials in z. In this case, $w = -a_1(z)/a_0(z)$ is a single-valued rational function of z; functions of this type are characterized by the condition that w be regular in the extended z-plane (z-sphere) except for a finite number of poles. If the poles occur at the points $b_1, b_2, \ldots, b_n$, then w may be expanded in partial fractions:

$$w = p(z) + h_1(z) + \cdots + h_n(z),$$

where

$$h_k(z) = \frac{c_{1,k}}{z - b_k} + \frac{c_{2,k}}{(z - b_k)^2} + \cdots + \frac{c_{m,k}}{(z - b_k)^m}$$

is the principal part of $w(z)$ at b_k and $p(z)$ is the polynomial in z which, to within a constant term, is the principal part of $w(z)$ at infinity. Any rational function $R(z, w)$ of z and this rational function w is also a rational function of z and has a partial-fraction expansion. Each integral

$$F(z) = \int_{z_0}^{z} R(z, w) \, dz$$

can be computed directly, yielding terms of the form $A \log (z - b)$, in addition to a rational function of z. Thus $F(z)$ is a multiple-valued function of z which changes value by $2\pi i A$ when z is continued around a small circle about any b which is a pole of $R(z, w)$ with nonzero residue A. Moreover, the change in value of $F(z)$ around any simple closed path is, by the residue theorem, $2\pi i$ times the sum of the residues of $R(z, w)$ at points interior to this path, so that the terms $A \log (z - b)$ account completely for the multiple-valuedness of $F(z)$. Thus we have some of the important properties of an algebraic function defined by a equation of degree 1 in w.

The next algebraic functions we shall consider are those defined by equations of degree 2 in w; that is, $a_0 w^2 + a_1 w + a_2 = 0$, where the $a_i = a_i(z)$ are polynomials in z, and $a_0 \neq 0$. If we make the simple change of variable $\zeta = 2a_0 w + a_1$, we obtain

$$\zeta^2 - p(z) = 0,$$

where $p(z) = a_1^2 - 4a_0 a_2$ is a polynomial in z. For any fixed z, ζ is a single-valued function of w, and conversely; here, we shall study $\zeta(z)$ instead of $w(z)$. We shall do this by starting with $p(z)$ of degree 1 in z and letting the degree of p increase in going from one case to the next.

The algebraic function defined by $w^2 - z = 0$ is not single-valued in the extended z-plane. For, using polar coordinates $z = re^{i\theta}$, we have $w = \sqrt{r}\, e^{\frac{1}{2} i\theta}$. Starting at some point $r_0 e^{i\theta_0}$, $r_0 \neq 0$, and continuing $w(z)$ along a closed path that winds once around the origin so that θ increases by 2π, $w(z)$ comes to the value $\sqrt{r_0}\, e^{\frac{1}{2} i(\theta_0 + 2\pi)} = -\sqrt{r_0}\, e^{\frac{1}{2} i\theta_0}$, which is just the negative of its original value. Continuation around this path once again leads back to the original value of $w(z)$. If we cut the extended z-plane along the positive real axis and restrict ourselves so as never to continue $w(z)$ over this cut, we get two single-valued branches of $w(z)$, namely, $w = \sqrt{r}\, e^{\frac{1}{2} i\theta}$, $0 \leq \theta < 2\pi$, and $w = \sqrt{r}\, e^{\frac{1}{2} i\theta}$, $2\pi \leq \theta < 4\pi$. To "build" the Riemann surface for $w(z)$, we take two replicas of the z-plane cut along the positive real axis and call them sheet I and sheet II. The cut on each sheet has two edges; label the edge of the first quadrant with a $+$ and the edge of the fourth quadrant with a $-$. Then attach the $+$ edge of the cut on I to the $-$ edge of the cut on II, and attach the $-$ edge of the cut on I to the $+$ edge of the cut on II. Thus, whenever we cross the cut, we pass from one sheet to the other.

Now the coordinate z determines a point in I and a point in II. It will be convenient to find a designation which will determine a single point on the Riemann surface. We associate to the point z on I the fixed value of $\sqrt{z}$ given by $\sqrt{r}\, e^{\frac{1}{2} i\theta}$, $0 \leq \theta < 2\pi$, and designate this point on I by $(z, \sqrt{z})$. Then, starting from $w = \sqrt{z}$, if we continue the function $w(z)$ defined by $w^2 - z = 0$ around a simple closed path about the origin, we cross the cut and pass into II, and when we return to the point in II having coordinate z, w has become $-\sqrt{z}$. We designate the point z on II by $(z, -\sqrt{z})$, which distinguishes it from $(z, \sqrt{z})$ on I. Thus each point of the Riemann surface may be considered as an ordered pair (z, w), where $w^2 - z = 0$, and two points (z_1, w_1) and (z_2, w_2) are identical on the Riemann surface if and only if $z_1 = z_2$ and $w_1(z) = w_2(z)$ about $z = z_1$. It is also clear that $w(z)$, satisfying $w^2 - z = 0$, is single-valued on the surface and assumes the value w at the point (z, w). In this case, there are two values of w for each base point z except $z = 0$ and $z = \infty$, which are branch points of $w = \sqrt{z}$.

Unfortunately, the two-sheeted surface we just constructed cannot be realized in our three-dimensional euclidean space as two sheets lying over the z-plane and attached crosswise along the given cuts, as will be readily apparent if we try to make it by cutting sheets of paper. It is this fact that lends an air of mystery to this surface, and which makes us suspicious and uncomfortable about Riemann surfaces in general. To dispel any such suspicion, we shall show that the two-sheeted surface can be mapped topologically onto a sphere.† Again we shall begin by imagining the surface as two sheets lying over the extended z-plane, each cut along the positive real axis. Using stereographic projection, we can consider the two sheets to be spheres cut along a meridian circle from the south pole to the north pole (Fig. 1–1) with each + edge attached to the − edge of the other sheet. Now pretend that the spheres are made of rubber and, by spreading the edges of the cuts, deform each sheet into a hemisphere. When each sheet

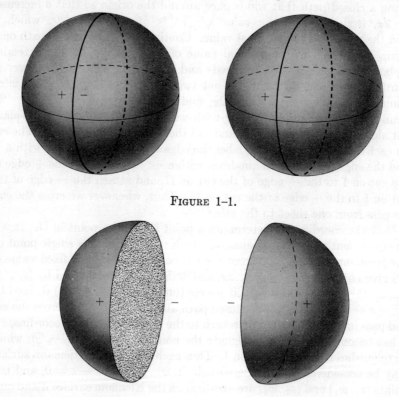

FIGURE 1–1.

FIGURE 1–2.

---

†A mapping is called *topological* if it is continuous and one-to-one with a continuous inverse.

is rotated so that the openings of the hemispheres face each other (Fig. 1–2), the edges marked $+$ and $-$ face each other and the two hemispheres may be pasted together to give us a sphere. This mapping is carried out analytically if we take each point $(z, \sqrt{z})$ of the Riemann surface into the point $t = \sqrt{z}$ of the extended t-plane (t-sphere).

Now what can we say about the integrals

$$F(z) = \int_{z_0}^{z} R(z, \sqrt{z}) \, dz,$$

where $R(z, w)$ is a rational function of z and w? If we consider this integral on the Riemann surface $(z, \sqrt{z})$ and map this surface onto the t-sphere by $t = \sqrt{z}$, our integral becomes

$$F(z) = \int_{\sqrt{z_0}}^{\sqrt{z}} R(t^2, t) 2t \, dt,$$

which is just the integral of a rational function of t. But this was treated in the first case, in which we saw that the only multiplicity arises from the residues of $2R(t^2, t)t$. Thus, $F(z)$ is a multiple-valued function on the Riemann surface of $w^2 - z = 0$, the multiplicity arising from the logarithmic singularities. Finally, in the z-plane itself, $F(z)$ has the additional two-valuedness due to the identification of the sheets.

The situation for $w^2 = a_0 z + a_1$ is essentially the same as that for $w^2 - z = 0$. Here we make the cut in the z-plane from $z = -a_1/a_0$ to $z = \infty$ instead of from 0 to ∞ and proceed as before. In fact, even the case $w^2 = a_0 z^2 + a_1 z + a_2$, $a_1^2 - 4a_0 a_2 \neq 0$, $a_0 \neq 0$, offers nothing essentially new, for, by factoring, we get $w^2 = a_0(z - r)(z - s)$, $r \neq s$. The two points $z = r$ and $z = s$ are branch points of this function, and we obtain two single-valued branches of $w = \sqrt{a_0(z - r)(z - s)}$ by cutting the z-plane along a curve joining r to s. Joining two replicas of the extended z-plane along this cut, we obtain a two-sheeted Riemann surface on which $w(z)$ is single-valued. It is clear that if the surface were made of rubber, it could be deformed continuously into that of $w^2 = z$ by moving r into 0 and s into ∞ and deforming the cut into the positive real axis. Thus this new surface may also be mapped topologically into a sphere. The mapping is executed analytically by first applying the linear fractional transformation $\tau = (z - r)/(z - s)$, which carries the z-plane in a one-to-one conformal manner onto the τ-plane with $r \to 0$ and $s \to \infty$. The two-sheeted Riemann surface over the z-plane maps onto a two-sheeted Riemann surface over the τ-plane, branched at $\tau = 0$ and $\tau = \infty$. Then $t = \sqrt{\tau}$ unwinds this Riemann surface and maps it onto the t-sphere as before.

We now consider the integral

$$\int_{z_0}^{z} R(z, \sqrt{a_0 z^2 + a_1 z + a_2})\, dz$$

of a rational function of z and w, where $w^2 = a_0 z^2 + a_1 z + a_2$. Using the change of variables above, which maps the Riemann surface over the z-sphere onto the t-sphere, we have $t = \sqrt{(z - r)/(z - s)}$, and

$$\int_{z_0}^{z} R(z, w)\, dz = \int_{(z_0 - r)/(z_0 - s)}^{(z - r)/(z - s)} R\left(\frac{\tau s - r}{\tau - 1}, \sqrt{a_0 \tau}\,\frac{s - r}{\tau - 1}\right)\frac{r - s}{(\tau - 1)^2}\, d\tau,$$

or

$$F(z) = \int_{\sqrt{(z_0 - r)/(z_0 - s)}}^{\sqrt{(z - r)/(z - s)}} R\left(\frac{t^2 s - r}{t^2 - 1}, \sqrt{a_0}\, t\,\frac{s - r}{t^2 - 1}\right)\frac{r - s}{(t^2 - 1)^2}\, 2t\, dt,$$

which is the integral of a rational function of t on the t-sphere. This integral is a multiple-valued function of $t = \sqrt{(z - r)/(z - s)}$ because of the logarithmic singularities corresponding to those poles for which the integrand has nonzero residue. Thus, as before, the multiple-valuedness of $F(z)$ in the z-plane arises from the logarithmic singularities of $F(z)$ and the two-valuedness of the map $z \to t$.

The picture changes significantly when we proceed to the case of the algebraic function defined by $w^2 = a(z - r_1)(z - r_2)(z - r_3)$, where r_1, r_2, r_3 are distinct. Again, to each z there correspond two values of w, one the negative of the other. We go from one to the other by continuing $w(z)$ over any closed path winding once around one of the roots r_1, r_2, r_3. For $w = \sqrt{a}\sqrt{z - r_1}\sqrt{z - r_2}\sqrt{z - r_3}$, and the factor $\sqrt{z - r_i}$ changes sign when $\arg(z - r_i)$ changes by 2π. If we cut the z-plane from r_1 to r_2, we cannot wind around either r_1 or r_2 alone without crossing the cut. However, we could choose a path which winds around both r_1 and r_2 (see the dotted path in Fig. 1–3). But now both $\arg(z - r_1)$ and $\arg(z - r_2)$ change by 2π, both the factors $\sqrt{z - r_1}$ and $\sqrt{z - r_2}$ change sign, and there is no change in w. We next cut the z-plane from r_3 to ∞. This prevents us from winding around all three of the roots r_1, r_2, and r_3. Thus either branch of $w(z)$ is single-valued in the cut plane. If we now take two copies of the cut z-plane (Fig. 1–3 or 1–4) and connect them crosswise over the cuts as before, we obtain a two-sheeted Riemann surface on which $w^2 = a(z - r_1)(z - r_2)(z - r_3)$ is single-valued. Again the points on this surface can be designated by $(z, w(z))$, where the z determines a point on both sheets and $w(z)$ says on which sheet the point lies.

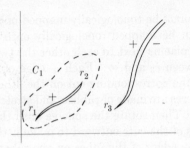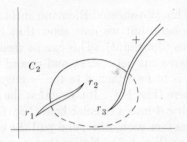

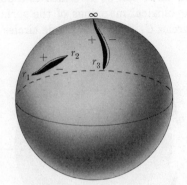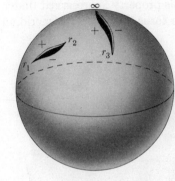

FIGURE 1-3.   FIGURE 1-4.

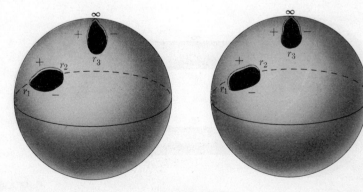

FIGURE 1-5.

FIGURE 1-6.

This two-sheeted Riemann surface *cannot* be topologically mapped onto a sphere, but we now show that it can be mapped topologically onto a torus (doughnut). This can be seen by placing next to each other the two spheres cut between r_1 and r_2 and between r_3 and ∞. Each $+$ edge of a cut is to be attached to the $-$ edge of the corresponding cut on the other sphere (Fig. 1–5). Imagine that the spheres are made of rubber, and stretch each cut into a circular hole (Fig. 1–6). Then rotate the spheres until the holes face each other, and pull the edges of the cuts outward to make little tubes (Fig. 1–7). Notice that now the $+$ edges of the tubes on one sphere are opposite the $-$ edges of the tubes on the other sphere. Thus we may join together the ends of the tubes to form the surface in Fig. 1–8, which can be topologically mapped onto a torus (Fig. 1–9).

It is easy to see that the torus cannot be mapped onto a sphere topologically. For on the sphere, any closed curve can be deformed to a point and this property is preserved under topological mappings of the surface. On the torus, however, the meridian circles C_1 and the latitude circles C_2

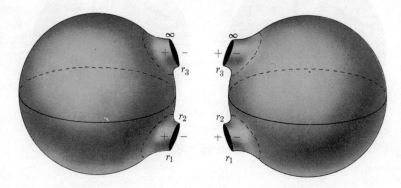

FIGURE 1–7.

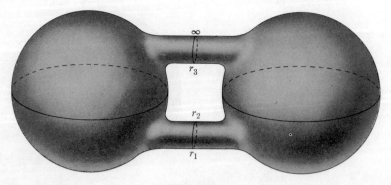

FIGURE 1–8.

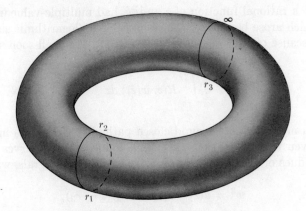

FIGURE 1–9.

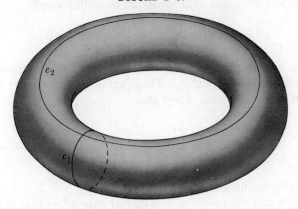

FIGURE 1–10.

indicated in Fig. 1–10 cannot be deformed continuously to a point on the surface of the torus. The curves marked C_1 and C_2 in Figs. 1–3 and 1–4 correspond to the meridian curves C_1 and latitude curves C_2 on the torus, respectively. In the two-sheeted Riemann surface of Fig. 1–4, the solid part of C_2 lies on one sheet and the dashed part on the other.

The existence on the surface of curves which, like C_1 and C_2, cannot be deformed to a point, affects the multiple-valuedness of the integrals of algebraic functions. Observe that around either C_1 or C_2, the function $w = \sqrt{a(z - r_1)(z - r_2)(z - r_3)}$ does not change its value.

In the cases studied previously, an integral

$$F(z) = \int_{z_0}^{z} R(z, w(z))\, dz,$$

where R is a rational function of z and w, had multiple-valuedness in the z-plane which arose because of the residues of R (logarithmic singularities of F) or because of the two-valuedness of $w(z)$. We shall soon see that

$$\int_{z_0}^{z} R(z, w(z))\, dz$$

can have a nonzero value around closed paths like C_1 and C_2 in Figs. 1–3 and 1–4 even though $w(z)$ remains single-valued on the curves and there are no residues of R enclosed by the curves. These integrals, with

$$w^2 = a(z - r_1)(z - r_2)(z - r_3),$$

are called *elliptic* integrals. The situation is similar when

$$w^2 = a(z - r_1)(z - r_2)(z - r_3)(z - r_4),$$

where r_1, r_2, r_3, r_4 are all distinct. In this case, cuts are made between r_1 and r_2 and between r_3 and r_4. These again can be opened and joined, as before, to give us a torus. Here also,

$$\int_{z_0}^{z} R(z, w)\, dz$$

is called an elliptic integral.

To complete the discussion of the special case $w^2 - p(z) = 0$, we take the function $w(z)$ defined by $w^2 = a(z - r_1)(z - r_2) \ldots (z - r_n)$, where the roots $r_1, r_2, \ldots, r_n$ are distinct. To each z correspond two values of w, so we get a two-sheeted Riemann surface with branch points at r_1, $r_2, \ldots, r_n$. As before, continuation of w along a path enclosing an odd number of the branch points leads to $-w$, while a path enclosing an even number of the branch points leads back to the original value of w. Thus, if we separate the branch points into pairs, say (r_1, r_2), (r_3, r_4), $\ldots$, and make cuts joining r_1 to r_2, r_3 to r_4, $\ldots$, we obtain two branches of $w(z)$, each single-valued in the cut plane. If n is odd, r_n is left over and we make a cut from r_n to ∞. This gives us $n/2$ cuts if n is even and $(n + 1)/2$ cuts if n is odd. If we connect two spheres, each cut between the branch points of w in pairs, as we did in the case $n = 3$ or 4, we obtain a surface such as that illustrated in Fig. 1–11. This surface consists of two spheres joined by $n/2$ tubes if n is even or $(n + 1)/2$ tubes if n is odd.

By momentarily fixing our attention on the two spheres and the one tube joining the cuts between r_1 and r_2 and closing the remaining cuts, we

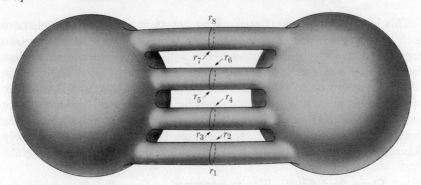

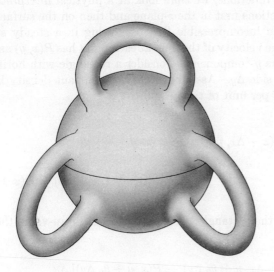

FIGURE 1–11.

FIGURE 1–12.

obtain a surface which is topologically a sphere. Now we restore the remaining g tubes on this new sphere; here g is $(n/2) - 1$ if n is even and $(n + 1)/2 - 1$ if n is odd. Each tube looks like a handle on the sphere; we get as the final topological model of the Riemann surface a sphere with g handles, as illustrated in Fig. 1–12. The number g is called the *genus* of the surface. Thus each algebraic function of the form $a_0(z)w^2 + a_1(z)w + a_2(z) = 0$, $a_0(z) \not\equiv 0$, has a Riemann surface which is topologically equivalent to a sphere with g handles. It can be shown that the Riemann surface for *any* algebraic function is topologically a sphere with g handles and that the algebraic function is a single-valued function of the points on this surface.

This leads us to our next step. Why not start with a surface in space such as a sphere with handles, determine which functions on the surface correspond to analytic functions in the z-plane, and see which of these functions are single-valued on the surface? This will classify the analytic functions according to their Riemann surfaces. Furthermore, knowledge of the single-valued and multiple-valued functions on the Riemann surface and the topological nature of the surface will enable us to determine the behavior of the integrals of the algebraic functions. This is precisely Riemann's approach to the study of algebraic functions and their integrals.

1–2 Plane fluid flows. We are interested in those functions which are defined and analytic on a surface in space. To get a clearer intuitive picture of such functions, we shall look at a physical interpretation of these analytic functions first in the z-plane and then on the surface.

Suppose an incompressible fluid is flowing in a steady state over the xy-plane. The velocity of the fluid at each point has $P(x, y)$ as x-component and $Q(x, y)$ as y-component. Consider a rectangle with horizontal side Δx and vertical side Δy. Assuming that the constant density has value 1, a mass of fluid per unit of time equal to

$$\int_0^{\Delta y} \{P(x + \Delta x, y + u) - P(x, y + u)\}\, du$$

$$+ \int_0^{\Delta x} \{Q(x + v, y + \Delta y) - Q(x + v, y)\}\, dv$$

flows out of the rectangle. According to the mean-value theorem, this is equal to

$$[P(x + \Delta x, y + \theta_2\, \Delta y) - P(x, y + \theta_2\, \Delta y)]\, \Delta y$$

$$+ [Q(x + \theta_3\, \Delta x, y + \Delta y) - Q(x + \theta_3\, \Delta x, y)]\, \Delta x,$$

where $0 < \theta_k < 1$, $k = 2, 3$. Next, the mean-value theorem yields for this expression

$$[P_x(x + \theta_1\, \Delta x, y + \theta_2\, \Delta y) + Q_y(x + \theta_3\, \Delta x, y + \theta_4\, \Delta y)]\, \Delta x\, \Delta y,$$

where $0 < \theta_k < 1$, $k = 1, 4$. If A is an arbitrary region, we may approximate A from within with a rectangular mesh. Then the mass flowing out of A per unit of time is approximated by the sum of the masses per unit time flowing out of the rectangles in the mesh. But this sum is the approximating sum for the integral

$$\iint\limits_{A} \left(\frac{\partial P}{\partial x} + \frac{\partial Q}{\partial y} \right) dx\, dy.$$

Since the fluid is incompressible, and we assume no fluid is created or destroyed in any region A, we must have

$$\iint\limits_{A} \left(\frac{\partial P}{\partial x} + \frac{\partial Q}{\partial y} \right) dx\, dy = 0$$

for all A, or $\partial P/\partial x + \partial Q/\partial y = 0$. This statement says that the fluid has zero divergence. The *circulation* of a fluid around a closed curve C is defined to be $\int_C P\, dx + Q\, dy$. We say that the flow is irrotational if its circulation around any curve C is zero. In this case $P\, dx + Q\, dy$ is an exact differential and there is a function $u(x, y)$ such that $P = \partial u/\partial x$, $Q = \partial u/\partial y$. The fact that the flow has zero divergence now implies that $\partial^2 u/\partial x^2 + \partial^2 u/\partial y^2 = 0$, that is, that u is a harmonic function. The function u is called the *velocity potential* of the flow.

The curves $u =$ constant are called *equipotential lines*. The tangent line to an equipotential line makes an angle α with the x-axis, given by $\tan \alpha = -(\partial u/\partial x)/(\partial u/\partial y)$ when $(\partial u/\partial x)^2 + (\partial u/\partial y)^2 \neq 0$. The velocity vector makes an angle β with the x-axis, given by $\tan \beta = Q/P = (\partial u/\partial y)/(\partial u/\partial x)$, from which we conclude that α and β differ by $90°$ and that the flow is perpendicular to the equipotential curves in the direction of increasing u.

If the harmonic function u is given, its conjugate harmonic function v is defined by the Cauchy-Riemann equations $\partial u/\partial x = \partial v/\partial y$, $\partial u/\partial y = -\partial v/\partial x$. Then $f(z) = u(x, y) + iv(x, y)$ is an analytic function of z, called the *complex potential* of the flow. The tangent to the curve $v =$ constant makes an angle γ with the x-axis, given by $\tan \gamma = -(\partial v/\partial x)/(\partial v/\partial y) = (\partial u/\partial y)/(\partial u/\partial x)$. Thus $\tan \beta = \tan \gamma$, and the fluid flows in the direction of the curves $v =$ constant, which are consequently called *streamlines*. The assumption $(\partial u/\partial x)^2 + (\partial u/\partial y)^2 \neq 0$ may be restated $f'(z) \neq 0$, and the streamlines are orthogonal to the equipotential lines except at points where $f'(z) = 0$.

When $u + iv$ is analytic, $v - iu$ is also analytic, since v, $-u$ satisfy the Cauchy-Riemann equations. Thus we may take the curves $u =$ constant as the streamlines and the curves $v =$ constant as the equipotential lines. The flow thus obtained is called the *conjugate flow* of the original one.

When the analytic function $w = f(z)$ is regular at z_0 but $f'(z_0) = 0$, the curves $u =$ constant and $v =$ constant do not intersect orthogonally at z_0. In particular, if

$$f(z) = a_0 + a_k(z - z_0)^k + a_{k+1}(z - z_0)^{k+1} + \cdots, \qquad a_k \neq 0,$$

†hen the curves $u = $ constant and $v = $ constant intersect at an angle of $\pi/2k$. In this case, k equipotential lines pass through z_0 with equal angles between them, and these angles are bisected by the k streamlines through z_0. Such a point z_0 is called a *stationary point* or *cross-point* of order $k - 1$. Figure 1–13 illustrates a cross-point of order 2 (dotted lines are equipotential lines, solid lines are streamlines).

By making use of stereographic projection, these flows may be pictured on a sphere rather than on a plane. To study the flow at $z = \infty$, we use the familiar device of replacing z by $1/\zeta$ and studying the resulting function of ζ in the neighborhood of $\zeta = 0$. Thus we obtain a cross-point of order $k - 1$ at $z = \infty$ if the series expansion of $f(z)$ in ascending powers of $1/z$ has $a_k(1/z)^k$ as its first nonconstant term.

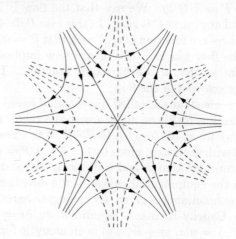

FIGURE 1–13.

Now let us consider the flow in the neighborhood of a point z_0 at which $f(z)$ becomes infinite. Let us restrict the discussion to analytic functions $f(z)$ for which $f'(z)$ has poles as its only singularities. Thus the principal part of the expansion of $f(z)$ about z_0 is

$$A \log (z - z_0) + \frac{A_1}{z - z_0} + \frac{A_2}{(z - z_0)^2} + \cdots + \frac{A_\nu}{(z - z_0)^\nu}.$$

The first term is called a logarithmic singularity, the second an algebraic infinity or pole of order 1, etc. We shall consider the effect of each singularity separately and then superimpose the flows to get the joint effect of the whole principal part. The coefficient A is called the *logarithmic residue* of the singularity.

We discuss the logarithmic singularity $A \log (z - z_0)$ first. We shall take the cases A real and A pure imaginary separately, and superimpose the two flow patterns to get the general case. If A is real, we set $z = z_0 + re^{i\varphi}$ and $A \log (z - z_0) = u + iv$ and get

$$u = A \log r, \qquad v = A\varphi.$$

The streamlines $v = $ constant are radial lines emanating from $z = z_0$, while the equipotential lines are circles about $z = z_0$ (Fig. 1–14). Thus $z = z_0$ is either a *source* from which fluid emerges or a *sink* into which fluid disappears, depending upon whether A is positive or negative, respectively. To calculate the *strength* of a source or sink, we integrate the magnitude of the velocity (speed) around an equipotential circle. Since the velocity is radial, the speed is given by $\partial u/\partial r = A/r$, so the strength of the flow is

$$\int_0^{2\pi} \frac{A}{r} r \, d\varphi = 2\pi A.$$

Next, if A is purely imaginary, we may set $A = iB$, B real, and obtain $u = -B\varphi$, $v = B \log r$. This is just the conjugate of the flow we discussed above; the streamlines now are the circles with center at z_0 and the equipotential lines are radial lines emanating from z_0 (Fig. 1–15). This flow about z_0 is a *vortex*, the flow being clockwise or counterclockwise according to whether B is positive or negative. The circulation is given by

$$\int_0^{2\pi} \frac{\partial u}{\partial \varphi} \, d\varphi = -2\pi B.$$

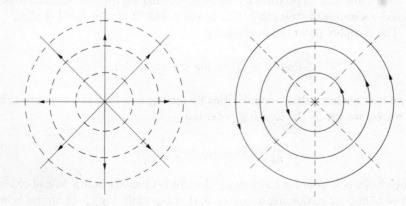

FIGURE 1–14.   FIGURE 1–15.

We next consider a pole of order 1, say $A_1/(z - z_0)$. If we set $z - z_0 = re^{i\varphi}$ and $A_1 = \rho e^{i\psi}$, we get $A_1/(z - z_0) = (\rho/r)e^{i(\psi - \varphi)}$, so that

$$u = \frac{\rho}{r} \cos (\psi - \varphi), \qquad v = \frac{\rho}{r} \sin (\psi - \varphi).$$

In this case the streamlines $v = $ constant are a coaxal family of circles which are tangent to the line $\varphi = \psi$ at $z = z_0$. The equipotential lines are the orthogonal coaxal family of circles which are tangent to the line $\varphi = \psi + \frac{1}{2}\pi$ at $z = z_0$ (Fig. 1–16).

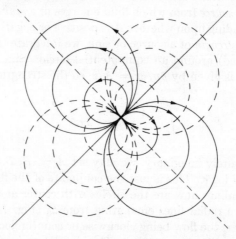

FIGURE 1–16.

Assuming that a source or sink can be produced experimentally by punching a hole in the surface and having fluid flow in or out of this hole, we shall show how to produce a pole by coalescing logarithmic singularities. Consider a source of strength $1/h$ at z_0 and a sink of strength $-1/h$ at $z_0 + h$. The complex potential is given by

$$\frac{1}{h} [\log (z - z_0) - \log (z - z_0 - h)].$$

If we now coalesce these singularities by letting $h \to 0$ as the strength $1/h$ increases, we get as the limiting potential

$$\frac{d}{dz} \log (z - z_0) = \frac{1}{z - z_0},$$

which has a pole of order 1 at $z = z_0$. Figure 1–17 shows how a pole of order 1 is obtained by coalescing a source and sink, while Fig. 1–18 shows how it may also be obtained by coalescing two oppositely oriented vortices.

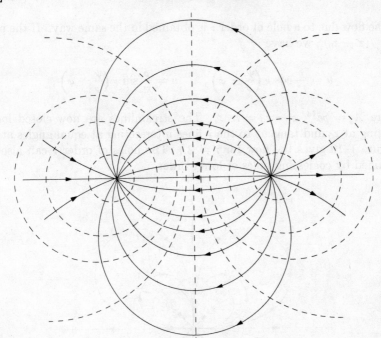

FIGURE 1–17.

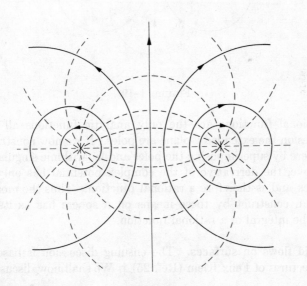

FIGURE 1–18.

The flow due to a pole of order ν is obtained in the same way. If the pole is $A_\nu/(z - z_0)^\nu$, we have

$$u = \frac{\rho}{r^\nu} \cos \nu \left(\frac{\psi}{\nu} - \varphi \right), \qquad v = \frac{\rho}{r^\nu} \sin \nu \left(\frac{\psi}{\nu} - \varphi \right),$$

where $A_\nu = \rho e^{i\psi}$, $z - z_0 = re^{i\varphi}$. The streamlines are now closed loops starting at z_0 and tangent to the ν lines intersecting at equal angles at z_0. (Figure 1–19 gives the flow for $\nu = 2$.) The poles of order ν can also be obtained by coalescing poles of lower order.

FIGURE 1–19.

The rational functions are the only analytic functions all of whose singularities on the extended z-plane are poles. If we now construct a flow on the sphere by superimposing the poles and logarithmic singularities discussed above, the derivative of the complex potential has only poles as singularities and is therefore a rational function. Thus the most general flow we can construct by these means on a sphere has as its complex potential the integral of a rational function.

1–3 Fluid flows on surfaces. The ensuing discussion is based largely upon the lectures of Felix Klein (Ref. 25).† We shall now discuss the flow

---

†References are at the rear of the book.

of an incompressible fluid on a surface S in space. Assume that the surface is given by the equations $x_i = x_i(p, q)$, $i = 1, 2, 3$, in the (x_1, x_2, x_3) space, where (p, q) may vary in some plane region. We may suppose that all the functions here have as many continuous derivatives as necessary for the simple calculations that follow. The pair (p, q) may be considered as the coordinates of a point on S. A curve C on S is given by $p = p(t)$, $q = q(t)$, $a \le t \le b$, and in terms of the vector $\mathbf{x} = (x_1, x_2, x_3)$ the element of arc length along C is given by

$$ds^2 = d\mathbf{x} \cdot d\mathbf{x} = (\mathbf{x}_p \, dp + \mathbf{x}_q \, dq) \cdot (\mathbf{x}_p \, dp + \mathbf{x}_q \, dq)$$

or

$$ds^2 = (\mathbf{x}_p \cdot \mathbf{x}_p) \, dp^2 + 2(\mathbf{x}_p \cdot \mathbf{x}_q) \, dp \, dq + (\mathbf{x}_q \cdot \mathbf{x}_q) \, dq^2.$$

It is customary to set $(\mathbf{x}_p \cdot \mathbf{x}_p) = E$, $(\mathbf{x}_q \cdot \mathbf{x}_q) = G$, and $(\mathbf{x}_p \cdot \mathbf{x}_q) = F$, so that

$$ds^2 = E \, dp^2 + 2F \, dp \, dq + G \, dq^2. \tag{1}$$

Since ds^2 is always positive, $W^2 = EG - F^2$ is also positive.

It is most convenient to select a special system of coordinates (u, v) instead of (p, q), in terms of which the element of arc length is

$$ds^2 = \lambda(u, v) \, (du^2 + dv^2). \tag{2}$$

That such coordinates, called *isothermal coordinates*, can be found in the vicinity of any point on S is made more apparent by factoring (1) to get

$$ds^2 = \left(\sqrt{E} \, dp + \frac{F + iW}{\sqrt{E}} \, dq \right) \left(\sqrt{E} \, dp + \frac{F - iW}{\sqrt{E}} \, dq \right).$$

If we can find an integrating factor $\sigma = \sigma_1 + i\sigma_2$ such that

$$\sigma \left(\sqrt{E} \, dp + \frac{F + iW}{\sqrt{E}} \, dq \right) = du + i \, dv, \tag{3}$$

then

$$\bar{\sigma} \left(\sqrt{E} \, dp + \frac{F - iW}{\sqrt{E}} \, dq \right) = du - i \, dv,$$

and finally

$$|\sigma|^2 \, ds^2 = du^2 + dv^2.$$

Setting $|\sigma|^2 = 1/\lambda$ gives us the desired isothermal coordinates (u, v). Thus we get isothermal coordinates by finding an integrating factor to make $\sqrt{E}\,dp + [(F + iW)/\sqrt{E}]\,dq$ an exact differential. The differential $du + i\,dv$ can be written as

$$du + i\,dv = \left(\frac{\partial u}{\partial p} + i\,\frac{\partial v}{\partial p}\right)dp + \left(\frac{\partial u}{\partial q} + i\,\frac{\partial v}{\partial q}\right)dq,$$

and comparison with (3) yields

$$\frac{\partial u}{\partial p} + i\,\frac{\partial v}{\partial p} = \sigma\sqrt{E}, \qquad \frac{\partial u}{\partial q} + i\,\frac{\partial v}{\partial q} = \sigma\left(\frac{F + iW}{\sqrt{E}}\right).$$

We may eliminate σ to get

$$E\left[\frac{\partial u}{\partial q} + i\,\frac{\partial v}{\partial q}\right] = (F + iW)\left[\frac{\partial u}{\partial p} + i\,\frac{\partial v}{\partial p}\right]$$

or simply

$$E\,\frac{\partial u}{\partial q} = F\,\frac{\partial u}{\partial p} - W\,\frac{\partial v}{\partial p}, \qquad E\,\frac{\partial v}{\partial q} = W\,\frac{\partial u}{\partial p} + F\,\frac{\partial v}{\partial p}.$$

Solving for $\partial v/\partial p$ and $\partial v/\partial q$ gives

$$\frac{\partial v}{\partial p} = \frac{F\,\partial u/\partial p - E\,\partial u/\partial q}{\sqrt{EG - F^2}}, \qquad \frac{\partial v}{\partial q} = \frac{G\,\partial u/\partial p - F\,\partial u/\partial q}{\sqrt{EG - F^2}}. \qquad (4)$$

Similarly,

$$\frac{\partial u}{\partial p} = \frac{E\,\partial v/\partial q - F\,\partial v/\partial p}{\sqrt{EG - F^2}}, \qquad \frac{\partial u}{\partial q} = \frac{F\,\partial v/\partial q - G\,\partial v/\partial p}{\sqrt{EG - F^2}}. \qquad (5)$$

From (4), we find that u satisfies

$$\frac{\partial}{\partial q}\left[\frac{F\,\partial u/\partial p - E\,\partial u/\partial q}{W}\right] + \frac{\partial}{\partial p}\left[\frac{F\,\partial u/\partial q - G\,\partial u/\partial p}{W}\right] = 0, \qquad (6)$$

which is called the *Beltrami equation*.

If another set of isothermal coordinates (x, y) in the vicinity of a point is known, then $ds^2 = \mu(dx^2 + dy^2)$. Using (x, y) instead of (p, q) in (4), we have $E = G = \mu$, $F = 0$, so that

$$\frac{\partial v}{\partial x} = -\frac{\partial u}{\partial y}, \qquad \frac{\partial v}{\partial y} = \frac{\partial u}{\partial x},$$

which are just the Cauchy-Riemann equations telling us that u and v are conjugate harmonic functions and that $f = u + iv$ is an analytic function of $z = x + iy$. The Beltrami equation (6) becomes the familiar Laplace equation $\partial^2 u/\partial x^2 + \partial^2 u/\partial y^2 = 0$. Thus, in general, we may say that a complex-valued function $f(p, q)$ defined on S is called a *complex potential function* on S if its real and imaginary parts satisfy (4). Thus the real and imaginary parts of a complex potential function on S give us isothermal coordinates in the neighborhood of each point on S.

To discuss angles on the surface S, we take two curves C_1 and C_2 which intersect at a point P on S. Take as parameter along C_i, $i = 1, 2$, the arc length s_i along C_i, so that C_i is given parametrically by $p = p_i(s_i)$, $q = q_i(s_i)$. Then the unit tangent vector $\mathbf{a}_i$ to the curve C_i at P is given by

$$\mathbf{a}_i = \mathbf{x}_p \frac{dp_i}{ds_i} + \mathbf{x}_q \frac{dq_i}{ds_i},$$

and the angle θ in which C_1 and C_2 intersect is given by the equations

$$\cos\theta = \mathbf{a}_1 \cdot \mathbf{a}_2 = E \frac{dp_1}{ds_1}\frac{dp_2}{ds_2} + F\left(\frac{dp_1}{ds_1}\frac{dq_2}{ds_2} + \frac{dp_2}{ds_2}\frac{dq_1}{ds_1}\right) + G\frac{dq_1}{ds_1}\frac{dq_2}{ds_2},$$

$$\sin\theta = \sqrt{(\mathbf{a}_1 \times \mathbf{a}_2) \cdot (\mathbf{a}_1 \times \mathbf{a}_2)} = \sqrt{(\mathbf{a}_1 \cdot \mathbf{a}_1)(\mathbf{a}_2 \cdot \mathbf{a}_2) - (\mathbf{a}_1 \cdot \mathbf{a}_2)^2}$$

$$= W\left(\frac{dp_1}{ds_1}\frac{dq_2}{ds_2} - \frac{dp_2}{ds_2}\frac{dq_1}{ds_1}\right).$$

The p-curves along which $q = $ constant and the q-curves along which $p = $ constant are called *parametric curves* on S. Along the p-curves $dq = 0$, while along the q-curves $dp = 0$. If we take for C_1 the p-curve through P and for C_2 the q-curve through P, we get for the angle between the parametric curves

$$\cos\theta = F\frac{dp_1}{ds_1}\frac{dq_2}{ds_2} = \frac{F}{\sqrt{EG}}.$$

Thus, parametric curves intersect orthogonally if and indeed only if $F = 0$. The whole family of p-curves is orthogonal to the whole family of q-curves if and only if $F \equiv 0$, in which case $(p/\sqrt{E}, q/\sqrt{G})$ are isothermal coordinates.

Next let S and $\tilde{S}$ be two surfaces with coordinates (p, q) and $(\tilde{p}, \tilde{q})$, respectively. We suppose we have a one-to-one mapping of S onto $\tilde{S}$, given by $\tilde{p} = \varphi(p, q)$, $\tilde{q} = \psi(p, q)$. Then (p, q) also determine a point on S and may be considered as coordinates on $\tilde{S}$. The element of arc length on

S and $\widetilde{S}$ can be given as

$$ds^2 = E\,dp^2 + 2F\,dp\,dq + G\,dq^2$$

and

$$d\widetilde{s}^2 = \widetilde{E}\,dp^2 + 2\widetilde{F}\,dp\,dq + \widetilde{G}\,dq^2,$$

respectively. The mapping $S \to \widetilde{S}$ is called *conformal* if the angle between two directed curves through P on S is always equal to the angle between the corresponding two directed curves through the corresponding point $\widetilde{P}$ on $\widetilde{S}$. We now prove that the mapping is conformal if and only if ds and $d\widetilde{s}$ are proportional; that is, $d\widetilde{s} = \rho(p, q)\,ds$.

Take $\widetilde{C}_1$ and $\widetilde{C}_2$ as the images of C_1 and C_2, and let $\widetilde{\theta}$ and θ be the corresponding angles of intersection. Then

$$\sin \theta = W\left(\frac{dp_1}{ds_1}\frac{dq_2}{ds_2} - \frac{dp_2}{ds_2}\frac{dq_1}{ds_1}\right)$$

and

$$\sin \widetilde{\theta} = \widetilde{W}\left(\frac{dp_1}{d\widetilde{s}_1}\frac{dq_2}{d\widetilde{s}_2} - \frac{dq_1}{d\widetilde{s}_1}\frac{dp_2}{d\widetilde{s}_2}\right).$$

If the mapping is conformal, $\theta = \widetilde{\theta}$ and

$$\frac{W}{ds_1\,ds_2} = \frac{\widetilde{W}}{d\widetilde{s}_1\,d\widetilde{s}_2}.$$

For the curves C_2 and $\widetilde{C}_2$, we select the p-curves through P and $\widetilde{P}$ along which $ds_2 = \sqrt{E}\,dp$ and $d\widetilde{s}_2 = \sqrt{\widetilde{E}}\,dp$. Then

$$\frac{W}{ds_1\sqrt{E}\,dp} = \frac{\widetilde{W}}{d\widetilde{s}_1\sqrt{\widetilde{E}}\,dp},$$

or simply

$$\frac{d\widetilde{s}_1}{ds_1} = \frac{\widetilde{W}\sqrt{E}}{W\sqrt{\widetilde{E}}} = \rho(p, q),$$

for any corresponding curves C_1 and $\widetilde{C}_1$, proving our assertion one way. Next, if the elements of arc are proportional along a p-curve, $d\widetilde{s} = \sqrt{\widetilde{E}}\,dp$ and $ds = \sqrt{E}\,dp$, so that $d\widetilde{s} = \rho\,ds$ implies that $\widetilde{E} = \rho^2 E$. Along a q-curve, $d\widetilde{s} = \sqrt{\widetilde{G}}\,dq$ and $ds = \sqrt{G}\,dq$, so that $\widetilde{G} = \rho^2 G$. Thus, in order that $d\widetilde{s} = \rho\,ds$, we must also have $\widetilde{F} = \rho^2 F$ and $\widetilde{W} = \rho^2 W$. Furthermore, $d\widetilde{s}_1 = \rho\,ds_1$ and $d\widetilde{s}_2 = \rho\,ds_2$, so that $\sin \theta = \sin \widetilde{\theta}$ and the mapping is conformal.

In particular, a mapping is conformal if and only if it maps an isothermal system of coordinates on S into an isothermal system of coordinates on $\widetilde{S}$. For on S, $ds^2 = \lambda(dp^2 + dq^2)$. The mapping is conformal when and only when $d\tilde{s} = \rho\, ds$, so that $d\tilde{s}^2 = \rho^2\lambda\,(dp^2 + dq^2) = \tilde{\lambda}\,(dp^2 + dq^2)$. This is just the property characterizing isothermal coordinates, which proves our assertion.

A complex potential function $f(p, q)$ on S can be considered as a function of the point (p, q) on $\widetilde{S}$, the conformal image of S. Since $\widetilde{E} = \rho^2 E$, $\widetilde{F} = \rho^2 F$, $\widetilde{G} = \rho^2 G$, and $\widetilde{W} = \rho^2 W$, and since equations (4) are homogeneous of degree zero, we conclude that $f(p, q)$ is also a complex potential function on $\widetilde{S}$. Conversely, if $f(p, q)$ is a complex potential function on S and $F(p, q)$ is one on $\widetilde{S}$, and if they assume the same values at corresponding points, the real and imaginary parts of each give us isothermal coordinates on S and $\widetilde{S}$, respectively, and the correspondence of these coordinates implies that the mapping of S onto $\widetilde{S}$ is conformal. Hence, from the point of view of studying the totality of complex potential functions on S, we may consider all the one-to-one conformal images of S as being equivalent and merely select one of these as a model on which to operate.

Let (x, y) be isothermal coordinates in a region N on S. A mapping may be defined from N to a region G of the $z = x + iy$ plane by taking the point (x, y) in N into the point $x + iy$ in the z-plane. This mapping is conformal, for on S, $ds^2 = \lambda\,(dx^2 + dy^2)$, whereas in the z-plane, $ds^2 = dx^2 + dy^2$. But any complex potential function $f = u + iv$ on N satisfies $\partial u/\partial x = \partial v/\partial y$, $\partial u/\partial y = -\partial v/\partial x$ and hence is an ordinary analytic function of the complex variable z in G.

Since the real and imaginary parts of any complex potential function $f = x + iy$ on S form a set of local isothermal coordinates, we can say that any complex potential function on S is an analytic function, in the ordinary sense, of any other complex potential function on S.

An irrotational, incompressible fluid flowing in a steady state on the surface S has a velocity potential $u(p, q)$ which satisfies the Beltrami equation (6) (which we have seen to be a generalization of the Laplace equation). The streamlines are given by the curves $v = $ constant, where v is the conjugate function to u defined by (4). We may now produce fluid flows on the surface S by placing sources, sinks, vortices, or poles obtained by coalescing them, at certain points on S. Each flow gives rise to a complex potential function $u + iv$, and each such complex potential function is an analytic function of every other.

A surface is said to be of genus g if g is the maximum number of non-intersecting closed curves (called *loop-cuts*) on the surface which do not divide the surface into disconnected pieces. To simplify the present discussion, we shall use the fact that any closed surface of genus g can be mapped topologically onto one of the models encountered earlier in this

chapter, namely, a sphere with g
handles. For $g = 0$, we get a sphere;
for $g = 1$, we get a torus; and for
$g = 3$, we get the surface illustrated
in Fig. 1-12. These models are called
the *normal surfaces of genus g*. Certain loop-cuts on the normal surface
of genus g are of special interest.
These are the meridian curve and the
curve of latitude in each handle. We

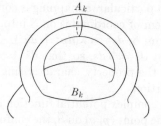

FIGURE 1-20.

shall denote the meridian curves by $A_1, A_2, \ldots, A_g$ and the latitude curves
by $B_1, B_2, \ldots, B_g$ (Fig. 1-20). It will be proved in Chapter 5 that every
closed curve on the surface S can be deformed into an integral combination
of the loop-cuts A_i and B_i, $i = 1, \ldots, g$. For example, on the torus, the
closed curve pictured in Fig. 1-21 can be deformed into $2A + B$ in
Fig. 1-22.

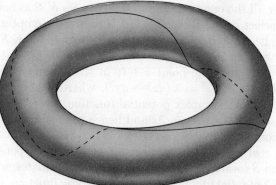

FIGURE 1-21.

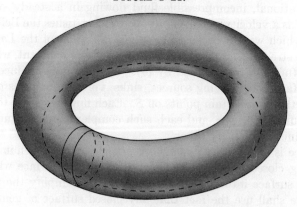

FIGURE 1-22.

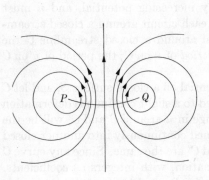

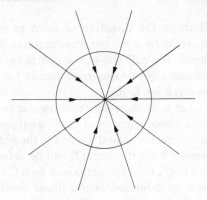

FIGURE 1–23.   FIGURE 1–24.

1–4 Regular potentials. Now let us see which flows are possible on the normal surfaces. We say that the potential u is *regular* at a point if the complex potential $u + iv$ is finite and differentiable at that point. On the sphere, there is no flow that has an everywhere regular potential, for the only everywhere finite analytic function on the sphere is a constant. The flows that are possible, then, arise only when certain singularities are

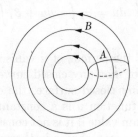

FIGURE 1–25.

introduced (sources, sinks, poles, vortices, etc.). These same devices can be used on a surface of genus g ($g > 0$) to produce flows on the surface. But now these are not the only possibilities, for if we can draw a loop-cut on the surface which does not divide the surface into disconnected pieces, this loop-cut can be made an equipotential line and the fluid will flow across the loop-cut.

To understand this better, consider an arc on the sphere with a vortex at each end, these vortices being oppositely oriented. The fluid will flow across the arc, as illustrated in Fig. 1–23. Next let the end points of the arc come together to form a closed curve. The flow will still be across the curve, but if the curve forms the boundary of an area (as it must on the sphere), there must be a sink or source in the area bounded by the curve (Fig. 1–24). On a surface of genus $g > 0$, the picture is different, for now the curve may be taken to be a loop-cut A, and the fluid may flow right around the loop-cuts B crossing A, as illustrated in Fig. 1–25 for the torus. This flow has no singularities and gives rise to an everywhere regular potential function u. This potential function, however, is not single-valued, for the fluid flows in the direction of most rapidly increasing potential, and u must increase by some constant amount on each circuit around a closed stream-line. We call the change in potential around a closed streamline C the *modulus of periodicity*, or simply the *period* of u on C; the period of u on C is given by $\int_C du$.

Let u be an everywhere regular potential on a closed surface S, and let C be a closed curve on S. If C is subjected to a slight continuous deformation into another closed curve C', the change in u around C and C' will be the same. Thus if a curve C can be deformed continuously into another closed curve C', then the periods of u on C and C' are the same. Since any curve C can be deformed into a linear combination, with integers as coefficients, of the loop-cuts $A_1, B_1, A_2, B_2, \ldots, A_g, B_g$, and because the integral is additive, we have

$$\int_C du = \alpha_1 \int_{A_1} du + \beta_1 \int_{B_1} du + \cdots + \alpha_g \int_{A_g} du + \beta_g \int_{B_g} du.$$

Thus if the periods of u vanish on all the A_i, B_i, $i = 1, \ldots, g$, then the period of u on any closed curve C is zero and u is single-valued.

On any closed surface, the only single-valued, everywhere regular potential function u is a constant. For at some point of S, u must have a maximum value if it is not constant. In the neighborhood of this maximum point, we may choose isothermal coordinates (x, y) so that the maximum occurs at (x_0, y_0). The potential u now satisfies $\partial^2 u/\partial x^2 + \partial^2 u/\partial y^2 = 0$ and is a harmonic function of (x, y), which cannot have a maximum point in a region of regularity.

If two potentials u and u' have the same periods over the loop-cuts A_i, B_i, $i = 1, \ldots, g$, their difference $u - u'$ has zero periods over the $2g$ loop-cuts and hence is everywhere regular and single-valued. Thus $u - u'$ is a constant. We then conclude that a potential u which is everywhere regular is determined up to an arbitrary additive constant by its periods over the $2g$ loop-cuts A_i, B_i, $i = 1, \ldots, g$.

It is now possible to construct a flow which has an everywhere regular potential u, with nonzero period on only one loop-cut. We shall illustrate this by showing the streamlines for these flows on surfaces of genus $g = 1$ and $g = 2$. It should be pointed out that even though we shall be able to specify the periods of u to be zero on all but one loop-cut, the harmonic conjugate v of u does not share this property; for v is completely determined by the equations (4) of Section 1–3 and we cannot specify its periods once u is given.

On the torus $(g = 1)$, we may take the meridian circle A as an equi-potential curve and get a flow whose streamlines are the circles of latitude. The potential for this flow has nonzero period around the latitude circle B

and zero period on A. Figure 1–25 shows the flow on the upper side of the torus; the flow on the bottom is in the same direction. If we take a latitude circle B as an equipotential, we obtain the conjugate flow in which the meridian circles are the streamlines. Figure 1–26 shows the streamlines on the upper side; the direction of flow is reversed on the

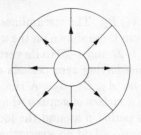

FIGURE 1–26.

lower side. Here we get zero period on B and nonzero period on A.

We may picture the surface of genus 2 as a "two-holed torus" (sphere with two handles). If we pull a tube out of the torus in Fig. 1–25 and bring it around to meet the torus again, the flow of Fig. 1–25 goes into that of Fig. 1–27, in which the left side corresponds to the original torus and the right side to the tube we pulled out of the torus. This flow has a potential which has nonzero period on the loop-cut B_1 and zero periods on A_1, B_2, A_2. The streamlines shown here are on the upper side; those on the lower side have the same directions. If two tubes are pulled out of the torus in Fig. 1–26 and their ends are brought together, we get the flow shown in Fig. 1–28. Here the potential has nonzero period on A_1 and zero periods

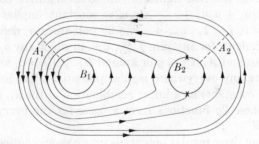

FIGURE 1–27.

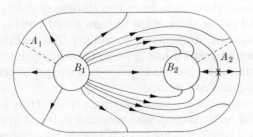

FIGURE 1–28.

on B_1, A_2, B_2. The streamlines on the lower side are to be directed oppositely from those shown on the upper side. If we reflect each of the surfaces in Figs. 1–27 and 1–28 in its vertical axis of symmetry, we obtain two more flows, one having zero periods on A_1, B_1, A_2 and the other having zero periods on A_1, B_1, B_2. A similar procedure can now be followed to get flows on a surface of genus g which have zero periods on all but one loop-cut. If u has period p around the loop-cut C, then u/p has period 1 around C. Thus we may find an everywhere regular potential u which has period 1 on a given loop-cut and zero periods on all other loop-cuts. In particular, let u_i be an everywhere regular potential function which has period 1 on A_i and zero periods on all other loop-cuts A_j, $j \neq i$, and all B_j, $j = 1, \ldots, g$; and let u_{g+i} have period 1 on B_i and zero periods on all B_j, $j \neq i$, and all A_j, $j = 1, \ldots, g$. Thus, given any periods p_i on A_i, $i = 1, \ldots, g$, and q_i on B_i, $i = 1, \ldots, g$, the potential

$$u = p_1 u_1 + \cdots + p_g u_g + q_1 u_{g+1} + \cdots + q_g u_{2g}$$

is everywhere regular and has the prescribed periods on the loop-cuts. If u' is any other everywhere regular potential with the same periods as u on the loop-cuts, then u' differs from u by an additive real constant.

The n functions u_1, u_2, $\ldots$, u_n on the surface S are said to be linearly independent over the real numbers (up to an additive constant) if any relationship $a_1 u_1 + a_2 u_2 + \cdots + a_n u_n \equiv$ constant implies that the real constants $a_i = 0$, $i = 1, \ldots, n$. The $2g$ potentials u_i defined above are linearly independent; for any sum $\sum_{i=1}^{2g} a_i u_i$ in which any a_j differs from 0 has period a_j around A_j if $j \leq g$ or around B_{j-g} if $j > g$, and hence is not constant. Since any everywhere regular potential u can be expressed (up to an additive constant) as a linear combination of the u_i, $i = 1, \ldots, 2g$, we say that these $2g$ functions form a *basis* for the everywhere regular potentials on S.

Before leaving these regular potentials u_i, we should notice an interesting fact. From Figs. 1–25 and 1–26, we see that these regular flows in the torus have no cross-points. In Figs. 1–27 and 1–28, we observe that on the surface of genus 2, these flows have two stationary points, and each time tubes are pulled out of the surface to form a new handle, two new cross-points are introduced. In general, we can say that an everywhere regular flow on a surface of genus g has $2g - 2$ stationary points. It can also be proved that if the potential has m poles on a surface of genus g, there will be $2m + 2g - 2$ stationary points.

Now let us study the complex potentials on S. If u_1 is an everywhere regular potential on S, its conjugate potential v_1 is also everywhere regular and $u_1 + iv_1$ is a complex potential. We begin by proving that u_1 and v_1 are linearly independent. In terms of isothermal coordinates, $\partial u_1 / \partial x =$

$\partial v_1/\partial y$, $\partial u_1/\partial y = -\partial v_1/\partial x$. If we assume that $au_1 + bv_1 \equiv$ constant, we have

$$a\frac{\partial u_1}{\partial x} + b\frac{\partial v_1}{\partial x} \equiv 0 \qquad \text{and} \qquad a\frac{\partial u_1}{\partial y} + b\frac{\partial v_1}{\partial y} \equiv 0.$$

But, by the Cauchy-Riemann equations,

$$a\frac{\partial u_1}{\partial x} - b\frac{\partial u_1}{\partial y} \equiv 0 \qquad \text{and} \qquad a\frac{\partial u_1}{\partial y} + b\frac{\partial u_1}{\partial x} \equiv 0.$$

Hence $(a^2 + b^2)\partial u_1/\partial x \equiv 0$ and $(a^2 + b^2)\partial u_1/\partial y \equiv 0$, or $u_1 \equiv$ constant, which is a contradiction.

If we next choose an everywhere regular potential u_2 which is linearly independent of u_1 and v_1 and take its conjugate v_2, the four potentials u_1, v_1, u_2, v_2 are linearly independent. For again assume that

$$au_1 + bv_1 + cu_2 + dv_2 \equiv \text{constant},$$

where $d \neq 0$ since u_1, v_1, and u_2 are linearly independent. Then differentiation and application of the Cauchy-Riemann equations give us the relations

$$(ac + bd)\frac{\partial u_1}{\partial x} + (-ad + bc)\frac{\partial v_1}{\partial x} + (c^2 + d^2)\frac{\partial u_2}{\partial x} \equiv 0,$$

$$(ac + bd)\frac{\partial u_1}{\partial y} + (-ad + bc)\frac{\partial v_1}{\partial y} + (c^2 + d^2)\frac{\partial u_2}{\partial y} \equiv 0.$$

Integration now gives us a linear relation between u_1, v_1, u_2, which is a contradiction. Proceeding in this way, we get the $2g$ linearly independent potentials

$$u_1, v_1, u_2, v_2, \ldots, u_g, v_g,$$

where u_j, v_j are conjugates. We can form the complex potentials $w_j = u_j + iv_j$, $j = 1, \ldots, g$, The functions $w_1, w_2, \ldots, w_g$ are linearly independent (up to an additive constant) over the complex numbers, for a relation

$$c_1w_1 + c_2w_2 + \cdots + c_gw_g \equiv \text{constant}$$

can be separated into two linear relations between the real and imaginary parts. But this is impossible by what was just proved.

Moreover, the most general everywhere finite complex potential function w is just of the form

$$w = c_1w_1 + \cdots + c_gw_g + k,$$

where k is a complex constant. For since the $u_1, v_1, \ldots, u_g, v_g$ are linearly independent over the reals, they form a basis for the regular potentials, and we may take a linear combination of these to have the same periods as the real part of w over the $2g$ loop-cuts. Thus

$$\operatorname{Re} w = \sum_{j=1}^{g} a_j u_j + b_j v_j + k_1, \qquad k_1 = \operatorname{Re} k,$$

and if we set $c_j = a_j - ib_j$, we get

$$w = \sum_{j=1}^{g} c_j w_j + k.$$

The functions $w_1, \ldots, w_g$ therefore form a basis for the everywhere finite complex potentials.

1–5 Meromorphic functions. Now we can obtain the form of an arbitrary complex potential f on S having prescribed singularities of the types we allow. Let $P_1, P_2 \ldots, P_r$ be r points on S at which f is to become infinite, as discussed earlier. First of all, the sum of the logarithmic residues of f must be zero. For if f has a singular term $(A + iB) \log (x + iy)$ when expressed in terms of the isothermal coordinates x, y, the A represents the strength of a source or sink in the flow whose potential is the real part of f. If this is to be a steady flow, the total strength of the sources must equal the strength of the sinks, so the sum of the real parts of the residues is zero. Similarly, the B is the strength of the source or sink in the conjugate flow, so that the sum of the B's is zero. In particular, this shows that we cannot have a complex potential with only one logarithmic singularity. Given any two points P and Q on S, we can construct a flow which has a source of given strength A at P and a sink of strength $-A$ at Q. The conjugate flows would then have vortices with equal but oppositely directed circulation. By coalescing logarithmic singularities, we can construct a flow whose complex potential has a pole at only one point of S and is otherwise finite.

We select a point Q on S, different from the points $P_1, P_2, \ldots, P_n$ at which f is singular. Construct the functions $F_1, F_2, \ldots, F_n$ such that F_j has at P_j the same singularity as f and is finite at all other points of S except Q, where F_j has a logarithmic singularity whose residue is the negative of that at P_j. Since the sum of the residues of f is zero, $F_1 + F_2 + \cdots + F_n$ has no singularity at Q and thus has precisely the same singularities on S as f. Then $f - F_1 - F_2 - F_3 - \cdots - F_n$ is an everywhere finite complex potential on S and may be represented as a linear combination of the w_i, $i = 1, 2, \ldots, g$. Hence

$$f = F_1 + F_2 + \cdots + F_n + c_1 w_1 + c_2 w_2 + \cdots + c_g w_g + k$$

is the most general complex potential on S having logarithmic singularities or poles as its only singularities. We may arbitrarily specify the singularities (the sum of whose residues is zero) and the periods of the real parts of f. Once this is done, f is completely determined, up to an additive constant; for if f' has the same singularities, and the real part of f' has the same periods as the real part of f, then $f - f'$ is everywhere finite and its real part has no periods. But then Re $(f - f')$ is a constant, which implies that $f - f' = $ constant.

An arbitrary complex potential function f on S can have moduli of periodicity of two kinds: (1) periods due to logarithmic singularities (vortices), and (2) periods due to the fact that some of the $2g$ loop-cuts are streamlines or equipotential curves. Thus for a complex potential to be single-valued, it *must* have poles as its only singularities. But then can there be *any* single-valued complex potentials?

A complex potential whose only singularities are poles and which is single-valued on S is called a *meromorphic function*. Since any pole of order n may be obtained by coalescing simple poles, we shall try to construct meromorphic functions having only simple poles. Let m points be given at which we want the simple poles to occur, and let $F_1, F_2, \ldots, F_m$ be any complex potential functions, not necessarily single-valued, each having a simple pole at one of the given points. Then the function

$$F = a_1 F_1 + a_2 F_2 + \cdots + a_m F_m + b_1 w_1 + \cdots + b_g w_g + c,$$

where the a_i, b_i, c are complex constants, is the most general function having simple poles at the m given points. Can we choose the constants a_j, b_j in such a way that F becomes single-valued? We compute the periods of F around each of the $2g$ loop-cuts and ask that these be zero:

$$\int_{A_j} dF = a_1 \int_{A_j} dF_1 + \cdots + a_m \int_{A_j} dF_m + b_1 \int_{A_j} dw_1 + \cdots + b_g \int_{A_j} dw_g = 0,$$

$$j = 1, \ldots, g,$$

$$\int_{B_j} dF = a_1 \int_{B_j} dF_1 + \cdots + a_m \int_{B_j} dF_m + b_1 \int_{B_j} dw_1 + \cdots + b_g \int_{B_j} dw_g = 0,$$

$$j = 1, \ldots, g.$$

This gives us $2g$ linear equations for the $m + g$ unknown constants $a_1, a_2, \ldots, a_m, b_1, \ldots, b_g$. If the rank of this system of equations is r, that is, if r of the equations are linearly independent, then $m + g - r$ of the a's and b's may be specified arbitrarily, and, counting the constant c, there are $m + g - r + 1$ arbitrary constants in F, for which any choice of values will make F single-valued. Since $r \leq 2g$, we can in general say that at least $m - g + 1$ constants are arbitrary, and if $m > g$, we are sure that there exists at least one meromorphic function on S with at most simple poles at the m prescribed points. This is part of the Riemann-Roch theorem, which gives a complete answer to the question of the number of independent meromorphic functions having prescribed poles.

Each of these meromorphic functions on the closed surface S shares an important property with polynomials and rational functions on the sphere. If the meromorphic function f takes on the value infinity exactly m times on S (that is, has m simple poles), then f assumes every value exactly m times on S. To get an idea of why this is true, we refer back to the lines of flow near a simple pole P, where each level curve $u = u_0$ (and $v = v_0$) is a circle which passes through P. For large values of u_0 and v_0, these circles intersect again near P, so there are m points, each near a pole, at which f assumes the value $u_0 + iv_0$. As u_0 and v_0 change continuously, the level curves $u = u_0$ and $v = v_0$ deform continuously and will always have one point of intersection. Two of the curves $u = u_0$ can intersect only at one of the finite number of cross-points, in which case we say that the value $u_0 + iv_0$ is assumed k times by f at a cross-point of order $k - 1$.

The complex-valued meromorphic function $f = u + iv$ maps the surface S onto the extended complex plane (sphere), and we have seen that this mapping is conformal. Since f assumes each complex value m times, the values of f cover the sphere with m sheets. A cross-point of order $k - 1$ of f on S maps into a branch point of order $k - 1$ of this m-sheeted covering of the sphere. Indeed, reference to Fig. 1–13 shows that the k curves $u = u_0$ passing through a cross-point P of order $k - 1$ divide the neighborhood of P into k sectors, in each of which f assumes the same set of values. The image of a path that passes from one of the k sectors to another will go from one sheet to another, and after traversing k sheets will return to its starting point.

The original surface S is thus conformally equivalent to an m-sheeted Riemann surface covering the complex sphere. We may then adopt as the basis for our study of the complex potential functions the m-sheeted covering surface over the sphere rather than the surface S in space, since any conformally equivalent surface can be selected as a model. We may well ask what advantage has been gained by considering surfaces in space rather than covering surfaces of the sphere right from the start. The advantages are that the surface in space had no branch points to plague us and the reason for the different kinds of periods of multiple-valued functions was obvious. Thus we avoided certain complications right from the beginning, only to learn later that we actually have studied only another representation of an m-sheeted covering surface of the sphere.

To understand better the nature of the meromorphic functions on S, let us take on the surface S a meromorphic function $z = x + iy$ with m simple poles, and use it to map S one-to-one and conformally onto an m-sheeted covering S^* of the sphere. Then any other meromorphic function $w = u + iv$ on S corresponds to an m-valued analytic function of the complex variable $z = x + iy$, since w is single-valued on the m-sheeted covering surface S^*. We have assumed that w has poles as its only singularities on S, and hence it has no essential singularities as a function of z. Thus w is an *algebraic function* of z.

There is considerable arbitrariness in the selection of the meromorphic function w, and if a w is taken which has different values $w_1, w_2, \ldots, w_m$ on a set of m distinct points at which z assumes one value, then it can be shown that the algebraic equation $f(z, w) = 0$ of degree m in w is irreducible. If n is the sum of the orders of the poles of w, then $f(z, w)$ is of degree n in z. To each point on S^* corresponds one pair of values (z, w) which satisfies the equation $f(z, w) = 0$ and, conversely, to each (z, w) corresponds in general one point of the surface. Thus S^* (or S) is precisely the Riemann surface of the algebraic function $f(z, w) = 0$.

If w_1 is another meromorphic function on S, it is also an algebraic function of z. We can say more about w_1, however, once we have selected the function w satisfying the irreducible equation $f(z, w) = 0$. Indeed, we now show that w_1 is just a rational function of z and w and, conversely, any rational function of z and w is a meromorphic function on S. The last part is clear, since any rational function of z and w is single-valued on S^* and has poles as its only singularities. As for the first part, let w_1 assume the m values $w_1^{(1)}, w_1^{(2)}, \ldots, w_1^{(m)}$ at the points corresponding to a given z, and let w assume the m values $w^{(1)}, w^{(2)}, \ldots, w^{(m)}$ at the same z. Then the sum

$$w_1^{(1)}[w^{(1)}]^\nu + w_1^{(2)}[w^{(2)}]^\nu + \cdots + w_1^{(m)}[w^{(m)}]^\nu$$

is a symmetric function and hence is single-valued as a function of z on the sphere. Since it is also algebraic, it must be a rational function of z for all integral powers ν. But from any m such linear equations in the $w_1^{(k)}$ (for different values of ν) we can solve for the $w_1^{(1)}, w_1^{(2)}, \ldots, w_1^{(m)}$ as rational functions of z and $w^{(1)}, w^{(2)}, \ldots, w^{(m)}$. From these we can get the desired result.

We have neglected for a while the multiple-valued potentials on S having only poles and logarithmic singularities. If W is one such function, then W must also be a multiple-valued function of z after S is mapped onto the

m-sheeted covering S^* of the sphere. The multiplicity of W on S^* is restricted to constant additive periods, and hence the derivative dW/dz is single-valued on S^* and has poles as its only singularities. But we have shown that dW/dz must then be a rational function of z, w; that is,

$$W = \int R(z, w) \, dz,$$

where R is a rational function of z and w. The converse is also true; namely, each integral of this type gives rise to a multiple-valued function on S having the prescribed type of singularities. Thus we see that the study of algebraic functions w of z and the integrals of rational functions of z and w is precisely the same as the study on S of (single-valued) meromorphic functions and the multiple-valued complex potentials having the prescribed types of singularities.

Now we see what we have gained by our approach. We had previously encountered difficulty in studying the multiplicity of values of the integrals $\int R(z, w) \, dz$. The periods due to logarithmic singularities were easily understood by use of the Cauchy residue theorem alone. But the study of the functions on a closed surface S has shown us clearly the nature of the other periods, those corresponding to integration around the loop-cuts of S. This gives us a complete picture of the possible multiplicity of values of these integrals. Our study even leads us to the possibility of making substitutions in this integral, for the z and w were any pair of independent meromorphic functions on S satisfying an irreducible algebraic equation. Any other two, say z_1 and w_1, could have been selected, where z_1 and w_1 are the rational functions of z and w, respectively, and z and w are in turn rational functions of z_1 and w_1. Thus we see that z_1 and w_1 may be substituted for z and w without changing the general character of the integral.

1–6 Function theory on a torus. To crystallize the preceding discussion, let us consider the simple case in which S is a torus. Here $g = 1$, and we may construct a meromorphic function on S which has two poles ($m > g$). This function has $2m + 2g - 2 = 4$ cross-points and must map S onto a two-sheeted covering of the sphere with four branch points, which is just what we showed previously from a topological point of view when we mapped the two-sheeted Riemann surface with four branch points onto a torus; however, the mapping is now *conformal*.

A conformal mapping of the torus onto a two-sheeted covering of the plane can easily be written explicitly. Consider the torus in (x, y, z)-space obtained by rotating the circle $(x - R)^2 + z^2 = \rho^2$, $y = 0$, about the z-axis:

$$x = (R + \rho \cos \alpha) \cos \varphi,$$
$$y = (R + \rho \cos \alpha) \sin \varphi,$$
$$z = \rho \sin \alpha,$$

where φ is the meridian angle and α is the latitude angle. To get a set of isothermal coordinates from (α, φ), we note that

$$ds = \sqrt{dx^2 + dy^2 + dz^2} = \sqrt{(R + \rho \cos \alpha)^2 \, d\varphi^2 + \rho^2 \, d\alpha^2}.$$

If we set $\xi = \varphi$ and

$$\eta = \int_0^\alpha \frac{\rho \, d\alpha}{R + \rho \, \cos \alpha},$$

this becomes

$$ds = (R + \rho \cos \alpha)\sqrt{d\xi^2 + d\eta^2};$$

(ξ, η) are then isothermal coordinates on the torus which map the torus conformally into the (ξ, η)-plane. As φ and α each vary between $-\pi$ and π, ξ varies between $-\pi$ and π, and η varies between $-p$ and p, where

$$p = \int_0^\pi \frac{\rho \, d\alpha}{R + \rho \cos \alpha},$$

so that (ξ, η) fills out a rectangle in the (ξ, η)-plane.

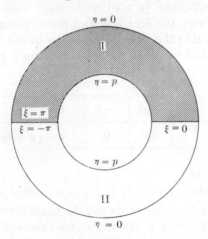

FIGURE 1–29.

In Fig. 1–29, only the upper half of the torus is visible. We have shaded one quarter of the torus and labeled it I. This is mapped into the shaded rectangle labeled I in Fig. 1–30. The other visible quarter of the torus is labeled II and is mapped into the unshaded rectangle labeled II. The area under I is to be unshaded and labeled IV while that under II is to be shaded and labeled III. Note that points on the lines $\xi = \pi$ and $\xi = -\pi$ having

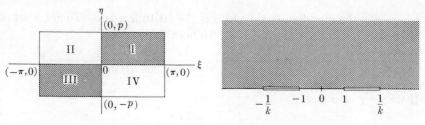

FIGURE 1–30.　　　　　　　　　　　　FIGURE 1–31.

the same η-coordinates correspond to the same point of the torus. Similarly, points on the lines $\eta = p$ and $\eta = -p$ having the same ξ coordinates correspond to the same point on the torus. To get the torus from this rectangle, we "identify" these pairs of lines.

Next consider in the $z = x + iy$ plane the four points $z = -1/k,\ -1,\ 1,$ $1/k,\ (k < 1)$. The function

$$\zeta = a + b \int_0^z \frac{dz}{\sqrt{(1 - z^2)(1 - k^2 z^2)}}$$

maps the upper half-plane $(y > 0)$ conformally into a rectangle in the $\xi + i\eta = \zeta$ plane, with the four specified points going into the vertices. We can choose k so that the rectangle is similar to rectangle I in Fig. 1–30, and then choose a and b so that $\zeta(z)$ actually maps $y > 0$ into rectangle I in such a way that

z	$-1/k$	-1	1	$1/k$
ζ	ip	0	π	$\pi + ip$

as shown in Fig. 1–32.

Each of the points $-1/k,\ -1,\ 1,\ 1/k$ is a branch point of order 2 for $\sqrt{(1 - z^2)(1 - k^2 z^2)}$, so that if we cut the plane between $-1/k$ and -1, and between 1 and $1/k$ (Fig. 1–31), and attach another sheet crosswise along these cuts, we find that $\zeta = \zeta(z)$ maps this two-sheeted Riemann surface conformally onto the whole rectangle in Fig. 1–30. The inverse mapping $z = z(\zeta)$ then gives us a one-to-one conformal map of the torus onto the two-sheeted Riemann surface. Indeed, the two edges of the rectangle on the lines $\xi = \pi$ and $\xi = -\pi$ are the images of the segments between 1 and $1/k$, while each of the edges on the lines $\eta = p$ and $\eta = -p$ is an image of the segment between $1/k$ and $-1/k$ through ∞, so that identified points on the edges of the rectangle are images of the same point on the two-sheeted Riemann surface.

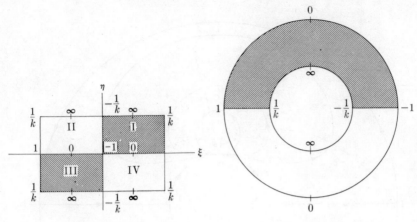

FIGURE 1–32.   FIGURE 1–33.

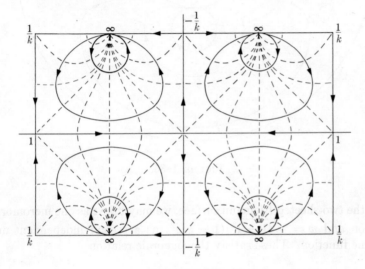

FIGURE 1–34.

The function $z = z(\zeta)$ mapping the torus one-to-one conformally onto the two-sheeted Riemann surface gives rise to a single-valued complex potential on the torus, with poles at the two points (indicated by ∞ in Fig. 1–33) which map into $z = \infty$ and with cross-points at the four points marked 1, $1/k$, $-1/k$, -1 in Fig. 1–33. This complex potential is the potential of the flows shown in Fig. 1–34 in the rectangle and in Fig. 1–35 on the torus. The dotted lines are the equipotential lines $x = $ constant, and the solid lines are the streamlines $y = $ constant, with arrows indicating the direction of flow.

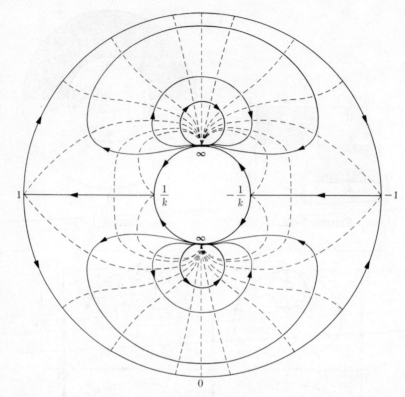

FIGURE 1–35.

On the two-sheeted Riemann surface, we may take z as one meromorphic function and $w = \sqrt{(1 - z^2)(1 - k^2 z^2)}$ as a second independent meromorphic function. These satisfy the algebraic relation

$$w^2 - (1 - z^2)(1 - k^2 z^2) = 0,$$

and any other meromorphic function on this Riemann surface, and hence on the torus, is a rational function of z and w. The multiple-valued complex potentials on the torus, is a rational function of z and w. The multiple-valued complex potentials on the torus are then of the form $\int R(z, w)\,dz$, where $w = \sqrt{(1 - z^2)(1 - k^2 z^2)}$. Integrals of this type are *elliptic integrals*.

Since $g = 1$, there is only one independent, everywhere finite (multiple-valued) complex potential, namely, that given in Fig. 1–25. The analytic function

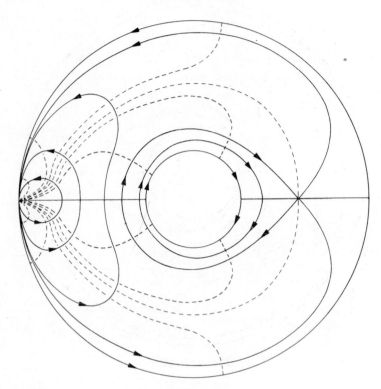

FIGURE 1–36.

$$\zeta(z) = \int_0^z \frac{dz}{w}$$

maps the two-sheeted surface into a rectangle and hence is finite on the surface. Thus this is (up to a constant multiplier) the only everywhere finite multiple-valued complex potential on the torus. It is known as an elliptic integral of the first kind, and is the canonical form for any elliptic integral which is finite on the two-sheeted surface. The multiple-valued functions on the torus that have poles as their only singularities are called elliptic integrals of the second kind, while those having logarithmic singularities as well are called elliptic integrals of the third kind. Flows corresponding to elliptic integrals of the second and third kinds are given in Figs. 1–36 and 1–37, respectively. The canonical forms for these integrals can also be readily found. This gives us a complete picture of the nature of the elliptic integrals and leads to their classification into three kinds.

Another question, which may have occurred to the reader, is that of the

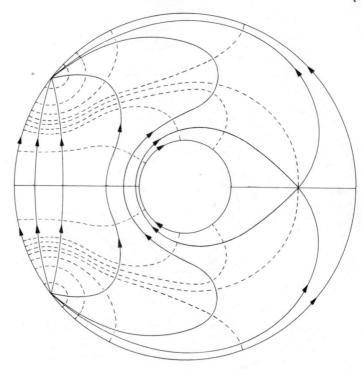

FIGURE 1–37.

isothermal coordinates. We have seen that on any surface we can find a system of isothermal coordinates which are valid in the vicinity of a given point and which give us a conformal mapping of the neighborhood of this point into a region in the complex plane. However, is it possible to find a system of isothermal coordinates valid on the whole surface? Later we shall show that if the surface has the property that any simple closed curve divides it into two pieces, then we can find isothermal coordinates which map the whole surface into a region of the extended complex plane in a one-to-one conformal manner. This gives us coordinates valid in the large, rather than the local coordinates we had before. We shall also show that in other cases it is possible to find isothermal coordinates $\sigma + i\tau = t$ with the property that different values of t determine different points on the surface, but to a single point on the surface will correspond many values of t. This is a situation similar to that which exists when we write the parametric representation of a curve, such as a circle $x^2 + y^2 = 1$ in the plane. If we set $x = \cos \theta$, $y = \sin \theta$, to each value of θ corresponds only one point on the circle, whereas each point on the circle has many θ's corresponding to it. If we consider the Riemann surface of the algebraic function $w(z)$ as being defined by the pairs (z, w), we may look upon this surface as an algebraic curve (in the same sense as the locus of points (x, y), for which $x^2 + y^2 = 1$, is a curve), and the coordinate t lets us write $z = z(t)$, $w = w(t)$ parametrically, as in the case of the circle, so that one point (z, w) corresponds to each value of t. We call t the *uniformizing parameter* of the Riemann surface.

Let us now chart, chapter by chapter, the course we follow through the rest of this book to carry out the study of abstract Riemann surfaces and their eventual connection with algebraic functions and their integrals. The second chapter discusses the basic notions of point-set topology, which we use to define an abstract Riemann surface or analytic manifold. Chapter 3 shows that the Riemann surface of an analytic function is also a Riemann surface in this abstract sense. In Chapter 4, covering surfaces and the fundamental group are treated. Such topics as the triangulability, orientability, and normal forms of surfaces are taken up in Chapter 5, and the notions of homology groups and their invariance are also included. In Chapter 6 we shall see that it is more natural to consider differentials and their integrals on a surface, rather than functions. These differentials form a Hilbert space, which is studied in Chapter 7. In Chapter 8 we come to the existence of harmonic and analytic differentials and functions on the abstract Riemann surfaces, corresponding to the flows we discussed in this introduction. The problem of finding a uniformizing parameter over the whole surface is taken up in Chapter 9, where automorphic functions are also discussed. Finally, the meromorphic functions and multiple-valued functions on the Riemann surface are studied in Chapter 10, connecting the study of closed Riemann surfaces and the study of algebraic functions.

PROBLEMS

1. Show that the n-sheeted Riemann surface of the algebraic function $w^n - z = 0$ is topologically a sphere.

2. Show graphically how the flow with the complex potential $1/z^2$ can be obtained by coalescing two simple poles.

3. In stereographic projection, a point $z = x + iy$ in the z-plane corresponds to the point (ξ, η, ζ) other than $(0, 0, 1)$ on the sphere $\xi^2 + \eta^2 + \zeta^2 = 1$, in which the line from $(0, 0, 1)$ to $(x, y, 0)$ intersects the sphere. Show that $x = \xi/(1 - \zeta)$, $y = \eta/(1 - \zeta)$, and that for the element of arc length $d\sigma$ on the sphere we have $d\sigma = (1 - \zeta)\,ds$, where $ds^2 = dx^2 + dy^2$, so that (x, y) are isothermal coordinates on the sphere except at $(0, 0, 1)$.

4. Find a uniformizing parameter t on the torus, using the material in Section 1–6.

CHAPTER 2

GENERAL TOPOLOGY

2–1 Topological spaces. In the introduction we saw that we are led to the study of multiple-valued functions of a complex variable through the study of functions on surfaces. In this chapter we shall lay the foundations for the study of surfaces. The backbone of analysis is the notion of convergence. General topology deals with the problem of introducing into an arbitrary collection of objects a notion of "vicinity" or "closeness" which enables us to discuss convergence questions. The terms *set* or *class* will mean any collection of objects; the objects will be referred to as *elements* or *points* of the set or class. Such a set becomes a *topological space* when a notion of convergence has been introduced into it which enables one to designate certain sequences as convergent. We shall here introduce a notion of convergence into sets in such a way as to obtain what is known as a *Hausdorff space*. Later certain additional conditions will be added to make these sets manifolds or surfaces.

Let E be any set of elements. A set A, all of whose elements are also elements of E, is called a *subset* of E. In the following explanation of notation, A and B denote subsets of E.

$p \in E$ means "p is an element of E," also read "p belongs to E" or "p is in E."

$p \notin E$ means "p is not an element of E."

$A \subseteq B$ means "A is a subset of B."

$A = B$ means "$A \subseteq B$ and $B \subseteq A$."

$A \subset B$ means "A is a *proper* subset of B"; that is, $A \subseteq B$ and $A \neq B$.

$A \cup B$ means "the *union* of A and B"; that is, the set consisting of those elements of A and B which are either in A or in B or in both.

$A \cap B$ means "the *intersection* of A and B"; that is, the set of those elements of A and B which belong to both A and B.

ϕ means "the *null* or *empty* set"; that is, the set containing no elements.

The sets A and B are called *disjoint* if $A \cap B = \phi$. By $A - B$ we shall mean the set of those elements of A which do not belong to B. If $A \subseteq E$, the *complement* of A in E is the set $E - A$. If E is understood from context, we shall simply write $\mathbf{C}A$ for the complement of A in E. It is not

42

difficult to verify that $\mathbf{C}(A \cup B) = (\mathbf{C}A) \cap (\mathbf{C}B)$ and $\mathbf{C}(A \cap B) = (\mathbf{C}A) \cup (\mathbf{C}B)$. For example, $\mathbf{C}(A \cup B)$ is the set of points belonging to neither A nor B. Thus $\mathbf{C}(A \cup B)$ is precisely the set of points belonging to both the complement of A and the complement of B, and we have proved the first of the two statements. We also note that the definition of complement yields immediately $\mathbf{C}(\mathbf{C}A) = A$.

Let I be a set which we shall call an *index set*. Let each $i \in I$ correspond to a subset A_i of a set E. Then $\cup_{i \in I} A_i$ denotes the set of all elements $x \in E$ such that there is *at least one* $i \in I$ for which $x \in A_i$. By $\cap_{i \in I} A_i$ is meant the set of all elements $x \in E$ such that $x \in A_i$ for *all* $i \in I$. It is easily verified that $\mathbf{C}(\cup_{i \in I} A_i) = \cap_{i \in I} (\mathbf{C}A_i)$ and $\mathbf{C}(\cap_{i \in I} A_i) = \cup_{i \in I} (\mathbf{C}A_i)$.

The set E will be called a *topological space* if some of its subsets are designated as *open sets*, and the open sets satisfy the following four axioms:

AXIOM 1. The empty set ϕ is open.

AXIOM 2. The whole set E is open.

AXIOM 3. The union of an arbitrary number of open sets is an open set.

AXIOM 4. The intersection of any finite number of open sets is an open set.

If, in addition, the topological space E satisfies the following "separation" axiom, it is called a *Hausdorff space*:

AXIOM 5. Given any two elements p and q in E, there exist two disjoint open sets A and B such that $p \in A$ and $q \in B$.

Before proceeding further, let us consider several examples of Hausdorff spaces. Let E be the set consisting of just two elements, p and q. Then the open sets can be defined to be the empty set ϕ, the single point p, the single point q, and the whole space E. It is clear that all the axioms 1 through 5 are satisfied. If, however, we had defined the open sets to be only the sets ϕ and E, axiom 5 would not have been satisfied, and the space E would not be a Hausdorff space.

A special class of Hausdorff spaces are the *metric spaces*. A metric space M is a set for which there is defined a real-valued *distance* function $d(p, q)$ of the two elements p and q of M which satisfies the following three conditions:

AXIOM a. $d(p, q) = 0$ if and only if $p = q$.

AXIOM b. $d(p, q) = d(q, p)$.

AXIOM c. $d(p, q) \leq d(p, r) + d(r, q)$ for all $p, q, r \in M$.

The open sets in M are defined by saying that a set A is open if to each point $p \in A$ corresponds a positive number ϵ such that $q \in M$ and $d(p, q) < \epsilon$ implies $q \in A$. Axioms 1 through 5 are satisfied. The set of points which satisfy $d(p, q) < \epsilon$ for some fixed point p in M is called a *spherical neighborhood of radius ϵ about p* and is denoted by $S(p, \epsilon)$. From axioms a, b, and c for a metric space, it follows directly that spherical neighborhoods are open sets in M. An example of such a metric space is the set of all n-tuples of real numbers $x = (x_1, x_2, \ldots, x_n)$, in which the distance between the points $x = (x_1, \ldots, x_n)$ and $y = (y_1, \ldots, y_n)$ is given by

$$d(x, y) = \sqrt{\sum_{k=1}^{n} (x_k - y_k)^2}.$$

This yields the n-dimensional euclidean space $\mathcal{E}^n$. In general, however, we shall deal with topological spaces in which no such metric has been defined, and we shall rely completely upon the properties of open sets derived from axioms 1 through 5.

In the following discussion, E is a fixed Hausdorff space. A subset A of E is called a *neighborhood* of an element p if there exists an open set B in E such that $p \in B \subseteq A$. An element p of a set A is called an *interior point* of A if A is a neighborhood of p. By the *interior* of A, we mean the set of interior points of A. We shall let A° denote the interior of A. We now prove several theorems about these concepts.

THEOREM 2–1. *$A^\circ = A$ if and only if A is an open set.*

If A is open, it follows from the definition of neighborhood that A is a neighborhood of any point p in A. If, on the other hand, A is a neighborhood of every point contained in A, then each point p belongs to an open set B_p which in turn is contained in A. If we represent the union of all the sets B_p by $\cup_{p \in A} B_p$, we have $A \subseteq \cup_{p \in A} B_p \subseteq A$. Therefore $A = \cup_{p \in A} B_p$ and is thus open by axiom 3.

THEOREM 2–2. *A° is an open set and is the largest open set contained in A; that is, if B is open and $B \subseteq A$, then $B \subseteq A^\circ$.*

Indeed, let B be open and $B \subseteq A$. Then A is a neighborhood of every point in B and $B \subseteq A^\circ$. To show that A° is open, let $p \in A^\circ$. Then there is an open set B_p such that $B_p \subseteq A$. But this implies $B_p \subseteq A^\circ$, and hence A° is a neighborhood of p. Thus A° is a neighborhood of each of its points and, by Theorem 2–1, is open.

THEOREM 2–3. *$A^\circ \cap B^\circ = (A \cap B)^\circ$.*

For $A^\circ \cap B^\circ$ is an open set by axiom 4, and $A^\circ \cap B^\circ \subseteq A \cap B$. Thus Theorem 2–2 tells us that $A^\circ \cap B^\circ \subseteq (A \cap B)^\circ$. We also have that $(A \cap B)^\circ$ is an open set and is contained in both A and B. Thus $(A \cap B)^\circ \subseteq A^\circ$ and $(A \cap B)^\circ \subseteq B^\circ$ or, finally, $(A \cap B)^\circ \subseteq A^\circ \cap B^\circ$, proving our assertion.

A set A is called *closed* if $\mathbf{C}A$ is open. The axioms 3 and 4 for open sets tell us that the union of a finite number of closed sets is closed and that the intersection of an arbitrary number of closed sets is closed. We shall say that an element p is *adherent* to a set A if every neighborhood of p contains at least one point of A. The *closure* of A, written $\overline{A}$, is the set of all points adherent to A. We note that $A \subseteq \overline{A}$. There is a close connection between the notions of closure of a set and interior of a set. In particular, we have

THEOREM 2–4. $\mathbf{C}\overline{A} = (\mathbf{C}A)^\circ$ *and* $\overline{\mathbf{C}A} = \mathbf{C}A^\circ$.

To prove the first of these, note that $p \in \mathbf{C}\overline{A}$ if and only if p has a neighborhood not meeting A, that is, a neighborhood in $\mathbf{C}A$. Thus $p \in \mathbf{C}\overline{A}$ means that $\mathbf{C}A$ is a neighborhood of p or, simply, $p \in (\mathbf{C}A)^\circ$. Similarly, the second statement is proved by observing that $p \in \mathbf{C}A^\circ$ if and only if A is not a neighborhood of p; that is, every open set containing p meets $\mathbf{C}A$. Hence $p \in \mathbf{C}A^\circ$ means that every neighborhood of p meets $\mathbf{C}A$ or, simply, $p \in \overline{\mathbf{C}A}$.

COROLLARY 2–1. $\overline{A}$ *is closed.*

For, by Theorem 2–2, $\mathbf{C}\overline{A} = (\mathbf{C}A)^\circ$ is open.

THEOREM 2–5. A *is closed if and only if* $\overline{A} = A$.

In fact, A is closed when and only when $\mathbf{C}A$ is open. But $\mathbf{C}A$ is open if and only if $\mathbf{C}A = (\mathbf{C}A)^\circ$. Since $(\mathbf{C}A)^\circ = \mathbf{C}\overline{A}$, we see that $\mathbf{C}A = \mathbf{C}\overline{A}$ and, finally, $A = \overline{A}$.

THEOREM 2–6. $\overline{A}$ *is the smallest closed set containing A in the sense that if B is closed and $A \subseteq B$, then $\overline{A} \subseteq B$.*

For if $A \subseteq B$, then $\overline{A} \subseteq \overline{B} = B$.

We observe here that there is a certain duality between theorems concerning open and closed sets. In particular, open and closed, interior and closure, union and intersection, are dual categories under the operation of complementation. A statement about open sets implies a statement about closed sets with the dual category substituted in the statement. For example, the statement "the union of arbitrarily many open sets is open" has as its dual statement "the intersection of arbitrarily many closed sets is closed"; and the statement "the intersection of finitely many open sets is open" has as its dual the statement "the union of finitely many closed sets is closed."

The *exterior* of a set A is defined to be the interior of the complement of A, that is, $(\mathbf{C}A)^\circ$. The *boundary* of A is the set of points common to both $\overline{A}$ and $\overline{\mathbf{C}A}$, that is, $\overline{A} \cap \overline{\mathbf{C}A}$. We see that for any set A in the space E, the whole space E is the union of the three mutually disjoint sets: the interior of A, the boundary of A, and the exterior of A. To illustrate, consider the two-dimensional euclidean space $\mathcal{E}^2$. The disk $x_1^2 + x_2^2 < 1$ is an open set. Its closure is the disk $x_1^2 + x_2^2 \leq 1$. Its boundary is the circle $x_1^2 + x_2^2 = 1$, while its exterior is the set $x_1^2 + x_2^2 > 1$.

The notions of open sets and neighborhoods allow us to discuss the convergence of sequences of points. First, by a *deleted* neighborhood of a point $p \in E$, we shall mean a neighborhood of p from which the point p is removed. We shall say that a point p is a *cluster point* or a *point of accumulation* of a set $A \subseteq E$ if every deleted neighborhood of p contains at least one point in A. The set of cluster points of A is called the *derived* set of A and is denoted by A'. It follows that a point is adherent to A if and only if it belongs either to A or to A', that is, $\overline{A} = A \cup A'$. A point p which belongs to A but is not a cluster point of A is called an *isolated* point of A.

A *sequence* $\{p_n\}$ of points in E is a correspondence between the positive integers and the set E which associates with each integer n, an element $p_n \in E$. We say that the sequence $\{p_n\}$ converges to a limit p if to each neighborhood U of p corresponds an integer N such that $p_n \in U$ if $n > N$. Axiom 5 enables us to say that a sequence cannot converge to two different limits; for if p and q are two different points, we can find two disjoint neighborhoods U_p of p and U_q of q. If $\{p_n\}$ converges to p, there exists an N such that for all $n > N$, $p_n \in U_p$. Thus for all $n > N$, $p_n \notin U_q$ and q is not a limit point of $\{p_n\}$.

If F is a subset of a topological space E, we may make F itself a topological space by defining open sets in F to be the intersections of open sets in E with the set F. Thus if A is an open set in E, $A \cap F$ is an open set in F. It can easily be verified that these sets satisfy axioms 1 through 5. The open sets defined in this way give us what is called the *relative topology* induced in F. A subset A of F is closed in F if and only if there is a closed set B in E such that $A = B \cap F$. Indeed, if such a set B exists, then $E - B = B_1$ is an open set in E and $F - A = B_1 \cap F$. Thus $F - A$ is open and A is closed in F. Conversely, if A is closed in F, $F - A$ is open in F and $F - A = B_1 \cap F$, where B_1 is open in E. Then the set $B = E - B_1$ and, clearly, $A = B \cap F$ where B is closed in E.

Let U_i represent an open set in the space E for each index i belonging to some index set I (such as the integers, real numbers, etc.). We say that the collection of open sets $\{U_i\}$ forms an *open covering* of E if $E = \cup_{i \in I} U_i$, that is, if each point of E is in at least one of the sets U_i. The open covering is called *finite* if there is only a finite number of different sets in the collection $\{U_i\}$. The space E is called *compact* if every open covering of E contains at least one finite open covering of E. If A is a subset of E, we say that A is compact if A is a compact space in the relative topology induced in A by E. Thus if $\{U_i\}$ is any collection of open sets in E and $A \subseteq \cup_{i \in I} U_i$, we say that $\{U_i\}$ is an open covering of A in E. A is then compact if and only if every such open covering of A contains a finite open covering of A. For example, the Heine-Borel theorem tells us that every closed, bounded subset of $\mathcal{E}^n$ is compact (see, for example, Ref. 3, p. 88).

THEOREM 2–7. *Every closed subset of a compact set is compact.*

Let E be compact and let A be a closed subset of E. Also let $\{U_i\}$ be an open covering of A. Then $\{U_i\}$ and $\mathbf{C}A$ form an open covering of E. There is a finite open covering of E contained in this covering. Thus A is also covered by a finite number of the $\{U_i\}$.

THEOREM 2–8. *If E is a compact space and A is a subset of E containing an infinite number of points, then $A' \neq \phi$; that is, every infinite subset of E has a cluster point in E.*

Let us assume that $A' = \phi$. Then $\overline{A} = A$, A is a closed set, and $E - A$ is an open set. Furthermore, since $A' = \phi$, to each point $p \in A$ corresponds an open set U_p containing p but no other point in A. The collection of open sets U_p together with $E - A$ form an open covering of E containing an innite number of sets, since A is infinite. The removal of any one of the sets U_p from the covering exposes the point p associated with U_p and destroys the covering of E. Therefore, this covering does not contain a finite open covering, and we have arrived at a contradiction to the compactness of E. Incidentally, this property of closed, bounded sets of $\mathcal{E}^n$ is just the familiar Bolzano-Weierstrass theorem.

THEOREM 2–9. *A compact set is closed.*

Assume that A is compact and that $p \in \mathbf{C}A$. Then for any $q \in A$, axiom 5 for a Hausdorff space implies that there are two disjoint open sets U_q and V_q with $q \in U_q$ and $p \in V_q$. Clearly, $A \subset \cup_{q \in A} U_q$, so that $\{U_q\}_{q \in A}$ forms an open covering of A. The compactness of A implies that a finite number of the $\{U_q\}$, say $U_{q_1}, U_{q_2}, \ldots, U_{q_n}$, cover A. Since $V_{q_i} \subset \mathbf{C}U_{q_i}$, we have

$$\bigcap_{i=1}^{n} V_{q_i} \subset \bigcap_{i=1}^{n} \mathbf{C}U_{q_i} = \mathbf{C}\bigcup_{i=1}^{n} U_{q_i} \subset \mathbf{C}A.$$

However, $\cap_{i=1}^{n} V_{q_i}$ is an open set containing p, so that $\mathbf{C}A$ is open and A is closed.

A space E is called *locally compact* if each point of E has a compact neighborhood. An example of a locally compact space is $\mathcal{E}^n$, since each point $x = (x_1, x_2, \ldots, x_n)$ has about it a compact sphere consisting of those points $y = (y_1, y_2, \ldots, y_n)$ for which $\sum_{k=1}^{n}(y_k - x_k)^2 \leq R^2$ for any positive number R.

If E_1 and E_2 are two Hausdorff spaces, a new Hausdorff space $E_1 \times E_2$, called the *topological product* of E_1 and E_2, is defined to be the set of all ordered couples (p_1, p_2) with $p_1 \in E_1$ and $p_2 \in E_2$ and with the following topology. If $A_1 \subseteq E_1$ and $A_2 \subseteq E_2$, then $A_1 \times A_2$ is the subset of $E_1 \times E_2$ consisting of all couples (p_1, p_2) with $p_1 \in A_1$ and $p_2 \in A_2$. The open sets of $E_1 \times E_2$ are the sets obtained by considering all possible unions of sets $A_1 \times A_2$ where A_1 is open in E_1 and A_2 is open in E_2. It is easy to verify axioms 1 through 5 for these sets. In this way, for example, we may consider the euclidean plane $\mathcal{E}^2$ as the topological product of two euclidean lines $\mathcal{E}^1 \times \mathcal{E}^1$. Similarly, the square $[0 \leq x_1 \leq 1, 0 \leq x_2 \leq 1]$ is the topological product of the two line segments $0 \leq x_1 \leq 1$ and $0 \leq x_2 \leq 1$.

A space E is said to be *connected* if it cannot be expressed as the union of two nonempty disjoint open sets. Since the complement of each open set is a closed set, we observe that E can be divided into two nonempty disjoint open sets if and only if it can be divided into two nonempty disjoint closed sets. In fact, E is connected if and only if it does not have a nonempty proper subset which is both open and closed. We say that a subset A of E is connected if it forms a connected space in the relative topology. Thus A is connected if and only if it is impossible to find two open (closed) sets B_1 and B_2 in E such that $A \cap B_1$ and $A \cap B_2$ are nonempty disjoint, and $A \subseteq B_1 \cup B_2$.

THEOREM 2–10. *Let* $\{A_i\}$, $i \in I$, *be a collection of connected sets in E all of which contain the common point p. Then $C = \cup_{i \in I} A_i$ is also connected.*

Suppose that $C = B_1 \cup B_2$, where B_1 and B_2 are relatively open in C and $B_1 \cap B_2 = \phi$; we shall prove that either B_1 or B_2 must be empty. Certainly the common point p belongs to either B_1 or B_2, say B_1. Then since $A_i \subseteq B_1 \cup B_2$, we may decompose A_i into $A_i = (A_i \cap B_1) \cup (A_i \cap B_2)$. The two parts $A_i \cap B_1$ and $A_i \cap B_2$ are relatively open in A_i and are disjoint; hence the connectedness of A_i implies that one must be empty. Since $p \in A_i \cap B_1$, we know that $B_2 \cap A_i = \phi$ for all $i \in I$; therefore $\cup_{i \in I} (B_2 \cap A_i) = \phi$. This, however, may be written as $B_2 \cap C = \phi$, and since $B_2 \subseteq C$, we conclude that $B_2 = \phi$. Thus C is connected.

The interval $I: a \leq x \leq b$ in $\mathcal{E}^1$ is connected; for otherwise $I = A \cup B$, where A and B are nonempty disjoint closed sets in I. Let $x_1 \in A$ and $x_2 \in B$ and suppose that $x_1 < x_2$. Then let c be the greatest lower bound of those points in the interval $x_1 < x < x_2$ which lie in B; $c > x_1$. Since B is closed, $c \in B$; but the interval $x_1 \leq x < c$ lies completely in A, and hence c is a limit point of points in A. Since A is closed, $c \in A$, which is impossible since A and B are disjoint. Theorem 2–10 enables us to use the connectedness of I to prove that $\mathcal{E}^1$ is connected, for $\mathcal{E}^1 = \cup_{n=1}^{\infty} I_n$, where I_n is the interval $-n \leq x \leq n$, and each I_n is connected. To show that $\mathcal{E}^2$ is connected, we observe that $\mathcal{E}^2$ is the union of all lines through a fixed point considered as an origin.

Consider next all the connected sets in the space E which contain the the fixed point p. According to Theorem 2–10, the union C of all these connected sets in E containing p is also a connected set. It is the largest connected set containing p; for if A is any connected set containing p, then A is one term in the union forming C, and $A \subseteq C$. We call this largest connected set containing p the *component* of E determined by p.

THEOREM 2–11. *Two components C_1 and C_2 of E are either disjoint or identical.*

For if C_1 and C_2 are not disjoint, they contain a common point q. Since C_1 and C_2 are both connected, $C_1 \cup C_2$ is also connected. But C_1 and C_2 are the largest connected sets containing fixed points p_1 and p_2, respectively. Thus $C_1 \cup C_2 \subseteq C_1$ and $C_1 \cup C_2 \subseteq C_2$, or $C_1 = C_2$.

A set which is open and connected will be called a *region* or *open domain*. A closed connected set will be called a *continuum*. The closure of a region is called a *closed domain*.

In a Hausdorff space E, let B be an indexed collection of open sets U_i, $i \in I$, for some index set I. This collection B of open sets forms a *base* for E when every open set $U \subset E$ is the union of sets in B. E is said to have a *countable base* when there are only a countable number of different sets in B.

A Hausdorff space E is called *metrizable* if one can define a distance function $d(p, q)$, $p,q \in E$, which satisfies the axioms of a metric space and such that open sets defined by this metric are exactly the open sets of E. This is clearly the case when each spherical neighborhood $d(p, q) < c$ is a neighborhood of q in E and when each neighborhood of $q \in E$ contains a spherical neighborhood about q.

A set A of points in a Hausdorff space E is called *dense* in E if $\overline{A} = E$. The Hausdorff space E is called *separable* if it contains a countable, dense set of points.

THEOREM 2–12. *A metrizable space E has a countable base if and only if it is separable.*

If E is separable, there is a countable set of points $A = \{p_1, p_2, \ldots\}$ dense in E. Let $U_{m,n}$ be the spherical neighborhood $S(p_m, 1/n)$, that is, the set of points $q \in E$ such that $d(q, p_m) < 1/n$. The sets $U_{m,n}$ are a countable collection of open sets, and we shall now prove that they form a base for E. Let V be an open set in E. Then for each $p \in V$, there is an $r > 0$ such that $S(p, r) \subset V$. Fix n such that $1/n < r$. There is a point $p_m \in A$ such that $d(p, p_m) < 1/4n$. An application of the triangle inequality (axiom c) for metric spaces yields $p \in S(p_m, 1/2n) \subset S(p, r) \subset V$. Therefore, to each p corresponds a set $U_{m,n}$ such that $p \in U_{m,n} \subset V$, from which it follows that V is equal to the union of these $U_{m,n}$ for all $p \in V$. Thus the $\{U_{m,n}\}$ form a countable base for E.

The other half of the theorem is easy to prove, for if E has a countable base $\{U_n\}_{n=1}^{\infty}$, then we merely select one point p_n in each U_n and let $A = \{p_n\}_{n=1}^{\infty}$. If $p \in E$, then every neighborhood V of p contains a set U_n and hence a point p_n. Thus p is a cluster point of A and $\overline{A} = E$. We have proved that A is countable and dense in E, so that E must be separable.

As a last remark in this section, we shall define another property of some metric spaces which we shall encounter later. A sequence of points $\{p_n\}$ in a metric space E is called a *Cauchy sequence* if, given any $\epsilon > 0$, there exists a positive integer N, depending upon ϵ, such that if $n > N$, $k > 0$, then $d(p_n, p_{n+k}) < \epsilon$. The metric space E is called *complete* if every Cauchy sequence in E converges to a point in E; that is, if $\{p_n\}$ is a Cauchy sequence of points in E, then there is a point $p \in E$ such that $\lim_{n \to \infty} p_n = p$. The euclidean plane is an example of a complete metric space.

2–2 Functions and mappings. A *function* f from a space E to a space F is a correspondence which assigns an element of F to each element in E. A function f from E to F is said to be a *mapping* of E *into* F. If under the function f, the element $y \in F$ corresponds to $x \in E$, we write $y = f(x)$ and call y the *image* of x by f. When every element of F is the image of at least one element of E, then we say that f maps E *onto* F. If each element of F which is the image of an element of E is the image of only one element of E, then f is said to be a *one-to-one* mapping of E into F. Thus f is one-to-one if $f(x_1) = f(x_2)$ implies that $x_1 = x_2$ in E.

If f is a mapping of a space E to a space F and g is a mapping of the space F to a space G, we shall denote by $g \circ f$ the composite mapping of E to G which assigns the element $g(f(x))$ of G to the element x of E.

If A is a set in E, then $f(A)$ represents the set of points in F which are images of points in A under the mapping f. On the other hand, the set of all points in E which have their images under f in the set B in F will be denoted by $f^{-1}(B)$, and called the *inverse image* of B. We shall now use the notion of neighborhoods in the topological spaces to define continuity. We say that f is *continuous* at a point $x \in E$ if for every neighborhood V of $f(x)$ in F there exists a neighborhood U of x in E such that $f(U) \subseteq V$. More briefly, this may be formulated as follows: f is continuous if and only if the inverse image of a neighborhood of $f(x)$ is a neighborhood of x. This definition is clearly modeled after the definition of continuity of a real-valued function of a real variable, in which case the neighborhood V is taken to be an ϵ-interval about $f(x)$ and the neighborhood U is taken to be a δ-interval about x. A function is said to be *continuous on a set A* if it is continuous at every point of A. An interesting criterion for the continuity of a function on E is given in the following theorem.

THEOREM 2–13. *A function f from E to F is continuous on E if and only if the inverse image of every open set in F is an open set in E.*

If f is continuous on E, then any open set $B \subseteq F$ is a neighborhood of any point $y \in B$. Then if $x \in f^{-1}(B)$, there is a neighborhood U_x of x in E such that $U_x \subseteq f^{-1}(B)$. Thus $f^{-1}(B)$ is a neighborhood of each of its points and hence is open. To prove the other half of the theorem, let $f^{-1}(B)$ be open for all open sets $B \subseteq F$, let x be an arbitrary point in E, and let V be any neighborhood of $f(x)$. Then V contains an open set B containing $f(x)$, $f^{-1}(B)$ is an open set containing x. Therefore $f^{-1}(B)$ is a neighborhood of x, and f is continuous at x.

Since $f^{-1}(CB) = Cf^{-1}(B)$, we may use our duality between open and closed sets to reformulate Theorem 2–13 to say "f is continuous on E if and only if $f^{-1}(B)$ is closed for each closed set $B \subseteq F$."

It should be remarked in connection with Theorem 2–13 that under a continuous mapping, open sets do not necessarily map into open sets. For example, we may give the trivial example of the constant function which maps the whole space $\mathcal{E}^1$ into a single point of $\mathcal{E}^1$. Here every open set is mapped into the closed set consisting of one point. On the other hand, compact sets and connected sets are preserved under continuous mappings, as the next theorems indicate.

THEOREM 2–14. *Let f map a space E continuously into a space F. Then any compact set A in E maps onto a compact set B in F.*

Let $\{U_i\}$, $i \in I$, form an arbitrary open covering of B. Then, by Theorem 2–13, $V_i = f^{-1}(U_i)$ is open for each i, and $\{V_i\}$, $i \in I$, forms an open covering of A. Since A is compact, we can extract a finite open covering from the $\{V_i\}$. Then the images of this finite covering, $U_i = f(V_i)$, form a finite open covering of B, and B is compact.

THEOREM 2–15. *Let f map E continuously into F. Then the image under f of a connected set is connected.*

Let $A \subseteq E$ be connected and let $f(A) = B$. Then suppose B is not connected. There would be a decomposition of B into the union of two disjoint nonempty open sets, B_1 and B_2. Then $f^{-1}(B_1)$ and $f^{-1}(B_2)$ are also open, disjoint, and nonempty, and $A \subseteq f^{-1}(B_1) \cup f^{-1}(B_2)$, which is impossible since A is connected.

When f is a one-to-one mapping of E onto F, we may define an inverse function f^{-1} mapping F onto E by setting $f^{-1}(f(x)) = x$. The inverse f^{-1} is defined on all of F, since each $y \in F$ is the image of exactly one $x \in E$. If f is, in addition, a continuous mapping of E onto F, we cannot in general conclude that f^{-1} is also continuous. For consider the function $u + iv = f(x) = e^{ix}$ defined on the space $E : 0 \le x < 2\pi$ (using the relative topology from $\mathcal{E}^1$) and having values in the space F consisting of the circle $u^2 + v^2 = 1$ (with the relative topology from $\mathcal{E}^2$). This function f is continuous and one-to-one from E onto F, but the inverse function has a discontinuity at

$u = 1$, $v = 0$. A continuous function with a continuous inverse is called *bicontinuous*. A function f which produces a one-to-one bicontinuous mapping of E onto F is called a *homeomorphism* of E onto F. Two spaces E and F are called *homeomorphic* if there is a homeomorphism mapping E onto F. Theorems 2–13 through 2–15 show us that under a homeomorphism the images of open sets are open, the images of closed sets are closed, the images of compact sets are compact, and the images of connected sets are connected. In general, properties that are preserved under homeomorphisms of one space onto another are called *topological invariants*.

Let A be a set of elements p, q, r, ... Suppose that there is given a relation $\Re$ between certain pairs of elements of A which we shall denote by $p \, \Re \, q$. This relation is called an *equivalence relation* if it satisfies the following three properties:

(a) $p \, \Re \, p$ for all $p \in A$, ($\Re$ is reflexive).

(b) If $p \, \Re \, q$, then $q \, \Re \, p$, ($\Re$ is symmetric).

(c) If $p \, \Re \, q$ and $q \, \Re \, r$, then $p \, \Re \, r$, ($\Re$ is transitive).

If $\Re$ is an equivalence relation, we say that all elements q of A which satisfy $q \, \Re \, p$ for some fixed p form an *equivalence class*, which we shall denote by E_p. According to (a), $p \in E_p$. Two equivalence classes E_p and E_q are either disjoint or identical; that is, $E_p \cap E_q = \phi$ or $E_p = E_q$. For if E_p and E_q have the element r in common, then $r \, \Re \, p$ and $r \, \Re \, q$, so (c) and (b) imply that $p \, \Re \, q$. Now if $s \in E_p$, then $s \, \Re \, p$ and $p \, \Re \, q$, so $s \, \Re \, q$ and $s \in E_q$. Hence $E_p \subseteq E_q$, and similarly $E_q \subseteq E_p$, so that $E_p = E_q$. This enables us to define a new set B whose elements are equivalence classes of elements in A. We say that B is formed by *identifying* equivalent elements in A. An element $q \in E_p$ is called a *representative* of the equivalence class E_p.

Consider all continuous mappings of intervals $a \leq t \leq b$ in $\mathcal{E}^1$ into a topological space E. We shall say that the continuous mapping α of $a \leq t \leq b$ in E is equivalent to the continuous mapping β of $c \leq t \leq d$ into E if

$$\alpha(t) = \beta \left(c + \frac{t - a}{b - a} (d - c) \right) \qquad \text{for all } a \leq t \leq b.$$

This defines an equivalence relation between mappings of intervals into E (which we shall denote by $\alpha \cong \beta$), for we may readily verify (a), (b), and (c) above. This equivalence relation divides the continuous mappings of intervals of $\mathcal{E}^1$ into E into equivalence classes. A *path* or *curve* C on E is defined to be an equivalence class of continuous mappings of closed intervals in $\mathcal{E}^1$ into E. Given any mappings of $a \leq t \leq b$ into E, we can find a mapping β of $0 \leq t \leq 1$ into E which is equivalent to α; we need only set $\beta(t) = \alpha(a + t(b - a))$ for $0 \leq t \leq 1$ to get $\alpha \cong \beta$. Unless otherwise stated, we shall take as a representative mapping for each curve C a continuous mapping α of the unit interval $I: 0 \leq t \leq 1$ and denote C by the ordered pair (α, I).

If C is a curve (α, I) on E, the image of I in E is a compact and connected set, which we shall call the *carrier* of C and denote by $|C|$. The point $\alpha(0)$ is called the *beginning* or *initial point* and $\alpha(1)$ is called the *terminal* or *end point* of C. If $\alpha(0) = \alpha(1)$, the curve C is called a *closed curve*. We define the *inverse curve* C^{-1} of $C = (\alpha, I)$ to be the curve $C^{-1} = (\beta, I)$ where $\beta(t) = \alpha(1 - t)$, $t \in I$. C^{-1} has $\alpha(1)$ as initial point and $\alpha(0)$ as terminal point. A path C is said to join the point $p \in E$ to $q \in E$ if $\alpha(0) = p$ and $\alpha(1) = q$. If every pair of points of the Hausdorff space E can be joined by a path, we say that E is *arcwise connected*.†

If p, q, and r are three points of E, $C_1 = (\alpha, I)$ is a curve joining p to q, and $C_2 = (\beta, I)$ is a curve joining q to r, we can define a curve (γ, I) joining p to r as follows:

$$\gamma(t) = \begin{cases} \alpha(2t), & 0 \leq t \leq \tfrac{1}{2}, \\ \beta(2t - 1), & \tfrac{1}{2} \leq t \leq 1. \end{cases}$$

The curve (γ, I) is called the *product* of C_1 and C_2 and is denoted by $C_1 C_2$.

THEOREM 2–16. *An arcwise connected space is connected.*

Suppose that E is arcwise connected but not connected. Then

$$E = A_1 \cup A_2,$$

where A_1 and A_2 are nonempty disjoint closed sets. There must be at least one point $p_1 \in A_1$ and one point $p_2 \in A_2$, and these points can be connected by a path C in E. The carrier of C is a closed connected set in E and may be decomposed as $|C| = |C| \cap E = (|C| \cap A_1) \cup (|C| \cap A_2)$. The two sets $|C| \cap A_1$ and $|C| \cap A_2$ are closed, disjoint, and also nonempty, since $p_1 \in |C| \cap A_1$ and $p_2 \in |C| \cap A_2$. This contradicts the connectedness of $|C|$, proving that E must be connected.

2–3 Manifolds. A connected Hausdorff space M is called a (2-dimensional) *manifold* if each point of M is contained in an open set which is

---

†An *arc* is a path (α, I) for which α is a homeomorphism. A general topological space E is called *arcwise connected* if every pair of points of E can be joined by an arc. It can be shown, however, that for Hausdorff spaces (to which we have restricted ourselves) a pair of points can be connected by an arc if and only if they can be connected by a path. Thus we are justified in replacing the word "arc" by the word "path" in the definition of arcwise connectedness. For a detailed discussion of this subject, see Hall and Spencer (Ref. 19, p. 208).

homeomorphic to an open set in the euclidean plane $\mathcal{E}^2$.† Thus "M is a manifold" means that to each point P_0 on M corresponds an open set U containing P_0 and a homeomorphism Φ of U onto an open set V in the (x_1, x_2)-plane. We shall say that for $P \in U$, $\Phi(P) = (\varphi_1(P), \varphi_2(P))$ where $\varphi_1(P)$ and $\varphi_2(P)$ are continuous real-valued functions of P with $\varphi_1(P_0) = a_1$, $\varphi_2(P_0) = a_2$. Since V is an open set in $\mathcal{E}^2$, for a small enough positive number r, the disk K: $(x_1 - a_1)^2 + (x_2 - a_2)^2 < r^2$ satisfies $\overline{K} \subset V$. Then $\Phi^{-1}(K)$ is an open set on M which contains P_0 and which is homeomorphic to a disk in $\mathcal{E}^2$. This allows us to say that a connected topological space M is a manifold if and only if each point of M is contained in an open set which is homeomorphic to a disk in $\mathcal{E}^2$.

The mapping Φ associates to each point P in the neighborhood U of the point P_0 in a one-to-one fashion a point $(\varphi_1(P), \varphi_2(P))$ of the euclidean plane, so that any couple (x_1, x_2) which lies in $V = \Phi(U)$ determines exactly one point P on M, and may be used as coordinates of the point P. We say that $(\varphi_1(P), \varphi_2(P))$ defines a *local coordinate system* about the point P_0 on M. The numbers $x_1 = \varphi_1(P)$, $x_2 = \varphi_2(P)$ are called *local coordinates* or *local (uniformizing) parameters* about P_0. The parametrized set of points D on M which have local coordinates $(x_1 - a_1)^2 + (x_2 - a_2)^2 < r^2$ is called a *coordinate disk* or *parametric disk*.

The euclidean plane is itself clearly a manifold, for each point (x_0, y_0) is contained in a disk $(x - x_0)^2 + (y - y_0)^2 < r^2$ which is carried into a euclidean disk by the identity mapping. Similarly, any region in the euclidean plane is a manifold. The sphere S^2: $\xi^2 + \eta^2 + \zeta^2 = 1$ in $\mathcal{E}^3$ is a manifold if we introduce the following local uniformizing parameters. At any point P_0 of S^2, we consider the tangent plane T touching S at P_0. In T, we introduce mutually orthogonal x,y-axes with P_0 as the origin, and let Φ be the orthogonal projection of the neighborhood of P_0 on S onto T. Analytically, we can express these local coordinates near P_0: (ξ_0, η_0, ζ_0) by rotating the sphere in such a way that P_0 goes into $(0, 0, -1)$ along a meridian, and then projecting the neighborhood of $(0, 0, -1)$ into the plane $\zeta = -1$. We have for the point P: (ξ, η, ζ) near P_0:

$$x = \varphi_1(P) = -\xi\zeta_0 + \xi\zeta\sqrt{\frac{1 - \zeta_0^2}{1 - \zeta^2}},$$

---

†More generally, a connected Hausdorff space M is called an n-dimensional manifold if each point of M is contained in an open set which is homeomorphic to an open set in euclidean n-dimensional space. Most of the concepts defined in the rest of this chapter can be extended in an obvious way to n-dimensional manifolds, but since we shall be mainly concerned with 2-dimensional manifolds, we shall restrict our discussion to these from the beginning. For additional information about n-dimensional manifolds, see Ref. 52 or 23.

$$y = \varphi_2(P) = -\eta\zeta_0 + \eta\zeta\sqrt{\frac{1 - \zeta_0^2}{1 - \zeta^2}}.$$

Other examples, like the torus, the paraboloid, etc., can be made into manifolds in the same manner. The cone K: $\xi^2 + \eta^2 = \zeta^2$ is not a manifold, using the relative topology from $\mathcal{E}^3$, since the point P_0: $(0, 0, 0)$ does not have a neighborhood homeomorphic to a disk. This is easily verified, for any neighborhood U of P_0 must contain points P_1 with $\zeta > 0$ and points P_2 with $\zeta < 0$. Were K a manifold, and U homeomorphic to a disk, the images of P_1 and P_2 in the disk could be joined by an arc not passing through the image of P_0. But this property is topologically invariant and does not hold on K, proving that K is not a manifold. On the other hand, if we consider only half of K, that is, $\xi^2 + \eta^2 = \zeta^2$, $\zeta \geq 0$, we do obtain a manifold in the same manner as the sphere.

In general, there is no unique manner in which the local coordinates must be prescribed about a given point P_0. Indeed, if $y_1 = \lambda(x_1, x_2)$ and $y_2 = \mu(x_1, x_2)$ is a homeomorphism of the euclidean neighborhood $V = \Phi(U)$ onto another euclidean neighborhood W, then the composite mapping $y_1 = \lambda(\varphi_1(P), \varphi_2(P))$, $y_2 = \mu(\varphi_1(P), \varphi_2(P))$ defines another local coordinate system (y_1, y_2) about P_0. Moreover, if U_1 and U_2 are two neighborhoods of P_0 homeomorphic to euclidean disks, then $U_1 \cap U_2$ is also a neighborhood of P_0. Let $\Phi(P) = (\varphi_1(P), \varphi_2(P))$ be a local parameter in U_1, and $\Psi(P) = (\varphi_1(P), \varphi_2(P))$ be a local parameter in U_2. Then both local parameters are valid in $U_1 \cap U_2$, and the mapping $(y_1, y_2) = \Psi[\Phi^{-1}(x_1, x_2)]$ defines a homeomorphism of the euclidean neighborhood $\Phi(U_1 \cap U_2)$ onto $\Psi(U_1 \cap U_2)$.

It should be noted that if G is a region on a manifold M, then G is itself a manifold, for each point $P \in G$ has about it an open set $U \in M$ which is homeomorphic to an open set of $\mathcal{E}^2$. Then $U \cap G$ is an open set in G and the mapping of U into $\mathcal{E}^2$ restricted to $G \cap U$ is one-to-one and bicontinuous. Since G is open in M, $G \cap U$ is open in M and maps into an open set in $\mathcal{E}^2$. Since G is also connected, G is a manifold.

THEOREM 2–17. *Every manifold is arcwise connected.*

Let A be the set of points in M that can be joined to some fixed point $P_0 \in M$ by a path on M. The set A is open, for if $P \in A$, we can put a parametric disk D about P and each point $Q \in D$ can be joined to P by a radial line L in D, which is a curve, since L is the continuous image of a radial line in a euclidean disk. Since P can be joined to P_0 by a curve C, the curve CL joins Q to P_0 and $Q \in A$. Thus $D \subseteq A$ and A is open. Moreover, $M - A$ is also open, for any point $P \in M - A$ has about it a parametric disk D each of whose points Q can be joined to P by a radial line L.

If P_0 could be joined to Q by a curve C, then CL would join P_0 to P and P would be in A, not in $M - A$. Thus both A and $M - A$ are open, and A is not empty, since P_0 can be joined to itself by the curve C for which $\alpha(t) = P_0$, $0 \leq t \leq 1$. Since, by definition, M is connected, $M - A$ must be empty, so $M = A$. Hence, given $P, Q \in M$, P can be joined to P_0 and P_0 to Q, so that P can be joined to Q. Thus M is arcwise connected.

Each point of a manifold M has about it a parametric disk. Thus the totality of parametric disks forms an open covering of M. We now prove

THEOREM 2–18. *A manifold M has a countable base if and only if it possesses a covering by countably many parametric disks.*

Assume that M has a countable base $B = \{U_n\}_{n=1}^{\infty}$. Then each point $p \in M$ has about it a parametric disk D and D is the union of the sets in B, so that for some n, $p \in U_n \subset D$. We denote this U_n by $U_n(p)$, and we make correspond to each $U_n(p)$ one of the parametric disks, say D_n, such that $U_n(p) \subset D_n$. These D_n form a countable covering of M by parametric disks.

Conversely, assume that M has a countable covering by parametric disks, $\{D_n\}_{n=1}^{\infty}$. Then select in each D_n the collection of all possible disks $S: (x - b_1)^2 + (y - b_2)^2 < r^2$, where b_1, b_2, and r are rational numbers selected so that $S \subset D_n$. The collection B of all such disks S for all D_n, $n = 1, 2, \ldots$, forms a countable set of open sets, which we shall prove to be a base for M. If $V \subset M$ is an open set and $p \in V$, then $p \in D_n$ for some n, and p has coordinates (c_1, c_2) in D_n. There is an $\epsilon > 0$ such that the disk $D: (x - c_1)^2 + (y - c_2)^2 < \epsilon^2$ satisfies $D \subset V$. If we select rational numbers r, b_1, and b_2 such that $r < \epsilon$, $|b_1 - c_1| < r/4$, and $|b_2 - c_2| < r/4$, then the disk $S_p: (x - b_1)^2 + (x - b_2)^2 < r^2/4$ is in B, $p \in S_p \subset V$, and $V = \cup_{p \in V} S_p$. This proves that B forms a base and completes the proof of the theorem.

For brevity, instead of saying "M has a countable base," we shall say "M is countable." That not all manifolds are countable was displayed in an example by Pruefer which we present here (see Radó, Ref. 39, p. 107, and Calabi and Rosenlicht, Ref. 11, p. 335).

For each real number t, consider the ordered triple (x, y, t), in which (x, y) is a point in the euclidean plane $\mathcal{E}_t$. Two such triples are equivalent [written $(x_1, y_1, t) \sim (x_2, y_2, s)$] if

(a) $y_1 = y_2$; and

(b) when $y_1 = y_2 \leq 0$, then $t = s$ and $x_1 = x_2$; when $y_1 = y_2 > 0$, then $x_2 y_2 + s = x_1 y_1 + t$.

This equivalence relation may be used to define each equivalence class as a point on a manifold M. Let V_t be the set of points (x, y, t) on M. For any point $(\bar{x}, \bar{y}, t)$ in V_t we call the set $D_r(\bar{x}, \bar{y}, t)$ of points of V_t satisfying $(x - \bar{x})^2 + (y - \bar{y})^2 < r^2$ a disk of radius r about $(\bar{x}, \bar{y}, t)$. We say that a set $U \subset V_t$ is open if each point of U is the center of a disk lying entirely within U. Thus, in essence, we are using the topology of $\mathcal{E}_t$ in V_t. Open sets lying entirely within one V_t are called *elementary sets*. If a set U lies in both V_t and V_s, and is open in V_t, then it is also open in V_s. For if $U \subset V_t \cap V_s$, then U is contained in the half-plane $y_t > 0$ in V_t and also in $y_s > 0$ in V_s. But the transformation $x_s = x_t + (t - s)/y_t$, $y_s = y_t$ is a homeomorphism of $y_t > 0$ onto $y_s > 0$, proving our assertion that U is open in V_s. We then define an arbitrary set U on M as open if it is the union of elementary open sets.

We must verify that this definition of open sets satisfies axioms 1 through 5 for a Hausdorff space. Axioms 1 through 4 are immediate; to verify 5, we check the several possibilities separately. Let $(\bar{x}_1, \bar{y}_1, s)$ and $(\bar{x}_2, \bar{y}_2, t)$ be two points of M, and let $D_1 = D_r(\bar{x}_1, \bar{y}_1, s)$ and $D_2 = D_r(\bar{x}_2, \bar{y}_2, t)$ be disks of radius r about these points. We now select r small enough for D_1 and D_2 to be disjoint.

(i) If $\bar{y}_1 \neq \bar{y}_2$, then select $r = \frac{1}{4}|\bar{y}_1 - \bar{y}_2|$.

(ii) If $\bar{y}_1 = \bar{y}_2$, $t = s$, then $\bar{x}_1 \neq \bar{x}_2$ and we select $r = \frac{1}{4}|\bar{x}_1 - \bar{x}_2|$.

(iii) If $\bar{y}_1 = \bar{y}_2 < 0$, $t \neq s$, then $r = \frac{1}{2}|\bar{y}_1|$ makes $D_1 \cap D_2 = \phi$.

(iv) If $\bar{y}_1 = \bar{y}_2 > 0$, $t \neq s$, then $\bar{x}_1\bar{y}_1 - \bar{x}_2\bar{y}_2 \neq s - t$. By continuity of $x_1y_1 - x_2y_2$, there is an r such that if $(x_1, y_1) \in D_1$ and $(x_2, y_2) \in D_2$, then $x_1y_1 - x_2y_2 \neq s - t$, so that D_1 and D_2 are disjoint.

Finally,

(v) If $\bar{y}_1 = \bar{y}_2 = 0$, $t \neq s$, there is an r such that if $(x_1, y_1, t) \in D_1$ and $(x_2, y_2, s) \in D_2$, then $|x_1y_1 - x_2y_2| < |s - t|$, for $x_1y_1 - x_2y_2 = 0$ at $y_1 = \bar{y}_1$, $y_2 = \bar{y}_2$.

Thus we conclude that $D_1 \cap D_2 = \phi$. M is therefore a topological space and each point $(\bar{x}, \bar{y}, t)$ of M is contained in the disk $D_r(\bar{x}, \bar{y}, t)$ which is homeomorphic to the euclidean disk $(x - \bar{x})^2 + (y - \bar{y})^2 < r^2$. Thus M is a manifold in which the points $(0, -1, t)$ form an uncountable number of isolated points. But this implies that M does not have a countable base, for if it did, one of the countable number of disks, say D_1, covering M would have to contain an infinite number of the points $(0, -1, t)$ and $\bar{D}$ would then contain a cluster point of $(0, -1, t)$, which is a contradiction. Thus we have an example of a manifold without a countable base.

A function f defined on a manifold M may be considered locally as a function of the local coordinates, and certain of its properties may be investigated in terms of these local coordinates. We must, however, take care that the properties studied in terms of local coordinates are not lost if we change to a different local coordinate system. For example, it is quite natural to talk about the continuity of a function f on a manifold in terms of the local coordinates; for f is continuous in the neighborhood

U of P_0 if and only if for the local coordinate system $\Phi(P) = (\varphi_1(P),$ $\varphi_2(P)) = (x_1, x_2)$, valid in U, $f(\Phi^{-1}(x_1, x_2)) = g(x_1, x_2)$ is a continuous function of the two real variables (x_1, x_2) in $\Phi(U)$. If we change to a new local coordinate system $\Psi(P) = (\psi_1(P), \psi_2(P)) = (y_1, y_2)$ valid in U, and related to (x_1, x_2) by the homeomorphism $x_1 = \lambda(y_1, y_2)$, $x_2 = \mu(y_1, y_2)$, then $f(\Psi^{-1}(y_1, y_2)) = g(\lambda(y_1, y_2), \mu(y_1, y_2)) = h(y_1, y_2)$ is still a continuous function of y_1, y_2.

On the other hand, it is not natural to talk about the differentiability of a real-valued function on a manifold. For if the real-valued function f is given on M, we may fix a local coordinate system $\Phi(P) = (\varphi_1(P), \varphi_2(P)) = (x_1, x_2)$ about P_0 and again ask whether $f(\Phi^{-1}(x_1, x_2)) = g(x_1, x_2)$ has partial derivatives $\partial g/\partial x_1$ and $\partial g/\partial x_2$. Even when these partial derivatives exist, when we change local coordinates to $\Psi(P) = (y_1, y_2)$, where $x_1 = \lambda(y_1, y_2)$, $x_2 = \mu(y_1, y_2)$ are continuous functions, there is no guarantee that $f(\Psi^{-1}(P)) = g(\lambda(y_1, y_2), \mu(y_1, y_2)) = h(y_1, y_2)$ will have partial derivatives $\partial h/\partial y_1$ and $\partial h/\partial y_2$; for a differentiable function of a continuous function need not be differentiable.

Since we shall want to talk about differentiability of functions, we are led to the notion of a differentiable manifold. A real-valued function defined in a region $R \subset \mathcal{E}^2$ is said to be of *class C^n* if all its partial derivatives of orders $\leq n$ exist and are continuous in R. Two real-valued functions f_1, f_2, each defined in a region $R \subset \mathcal{E}^2$, yield a mapping of R into a subset of $\mathcal{E}^2$. This mapping is said to be of class C^n if f_1 and f_2 are both of class C^n in R.

We say that the manifold M is a differentiable or C^1 manifold

(i) *if there is given a collection $\{U_i, \Phi_i\}_{i \in I}$, where, for some index set I, $\{U_i\}_{i \in I}$ is an open covering of M, and Φ_i is a homeomorphism of U_i onto an open set of $\mathcal{E}^2$ (the mapping Φ_i defines a system of local coordinates in the set U_i); and*

(ii) *if, when $U_i \cap U_j \neq \phi$, then $\Phi_j(\Phi_i^{-1})$ is a C^1 mapping of $\Phi_i(U_i \cap U_j)$ onto $\Phi_j(U_i \cap U_j)$.*

We say that the collection $\{U_i, \Phi_i\}_{i \in I}$ defines a *differentiable structure* in the manifold M. If another covering $\{V_j\}, j \in J$, and the corresponding system of homeomorphisms Ψ_j of V_j into $\mathcal{E}^2$ are given which satisfy (i) and (ii), then another differentiable structure is defined on M. We say that these two differentiable structures are the same, or that they define the same differentiable manifold, when the covering obtained by taking all open sets in both $\{U_i\}$ and $\{V_j\}$ with the corresponding mappings Φ_i and Ψ_j satisfies the conditions (i) and (ii). It should be borne in mind that a differentiable manifold is defined as a manifold plus a set of allowed local coordinate systems, and only these local coordinates are to be used.

Let f be a real-valued function on a C^1 manifold M. In each parametric disk U, f may be expressed as a function of the local coordinates in U. If f is a C^1 function of the local coordinates in each parametric disk, we say that f is of *class* C^1 *on* M. This property is independent of the particular choice of local coordinates, since changes of local coordinates are all C^1 mappings and a C^1 function of C^1 functions is again a C^1 function.

It is clear that $\mathcal{E}^2$ is a C^1 manifold; the disks of radius 1 about any point and the identity mappings of these disks define a differentiable structure in $\mathcal{E}^2$. It can also be shown that the sphere with the local coordinates introduced before is a differentiable manifold.

In order to discuss higher-order differentiability, we must demand that the coordinate changes be restricted to a higher order of differentiability. The manifold M is called a C^n *manifold* if the mappings $\Phi_j(\Phi_i^{-1})$ in (ii) are required to be of class C^n. It is our intention to study complex-valued analytic functions on a manifold in terms of the local coordinates. In order to do this, we must ask that coordinate changes be accomplished by analytic functions and hence conformal mappings of the plane sets in (ii). For completeness, we shall restate the definition of an analytic manifold.

The manifold M is called a (complex) analytic manifold or an (abstract) Riemann surface

(i) *if there is given a collection* $\{U_i, \Phi_i\}_{i \in I}$, *where, for the index set* I, $\{U_i\}_{i \in I}$ *is an open covering of* M *and* Φ_i *is a homeomorphism of* U_i *onto an open set in the complex* z-*plane* $(z = x + iy)$; *and*

(ii) *if, when* $U_i \cap U_j \neq \phi$, *then* $\Phi_j(\Phi_i^{-1})$ *is a conformal sense-preserving mapping of* $\Phi_i(U_i \cap U_j)$ *onto* $\Phi_j(U_i \cap U_j)$; *that is,* $w = \Phi_j(\Phi_i^{-1})(z)$ $= f(z)$ *is an analytic function of* z *in* $\Phi_i(U_i \cap U_j)$.

The fact that $\Phi_j(\Phi_i^{-1})$ is one-to-one assures us that $f'(z) \neq 0$. The mapping Φ_i defines a local uniformizing parameter (or local coordinate) in the set U_i. As before, we say that the collection $\{U_i, \Phi_i\}_{i \in I}$ defines an *analytic structure* in the manifold M. We say that another collection $\{V_j, \Psi_j\}_{j \in J}$ defines the same analytic structure on M when the covering obtained by taking all open sets of both coverings and the corresponding mappings gives rise to a collection which satisfies conditions (i) and (ii). Once again, we stress that a Riemann surface is a manifold together with a certain set of allowed local coordinate systems, and only these coordinates are to be used.

If P_0 is a point on M, P_0 may be contained in several of the sets U_i, so there may be several different local parameters valid about P_0. We may, however, get new local parameters by observing that if $\Phi(P) = z$ defines one local coordinate system about P_0 in U and if $w = f(z)$ is any one-to-one conformal mapping of $\Phi(U)$ onto an open set of the w-plane, then $f(\Phi(P)) = w$ is also a local uniformizing parameter about P_0. In particular, if $\Phi(P_0) = z_0$, then the disk $|z - z_0| \leq r$ for small enough r is contained in

U, and if we set $w = (z - z_0)/r$, we get a new local parameter $w = \Psi(P)$, with $\Psi(P_0) = 0$ and $|w| \leq 1$. Thus each point P_0 of M is the *center* of a parametric disk $D: |w| < 1$.

A complex-valued function f on M is called *(regular) analytic*, or *holomorphic* at the point P_0 if in terms of the local parameter $z = \Phi(P)$, $0 = \Phi(P_0)$, the function $f(\Phi^{-1}(z))$ is a regular analytic function of z for $|z| < r$ for some $r > 0$; that is, $f(\Phi^{-1}(z)) = \sum_{n=0}^{\infty} a_n z^n$. This notion is invariantly defined, for if we change to another system of local coordinates, the new parameter is related to z by an analytic function, and an analytic function of an analytic function is analytic.

It should be noticed that the mapping relating two local coordinate systems is conformal, so that angles are preserved in each coordinate system, and we may define the angle between two intersecting curves on M as the angle between their tangents in any one system of local coordinates. Thus we may speak of angles on the analytic manifold because they are invariant under conformal mapping. However, distances are not preserved under conformal mappings, so we cannot speak about the distance between points on an analytic manifold.

The definition of analytic manifold given here is the same as that given for an abstract Riemann surface by H. Weyl (Ref. 50, pp. 35–36) and T. Radó (Ref. 39, p. 101). Weyl originally assumed the manifold triangulable, but Radó showed that this assumption is unnecessary.

The complex z-plane forms an example of a Riemann surface; all unit disks with the identity mappings define an analytic structure in the z-plane. In this case, we have one system of coordinates valid over the whole surface. The sphere with local coordinates defined by orthogonal projections onto tangent planes is *not* a Riemann surface, because angles are not preserved under such projections.

The sphere, however, may be made into a Riemann surface by defining local coordinates by means of *stereographic projection*. We consider the sphere $S^2: \xi^2 + \eta^2 + \zeta^2 = 1$ in $\mathcal{E}^3$, and the equatorial plane $T: \zeta = 0$. We shall denote by V_1 the set consisting of the whole sphere S^2 with the north pole $(0, 0, 1)$ removed, while by V_2, we shall denote S^2 with the south pole $(0, 0, -1)$ removed. Then any point $P: (\xi, \eta, \zeta)$ on S^2 has either V_1 or V_2 (or both) as a neighborhood. In V_1 we introduce the local coordinates

$$z_1 = \frac{\xi + i\eta}{1 - \zeta},$$

whereas in V_2 we define the local coordinates

$$z_2 = \frac{\xi - i\eta}{1 + \zeta}.$$

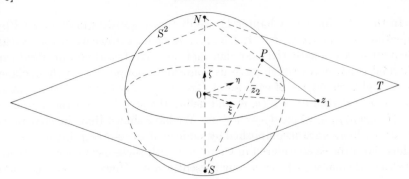

FIGURE 2–1.

The correspondence between points of V_1 and V_2 and the complex plane T is obtained geometrically by noting that z_1 is the point of intersection of a line L_1 through the north pole and the point P: (ξ, η, ζ) with the plane T, whereas $\bar{z}_2$ is the intersection with the plane T of the line L_2 through the south pole and P (Fig. 2–1).

For any point P in $V_1 \cap V_2$, the two local coordinates are related by

$$z_1 z_2 = \frac{\xi^2 + \eta^2}{1 - \zeta^2} = 1.$$

If $P \in V_1 \cap V_2$, then P is not at the north or south pole, so that $z_1 \neq 0$ and $z_2 \neq 0$, and the mapping $z_2 = 1/z_1$ is conformal. Thus the prescribed local parameters make the sphere into a Riemann surface.

The functions considered on a Riemann surface so far have been complex-valued functions, hence functions which map the Riemann surface into the complex plane. We shall also be interested in functions f defined on one Riemann surface S_1 and taking values in another Riemann surface S_2. If $P_0 \in S_1$, and $f(P_0) = Q_0$, we may take $z = \Phi(P)$ as local parameter about P_0 and $w = \Psi(Q)$ as local parameter about Q_0. Then we say that f is *analytic* on S_1 if the composite function $w = \Psi[f\{\Phi^{-1}(z)\}] = g(z)$ is an analytic function of z for all $P_0 \in S_1$. Two Riemann surfaces S_1 and S_2 are said to be *conformally equivalent* if there is a one-to-one analytic mapping f of S_1 onto S_2. Any complex-valued analytic function g on S_1 is carried into a complex-valued analytic function gf^{-1} on S_2 and, conversely, any complex-valued analytic function h on S_2 is carried into a complex-valued analytic function hf on S_1. Hence from the point of view of studying the class of complex-valued analytic functions on a Riemann surface, we may as well consider two conformally equivalent Riemann surfaces as being the same.

In the introduction (Chapter 1), we discussed surfaces in $\mathcal{E}^3$ defined by equations $x_i = x_i(p, q)$, $i = 1, 2, 3 \ldots$. On such a surface we introduced an element of arc length (Riemannian metric). We found certain local isothermal coordinates which gave us conformal mappings into the z-plane. In a neighborhood U_P of each point P of the surface S, we select a system of isothermal coordinates (u, v) and define the structure on the surface S by $\{U_P, \Phi_P\}_{P \in S}$, where $\Phi_P = u + iv$. We have shown that the changes of local coordinates are accomplished by conformal sense-preserving mappings. Thus the surfaces considered in Chapter 1 with these local coordinates are abstract Riemann surfaces in our present sense. However, our Riemann surfaces are now more general, since they are not embedded in $\mathcal{E}^3$ nor do they have on them a Riemannian metric. We have obtained our surfaces essentially by patching together small neighborhoods in such a way that overlapping pieces fit together conformally. In the next chapter, we shall see that the Riemann surface of an analytic function is precisely such an abstract Riemann surface.

Problems

1. Show that in a Hausdorff space the set consisting of one point is closed. Show that if axiom 5 were disregarded, one could construct a space satisfying axioms 1 through 4 in which a single point is not a closed set.

2. Show that the axioms for a metric space can be replaced by the following two axioms:

   (a) $\rho(p, q) = 0$ if and only if $p = q$;

   (b) $\rho(p, q) \leq \rho(p, r) + \rho(q, r)$ for any three points p, q, and r.

3. Prove that the topological product of two compact Hausdorff spaces is compact.

4. Prove that a Hausdorff space is connected if and only if it contains no proper subset which is simultaneously open and closed.

5. Prove that every compact metric space is separable and hence has a countable base.

6. Prove that on a compact set in a Hausdorff space, a continuous real-valued function assumes a maximum and a minimum value.

7. Show that the torus is the topological product of two circles. Similarly, show that a cylinder is the topological product of a circle and a line. Introduce isothermal coordinates on the cylinder to show that it is an analytic manifold.

CHAPTER 3

RIEMANN SURFACE OF AN ANALYTIC FUNCTION

3-1 The complete analytic function. The study of analytic functions in the z-plane leads to the introduction of Riemann surfaces on which the analytic functions are single-valued. One usually pictures these surfaces as composed of several sheets lying over the z-plane. We shall now show that this type of surface is just a Riemann surface in the abstract sense defined in Chapter 2.

The building blocks for the Riemann surface of an analytic function are the power series

$$P(z - a) = \sum_{n=0}^{\infty} a_n(z - a)^n,$$

which converge either in the whole z-plane or in a disk $|z - a| < r$ and possibly on part of the boundary $|z - a| = r$. The power series $P(z - a)$ converges to a regular analytic function in $|z - a| < r$ ($r = \infty$ for the whole plane). We shall call this power series a *(regular) function element*. We shall build up the complete analytic function by a process of analytic continuation. The point $z = a$ is called the *center* of the function element.

If we expand each expression $(z - a)^n = (z - b + b - a)^n$ in powers of $z - b$, where $|a - b| < r$, by the binomial theorem, and then regroup the terms to give a power series

$$Q(z - b) = \sum_{n=0}^{\infty} b_n(z - b)^n,$$

the new power series $Q(z - b)$ converges in a disk of radius at least equal to $r - |b - a|$. If the radius of convergence of $Q(z - b)$ is larger than $r - |b - a|$, we have extended the function beyond the original disk $|z - a| < r$. We say that $Q(z - b)$ is a *direct analytic continuation* of $P(z - a)$.

Let $K_1, K_2, \ldots, K_n$ be a finite sequence of disks in the z-plane so arranged that the center a_{i+1} of K_{i+1} lies within the disk K_i, $i = 1, 2, \ldots,$ $n - 1$. Such a sequence of disks is called a *chain*. If $P_i = P_i(z - a_i)$ is a function element with K_i as its disk of convergence, and if P_{i+1} is a direct analytic continuation of P_i, $i = 1, 2, \ldots, n$, we say that P_1 has been *continued analytically along the chain of disks.*

In a similar way, we may define analytic continuation along a path in the z-plane. Let $C = (\alpha, I)$ represent a path in the z-plane defined by $z = \alpha(t)$, $0 \leq t \leq 1$, such that $\alpha(0) = a$ and $\alpha(1) = b$. Suppose that to each value of t, we associate a function element $P_t = P_i(z - \alpha(t))$. For any t_0, if t_1 has the property that $\alpha(t)$ lies within the disk of convergence of P_{t_0} for all t in the interval $t_0 \leq t \leq t_1$, we shall require that P_{t_1} be a direct analytic continuation of P_{t_0}. We then say that $P_1 = P_1(z - b)$ has been obtained by *analytically continuing* $P_0 = P_0(z - a)$ *along the path C.* Conversely, P_0 is obtained by analytically continuing P_1 along the path C^{-1}.

THEOREM 3–1. *Analytic continuation of a given function element P_0 along a given curve C always leads to the same function element P_1.*

For if P_t and Q_t are two continuations of the same function element $P_0 \equiv Q_0$ along the curve $C = (\alpha, I)$, we shall show that the subset E of the interval $I: 0 \leq t \leq 1$ consisting of those t for which $P_t \equiv Q_t$ is both open and closed relative to I. First, we note that $t = 0$ belongs to E, so E is not empty. For any t_0, P_{t_0} and Q_{t_0} both converge in a circle $|z - \alpha(t_0)| < \epsilon(t_0)$, where $\epsilon(t_0)$ is the smaller of their radii of convergence. Then there is a $\delta = \delta(t_0) > 0$ such that $|\alpha(t_0) - \alpha(t)| < \epsilon(t_0)$ for all $|t - t_0| < \delta$. Hence P_t and Q_t are direct continuations of P_{t_0} and Q_{t_0}, respectively, if $|t - t_0| < \delta$. If $t_0 \in E$, then $P_{t_0} \equiv Q_{t_0}$ and their direct continuations P_t and Q_t are identical (or $t \in E$) for $|t - t_0| < \delta$. Thus E is open relative to I. On the other hand, if t_0 is a cluster point of E, there is a $t_1 \in E$ such that $|t_0 - t_1| < \delta(t_0)$ and $P_{t_1} \equiv Q_{t_1}$. But the disks of convergence of P_{t_1} and of P_{t_0} and Q_{t_0} overlap; in the overlapping area, they are all identical. Thus $P_{t_0} \equiv Q_{t_0}$ and $t_0 \in E$. Thus E is closed as well as open relative to I, and since E is nonempty, $E = I$. Thus $P_t \equiv Q_t$ for all $t \in I$ and, in particular, $P_1 \equiv Q_1$.

THEOREM 3–2. *The radius of convergence $r(a)$ of the series $P(z - a)$ is either identically infinite or is a continuous function of the center a.*

For if $r(a) < \infty$, and $|b - a| < \frac{1}{2}r(a)$, then $r(b) \geq r(a) - |b - a| \geq \frac{1}{2}r(a)$. Therefore a lies in the circle of convergence of $P(z - b)$ and $r(a) \geq r(b) - |b - a|$. Consequently, $|r(b) - r(a)| \leq |b - a|$ and $r(a)$ is a continuous function of a.

THEOREM 3–3. *If the continuation of the function element P_0 along a curve $C = (\alpha, I)$ is possible, it can always be accomplished by analytic continuation along a finite chain of disks.*

This is easily verified by noting that the radius of convergence $r(\alpha(t))$ of the function element P_t is a continuous function of t and hence has a positive lower bound δ. If the sequence of values $0 = t_0 < t_1 < t_2 < \cdots$ $< t_n = 1$ is chosen so that $|\alpha(t_i) - \alpha(t_{i+1})| < \delta$ for $i = 1, 2, \ldots, n$, the disks $K_i : |z - \alpha(t_i)| < r(\alpha(t_i))$, $i = 0, 1, \ldots, n$, form a finite chain, and $P_0, P_{t_1}, P_{t_2}, \ldots, P_1$ form an analytic continuation along this chain of disks.

If P_0 is continued analytically along the curve $C\colon z(t)$ from a to b, then analytic continuation of P_0 along any curve joining a to b and sufficiently near to C (in a sense to be described) leads to the same function element P_1. More precisely, we have the following theorem:

THEOREM 3–4. *Let δ be the minimum of the radius of convergence $r(\alpha(t))$ of the function element P_t. Let $C_1 = (\alpha_1, I)$ be any other curve with $\alpha_1(0) = a$ and $\alpha_1(1) = b$, such that $|\alpha_1(t) - \alpha(t)| < \delta/4$. If we denote by Q_t the function element obtained by continuing $P_0 = Q_0$ along the curve C_1, then $P_1 \equiv Q_1$.*

Consider a sequence $0 = t_0 < t_1 < \cdots < t_n = 1$ such that for all t in the interval $t_{i-1} \leq t \leq t_i$, we have $|\alpha(t) - \alpha(t_{i-1})| < \delta/4$, $i = 1, 2, \ldots, n$. The chain of disks $K_i : |z - \alpha(t_i)| < r(\alpha(t_i))$ gives us the continuation of P_0 to P_1 by a finite succession of direct continuations. Let L_i represent the line segment joining $\alpha(t_i)$ to $\alpha_1(t_i)$. Continuation along any path lying entirely within the disk of convergence of a function element leads to the same element, for each direct continuation is merely a rearrangement of the original series. Thus continuation of P_0 from a to $\alpha(t_1)$ along the curve C and along the composite path composed of C_1 from a to $\alpha_1(t_1)$ and then to $\alpha(t_1)$ along L_1^{-1} both lead to the same function element P_{t_1}. We now continue P_{t_1} from $\alpha(t_1)$ to $\alpha(t_2)$ along C to obtain P_{t_2}; we may, however, continue P_{t_1} from $\alpha(t_1)$ to $\alpha(t_2)$ along the composite path L_1 followed by C_1 from $\alpha_1(t_1)$ to $\alpha_1(t_2)$, and then L_2^{-1}, obtaining the same element P_{t_2}, since we never left the circle of convergence of P_{t_1}. In this process we traced L_1 successively in both directions, the net effect being that we get the same result as if we left out L_1. Thus we have continued P_0 along two paths to get P_{t_2}; namely, C from a to $\alpha(t_2)$ or C_1 from a to $\alpha_1(t_2)$ followed by L_2^{-1}. We repeat this stepwise process to b in a finite number of steps and end with $P_1 \equiv Q_1$.

Sometimes analytic continuation is not possible along a given curve $C = (\alpha, I)$. If there is a value of t, say $t = \tau$, such that the function element P_0 can be continued analytically along the arc $0 \leq t \leq t_0$ of C for any $t_0 < \tau$, but not for $t_0 > \tau$, we say that the point $\alpha(\tau)$ is a *singular* point relative to C and P_0.

We can now formulate the Weierstrass definition of an analytic function: *The (complete) analytic function is the set A of all function elements obtainable from a given function element by analytic continuation.*

From this definition, it is clear that each function element of A can be obtained from any other by analytic continuation. Furthermore, two analytic functions A_1 and A_2 which have a single function element in common are identical; i.e., each element of A_1 is contained in A_2 and vice versa. If the function element

$$P(z - a) = a_0 + a_1(z - a) + a_2(z - a)^2 + \cdots$$

belongs to an analytic function A, then a_0 is called a *value* of A at the point $z = a$.

The analytic function which we have defined here is not a function in the ordinary sense, for to a given value of z is associated not necessarily a single value of the function, but possibly many values, depending upon whether continuation of the function elements leads to the same or to different values when we return to the given point. In order to consider A as a function in the ordinary sense, we shall associate to A an analytic manifold, M_A, on which A will be a single-valued function. To this end, we recall that the analytic function A is the totality of function elements $P(z - a)$ obtained from a given element by analytic continuation. We consider the set of ordered pairs $(a, P(z - a))$ and call two such pairs equivalent if the following two conditions are satisfied:

(i) $a = b$,

(ii) $P(z - a) \equiv Q(z - b)$ in their common circle of convergence.

This is clearly an equivalence relation, and each equivalence class $(a, P(z - a))$ defines a point of the set M_A.

We now define a topology in M_A to make it an analytic manifold. Let $(a, P(z - a))$ be a point of M_A, and let $K_\rho(a)$ be any disk $|z - a| < \rho$ with radius smaller than the radius of convergence $r(a)$ of the function element $P(z - a)$. A disk D about the point $(a, P(z - a))$ on M_A consists of all points $(b, Q(z - b))$ in M_A such that $b \in K_\rho(a)$ and $Q(z - b)$ is a direct analytic continuation of $P(z - a)$. A subset V of M_A is called open if each point $(a, P(z - a))$ of V is contained in a disk D about $(a, P(z - a))$ with $D \subseteq V$. Thus the subset V of M_A is open if to each point $(a, P(z-a)) \in V$ corresponds a disk $K_\rho(a)$, $\rho < r(a)$, such that all points $(b, Q(z - b)) \in M_A$ with $b \in K_\rho(a)$ and Q a direct analytic continuation of $P(z - a)$ belong to the set V. It is clear that each disk D is an open set.

We shall first verify that this definition makes M_A a topological space:

(a) The null set ϕ is an open set, since no element of ϕ fails to satisfy the above condition.

(b) The whole set M_A is an open set, since any disk about each point of M_A is in M_A.

(c) The union of arbitrarily many open sets is open, for any point (a, P) in the union must be in at least one open set contained in the union. This open set contains a disk about (a, P).

(d) The intersection of any finite number of open sets is open; for if $V_1, V_2, \ldots, V_n$ are open, any point (a, P) in their intersection V belongs to each V_i, and each V_i contains points (b, Q) where b is any point of the disk $K_i(a): |z - a| < \rho_i$, $\rho_i < r(a)$, and Q is a direct continuation of P. The intersection V thus contains all points (b, Q) where $b \in K_\rho(a)$, $\rho = \min (\rho_i)$, $i = 1, \ldots, n$, and Q is a direct continuation of P, and these points form a disk about (a, P) in V.

(e) If (a, P) and (b, Q) are two points of M_A, we must display disjoint open sets each containing one of the given points. There are two cases in which $(a, P) \neq (b, Q)$:

$$\text{(i)} \quad a \neq b, \quad \text{and} \quad \text{(ii)} \quad a = b \text{ by } P \not\equiv Q.$$

In case (i) we can find two disjoint disks $K(a)$ and $K(b)$ with P converging in $K(a)$ and Q converging in $K(b)$. Then let U be the open set consisting of points (a_1, P_1) such that $a_1 \in K(a)$ and P_1 is a direct continuation of P; and let V be the open set consisting of points (b_1, Q_1) where $b \in K(b)$ and Q_1 is a direct continuation of Q. We have $(a, P) \in U$ and $(b, Q) \in V$ and $U \cap V = \phi$, since $K(a) \cap K(b) = \phi$. In case (ii), we can find a common disk $K_\rho(a)$ in which both P and Q converge. Let U be the open set consisting of points (a_1, P_1) where $a_1 \in K_\rho(a)$ and P_1 is a direct continuation of P; let V be the open set consisting of points (b_1, Q_1) where $b_1 \in K_\rho(a)$ and Q_1 is a direct continuation of Q. If U and V have a point $(a_1, P_1) = (b_1, Q_1)$ in common, then $a_1 = b_1$ and $P_1 \equiv Q_1$. But this means that we have continued P from a to a_1 and back to a, remaining in $K(a)$, and have arrived at a different function element Q, which is impossible since both direct continuations are merely rearrangements of the series P. Thus $(a, P) \in U$ and $(b, Q) \in V$ and $U \cap V = \phi$, completing the proof that M_A is a topological space.

If (a, P) is a point of M_A, then the point $z = a$ in the complex plane is called the *projection* of (a, P) on the z-plane. If V is a set of points on M_A, the projection of V on the z-plane is just the set of projections of all points in V on the z-plane.

If (a, P) and (b, Q) are two points on M_A, we can find a curve $C = (\alpha, I)$ joining a to b in the z-plane such that the continuation P_t of P along C leads to the function element Q; thus, $P_0 = P$, $P_1 = Q$. If we consider the points $(\alpha(t), P_t)$ on M_A, we obtain a path Γ on M_A joining (a, P) to (b, Q). To prove that Γ is a path, we must show that $(\alpha(t), P_t)$ is a continuous mapping of the interval I into M_A. Given any neighborhood U of the point $(\alpha(t_0), P_{t_0})$ on M_A, we can find a disk $K_\rho(\alpha(t_0))$ lying within the projection of U on the z-plane. We may choose ρ small enough so that $K_\rho(\alpha(t_0))$ is within the disk of convergence of P_{t_0}. We then can find a positive number δ such that for $|t - t_0| < \delta$, $\alpha(t) \in K_\rho(\alpha(t_0))$. Then P_t, $|t - t_0| < \delta$, is a direct continuation of P_{t_0}, and the points $(\alpha(t), P_t)$ lie inside of U when $|t - t_0| < \delta$. Thus Γ is a path on M_A joining (a, P) to (b, Q), so that M_A is arcwise connected and hence connected.

It remains yet to introduce local coordinates on M_A to make M_A an analytic manifold. For an arbitrary point (a, P) on M_A, let D be the disk about (a, P) consisting of all points (b, Q) with $b \in K_\rho(a)$, $K_\rho(a)$ contained in the disk of convergence of P, and Q a direct continuation of P. Then the projection of D on the z-plane is the disk $K_\rho(a)$. This defines a one-to-one bicontinuous mapping of D onto $K_\rho(a)$. If two such disks D_1 and D_2 overlap, the common points (a, P) map into the point a under both coordinate mappings, so different local parameters are related by the identity mapping of the z-plane, which is a conformal mapping. Thus we have proved the following theorem.

THEOREM 3–5. M_A is an analytic manifold.

The analytic manifold M_A is called the *analytic manifold of the regular function elements of A.*

To the point (a, P) of M_A, we may associate the value of A at the point $z = a$, which is obtained from the function element P. This defines a single-valued function f on M_A which is, moreover, an analytic function on M_A. For in terms of the local parameter $z =$ projection of (z, Q) about (a, P), we obtain the analytic function

$$f(z, Q) = P(z - a) = a_0 + a_1(z - a) + a_2(z - a)^2 + \cdots.$$

Thus the complete analytic function A in the sense of Weierstrass defines a single-valued function f on the analytic manifold M_A. Another single-valued analytic function on M_A is obtained when we consider the projection function which assigns to each point (a, P) on M_A the complex number $z = a$.

The analytic manifold M_A associated with any entire function is the whole z-plane; for in this case, the projection mapping is a one-to-one conformal mapping of M_A onto the complex plane. The function $\sqrt{z}$ presents a different situation. If we begin with the function element

$$P(z - 1) = 1 + \tfrac{1}{2}(z - 1) - \tfrac{1}{8}(z - 1)^2 + \tfrac{1}{16}(z - 1)^3 + \cdots$$

about $z = 1$, we note that the radius of convergence is 1. Expressing $z = 1 + re^{i\theta}$, we note that

$$P(z - 1) = \sqrt{r}\, e^{\frac{1}{2} i\theta}.$$

If we now continue $P(z - 1)$ along the path γ: $z = e^{2\pi it}$, $0 \leq t \leq 1$, we find that P_t converges in the circle $|z - e^{2\pi it}| < 1$ and has the form

$$P_t = e^{\pi it} + \tfrac{1}{2}e^{-\pi it}(z - e^{2\pi it}) - \tfrac{1}{8}e^{-3\pi it}(z - e^{2\pi it})^2 + \cdots.$$

Thus for $t = 1$, $z(1) = -1$ and $P_1 \equiv -P_0$. Therefore the two points $(1, P_0)$ and $(1, -P_0)$ have the same projections. If we now continue the element $P_1 = -P_0$ around the same path again, we return to the original element P_0. The same situation persists for each point in the z-plane different from $z = 0$. The two points $(z, \sqrt{z})$ and $(z, -\sqrt{z})$ project into the same point z. As z traverses any path winding around the origin once, the corresponding point on $M_{\sqrt{z}}$ projecting into z moves from $(z, \sqrt{z})$ to $(z, -\sqrt{z})$. This leads to the familiar model for the Riemann surface of $\sqrt{z}$ if we picture $M_{\sqrt{z}}$ to consist of an ascending spiral ramp which winds around the center axis twice and then penetrates back to the starting place.

3–2 The analytic configuration. Up to now, we have considered only the regular function elements of the analytic function. Now we shall add to the discussion certain singular elements. Let $S(\zeta)$ represent the function element

$$S(\zeta) = \sum_{n=\nu}^{\infty} a_n \zeta^n, \tag{1}$$

where ν is an integer. Consider the set of ordered pairs

$$(a, S(\sqrt[k]{z - a})), \tag{2}$$

where k is a positive integer. For brevity, we shall write this as $(a, S)_k$. If $a = \infty$, we consider the pair

$$(\infty, S(\sqrt[k]{1/z})) \tag{3}$$

or, briefly, $(\infty, S)_k$. If $k = 1$, and $\nu \geq 0$, the pair $(a, S)_1 = (a, S)$ is just a regular function element as discussed in the previous section.

The function $\zeta = \sqrt[k]{z - a}$ for $k \neq 1$ is not single-valued, but assumes exactly k different values at each point z in the deleted neighborhood of $z = a$. In general, however, we cannot say the same about $S(\sqrt[k]{z - a})$, as the simple case $k = 4$, $S(\zeta) = \zeta^2$ illustrates; here $S(\sqrt[4]{z - a}) = \sqrt{z - a}$ assumes only two different values at each point near a. In this case, we would obtain the same function if we had taken $k = 2$, $S(\zeta) = \zeta$. Suppose that $S(\zeta) = \sum_{n=\nu}^{\infty} a_n \zeta^{nl}$ for some positive integer l, and that for the element $(a, S)_k$, the integers l and k have greatest common divisor $m > 1$. Then $l = \lambda m$ and $k = \kappa m$, where $\lambda \neq l$ and $\kappa \neq k$. If we let ϵ represent a primitive kth root of 1, then

$$S(\epsilon^\kappa \zeta) \equiv \sum_{n=\nu}^{\infty} a_n (\epsilon^\kappa \zeta)^{nm\lambda} \equiv \sum_{n=\nu}^{\infty} a_n \epsilon^{kn\lambda} \zeta^{nl} \equiv \sum_{n=\nu}^{\infty} a_n \zeta^{nl} \equiv S(\zeta)$$

since $\epsilon^k = 1$. It is also clear that if $T(\zeta) = \sum_{n=\nu}^{\infty} a_n \zeta^{n\lambda}$, then $S(\sqrt[k]{z-a})$ and $T(\sqrt[\kappa]{z-a})$ represent the same function. To eliminate this ambiguity, we shall assume that $S(\zeta) \not\equiv S(\epsilon\zeta)$ if $\epsilon^k = 1$ and $\epsilon \neq 1$.

Furthermore, two pairs $(a, S)_k$ and $(b, T)_l$ will be called equivalent (written $(a, S)_k \cong (b, T)_l$) if and only if

(i) $a = b$ and $k = l$, and
(ii) there exists an ϵ with $\epsilon^k = 1$ such that $S(\zeta) \equiv T(\epsilon\zeta)$.

It is immediately verified that this is an equivalence relation. The set of equivalence classes of these ordered pairs will be denoted by R. Where there is no possibility for ambiguity, we shall use the notation $(a, S)_k$ for the ordered pair itself or for the class of pairs equivalent to $(a, S)_k$. An ordered pair $(a, S)_k$ which is not equivalent to a regular function element is called a *singular function element*.

Let $r(S)$ represent the radius of convergence of the regular terms $\sum_{n=0}^{\infty} a_n \zeta^n$ of the series $S(\zeta)$. A *disk* D about the point $(a, S)_k$ of R, $a \neq \infty$, will consist of the point $(a, S)_k$ itself and all regular function elements (b, P) of R with $|b - a| < \rho^k$, $\rho < r(S)$, and $P = P(z - b)$ converging to a function which is identically equal to one of the k determinations of $S(\sqrt[k]{z-a})$ in their common region of definition; that is, $P(z - b) \equiv S(\epsilon\sqrt[k]{z-a})$ where ϵ ($\epsilon^k = 1$) fixes one determination of the kth root about $z = b$. (Where no ambiguity arises, we use P and S to represent the functions to which the series converge as well as the series themselves. The identity has meaning only in the common region of definition of P and S.) We shall call ρ the radius of the disk D. As a disk D about $(\infty, S)_k$, we take in addition to $(\infty, S)_k$ all regular function elements (b, P) with $|b|^{-1} < \rho^k$, $\rho < r(S)$, and $P = P(z - b)$ converging to a function which is identically equal to a determination of $S(\sqrt[k]{z-a})$ in their common region of definition. A set V on R is defined to be an open set if each point $(a, S)_k$ of V is contained in a disk D about $(a, S)_k$ with $D \subseteq V$. Again it is easily verified that the disk D is itself an open set.

This definition of open sets makes R into a topological space. The first four axioms of a topological space are easily verified again for R. The separation axiom (e) is checked by observing that if $(a, S)_k$ and $(b, T)_l$ are two distinct points of R, the case $a \neq b$ presents no difficulty; when $a = b$, however, we consider the disks U and V about $(a, S)_k$ and $(a, T)_l$, respectively, each of radius ρ, $\rho < r(S)$ and $\rho < r(T)$. Then if U and V have a point (c, P) in common, we know that $P(z - c) \equiv S(\sqrt[k]{z-a})$ and $P(z - c) \equiv T(\sqrt[l]{z-a})$ in some neighborhood of $z = c$.

Let t be an lth root of $\sqrt[k]{z-a}$ chosen in such a way that near $[(c-a)^{1/k}]^{1/l}$, we have $t^l = \sqrt[k]{z-a}$ and $\sqrt[l]{z-a} = \epsilon_l t^k$, where ϵ_l is a primitive lth root of 1 and α is a positive integer $\leq l$. Then $S(t^l) \equiv T(t^k \epsilon_l^\alpha)$ in some neighborhood of $[(c - a)^{1/k}]^{1/l}$. But this means that these analytic functions are also identical in the larger disk about $z = a$ which contains the point $z = a$. If we replace t by $\epsilon_l t$, we find that

$$T(\epsilon_l^k \epsilon_l^\alpha t^k) \equiv S(\epsilon_l^l t^l) \equiv S(t^l) \equiv T(t^k \epsilon_l^\alpha).$$

If we set $\zeta = \epsilon_l^\alpha t^k$, then

$$T(\zeta) \equiv T(\epsilon_l^k \zeta).$$

If $\epsilon_l^k = \epsilon$, we note that $\epsilon^l = 1$, so that $T(\zeta) \equiv T(\epsilon \zeta)$, and this holds only if $\epsilon = 1$; therefore k is a multiple of l. In a similar manner, we show that l is a multiple of k and hence $k = l$.

We now have, in a neighborhood of $z = a$, $S(\sqrt[k]{z - a}) \equiv T(\eta \sqrt[k]{z - a})$, where $\eta^k = 1$. Thus $(a, S)_k$ and $(b, T)_l$ represent the same point on R, contrary to hypothesis, proving the separation axiom.

Let us now consider a regular function element $P(z - a)$. We have defined the analytic function A containing $P(z - a)$ to be the set of all regular function elements $Q(z - b)$ which can be obtained from $P(z - a)$ by analytic continuation. Each such regular function element $Q(z - b)$ defines a regular function element (b, Q) of R. The set M_A, which we called the analytic manifold of the regular function elements of A, consists of pairs (b, Q) where $Q(z - b)$ is a regular function element obtained by analytic continuation from $P(z - a)$. The identification $(b_1, Q_1) \cong (b_2, Q_2)$ in M_A (when $b_1 = b_2$ and $Q_1 \equiv Q_2$ in their common region of definition) coincides exactly with the identification of regular function elements in R, and we may therefore identify M_A with a subset of R. A disk about the point (b, Q) in M_A, which was used to define the topology in M_A, consists of exactly the same elements as a disk about the regular function element (b, Q) in R. Thus a set in M_A is open in M_A if and only if it is open when considered as a set in R. Since M_A is arcwise connected, we know that M_A lies in one component R_A of R.

We may therefore make the following definition. The totality of function elements (regular or singular) in the component R_A of R which contains the function elements in the complete analytic function A is called the *analytic configuration* of the analytic function A.

THEOREM 3–6. *The analytic configuration of an analytic function A together with the structure given in terms of the disks in R defined above is an analytic manifold.*

From its definition as a component of R, R_A is connected. We shall show that the disks in R are homeomorphic to euclidean disks and define an analytic structure on R_A.

Recall first that at a regular function element of R_A, the projection mapping $(a, P) \rightarrow a$ gives us the desired homeomorphism onto a euclidean disk. The projection mapping at points $(a, S)_k$, $k \neq 1$, would not be one-to-one but would make k points of R correspond to each point of the euclidean disk; that is, all k points (ζ, P) with $P(z - \zeta) \equiv S(\epsilon\sqrt[k]{z - a})$ in their common region of definition, where ϵ assumes the k different kth roots of unity, project into the same point $z = \zeta$. Thus, to make the mapping one-to-one, we consider the point (ζ, P) in the disk D of radius ρ about $(a, S)_k$, so that $P(z - \zeta) \equiv S(\epsilon\sqrt[k]{z - a})$ in their common region of definition, where ϵ with $\epsilon^k = 1$ fixes a determination of $\sqrt[k]{z - a}$ in a neighborhood of $z = \zeta$. This point (ζ, P) is mapped into the point $z = \epsilon\sqrt[k]{\zeta - a}$ of the disk $|z| < \rho$ with $(a, S)_k \to z = 0$. In the disk D of radius ρ about $(\infty, S)_k$, we map each point (ζ, P) where $P(z - \zeta) \equiv S(\epsilon\sqrt[k]{1/z})$, $\epsilon^k = 1$, in their common region of definition, into the point $z = \epsilon\sqrt[k]{1/\zeta}$, again with $(\infty, S)_k \to 0$. Then each of the k points of R projecting into $z = \zeta$ now maps into a different kth root of $\zeta - a$. Thus D is homeomorphic to a euclidean disk. D is hence connected, and it follows that all of D belongs to R_A when its center $(a, S)_k$ belongs to R_A. Therefore, the homeomorphism of D onto a euclidean disk gives us a local coordinate system about $(a, S)_k$ in R_A.

These local coordinates make R_A into an analytic manifold. For two disks D_1 about $(a, S)_k$ and D_2 about $(b, T)_l$ can have only ordinary points (ζ, P) in common. The parameter in D_1 at (ζ, P) is $z = \epsilon_1\sqrt[k]{\zeta - a}$, $\epsilon_1^k = 1$, and that in D_1 at (ζ, P) is $w = \epsilon_2\sqrt[l]{\zeta - b}$, $\epsilon_2^l = 1$. Since $\zeta \neq a$, $\zeta \neq b$, we have that $w = \epsilon_2\sqrt[l]{z^k + a - b}$ determines w as an analytic function of z. This completes the proof of the theorem.

We now define the *Riemann surface of the analytic function* A to be the analytic manifold R_A obtained by putting the above analytic structure on the analytic configuration of A.

We have obtained the analytic configuration by adding to the analytic function A the function elements of R which lie in the same component as A. We shall next prove that no new regular function elements have been added to A by this process.

THEOREM 3–7. *The regular function elements of the analytic configuration of an analytic function A are function elements of A.*

We know that any regular element (b, Q) of R_A can be joined to a fixed element (a, P) of A by a curve on R_A. To show that (b, Q) itself belongs to A, we must prove that (b, Q) can be joined to (a, P) by a curve in the submanifold M_A of R_A, where M_A is the analytic manifold of the regular function elements of A. Each function element (regular or singular) of R_A has about it a disk which except for its center point is composed entirely of regular function elements. Thus the singular function elements form a set F of isolated points on R_A which has no cluster point on R_A, and $G = R_A - F$ is an open set on R_A. We proceed to prove that G is also connected. (The proof will show, incidentally, that the set of points obtained by deleting a set of isolated points without a cluster point from a manifold is still a manifold.)

If G were not connected, G could be separated into the union of two disjoint nonempty open sets G_1 and G_2. But in R_A, $\overline{G}_1 \cap \overline{G}_2 \neq \phi$; for if $\overline{G}_1 \cap \overline{G}_2 = \phi$, then the fact that each element of F has a deleted neighborhood composed of elements of G implies that $R_A = \overline{G} = \overline{G_1 \cup G_2} = \overline{G}_1 \cup \overline{G}_2$. This, however, is a decomposition of R_A into two disjoint nonempty closed sets, which contradicts the connectedness of R_A. It is also clear that $\overline{G}_1 \cap \overline{G}_2 \subset F$; for if $p \notin F$, then $p \in G_1$ or $p \in G_2$. If, for example, $p \in G_1$, then G_1 is a neighborhood of p which contains no elements of G_2, so $p \notin \overline{G}_2$. Thus $\phi \neq \overline{G}_1 \cap \overline{G}_2 \subset F$, and we may select some point $p \in \overline{G}_1 \cap \overline{G}_2$ and let D be a disk about p such that $D - p \subset G$. Then $D - p = (D \cap G_1) \cup (D \cap G_2)$, where $D \cap G_1$ and $D \cap G_2$ are open nonempty disjoint sets. But $D - p$ is the image of a punctured euclidean disk and is hence connected, which gives us the desired contradiction and proves the assertion that $R_A - F$ is connected. Thus $R_A - F$ is a manifold and is arcwise connected, which proves that any pair of regular function elements of R_A may be joined by a path composed entirely of regular function elements, or that $R_A - F = M_A$. This proves Theorem 3–7.

If $(a, S)_k$ is a singular function element of R_A, the deleted disk D about $(a, S)_k$ contains only regular function elements. Let (b, P) be a regular function element in D. This means that in terms of the local coordinates in D, (b, P) has the coordinates $\epsilon \sqrt[k]{b - a}$, where $\epsilon^k = 1$, and $P(z - b) \equiv S(\epsilon \sqrt[k]{z - a})$ in their common region of definition. We define a path $(\alpha(t), P_t)$, $t \in I$, in D by saying that $\epsilon \sqrt[k]{\alpha(t) - a}$, $t \in I$, shall be the line segment from $\epsilon \sqrt[k]{b - a}$ to 0 and $P_t(z - \alpha(t)) \equiv S(\epsilon \sqrt[k]{z - a})$, $0 \leq t < 1$, in their common region of definition, while $P_1(z - a) \equiv S(\sqrt[k]{z - a})$.

We have proved that each singular function element of R_A can be joined to any regular function element by a path which, except for its end point, lies entirely in M_A. This prompts us to make the following definition. A function element $(a, S)_k$ (regular or singular) is said to be *joined analytically* to a regular function element (b, P) if there is a path (α, I), $\alpha(0) = b$, $\alpha(1) = a$, in the complex plane (or sphere) such that $(\alpha(t), P_t)$, $0 \leq t < 1$, are regular function elements forming an analytic continuation of P and if for all t sufficiently near 1, P_t is identically equal to a fixed determination of S while $(a, P_1) = (a, S)_k$. We have therefore proved

THEOREM 3–8. *The analytic configuration of the analytic function A consists of the totality of function elements (regular or singular) which can be joined analytically to a given regular function element in A.*

The Riemann surface R_A of the analytic function A therefore contains as a submanifold the manifold M_A of regular function elements in A.

The singular function elements $(a, S)_k$, $k > 1$, which are added to M_A to form R_A are called *algebraic branch points* of R_A. We remark that the analytic function A stands in the same relationship to the analytic manifold M_A of regular function elements as the analytic configuration of A stands with respect to the Riemann surface R_A of the analytic function A. At a point $(a, S)_k$ of the form (2) or (3), we say that the analytic function A assumes the value a_0 (see (1)) when $\nu \geq 0$ and the value ∞ when $\nu < 0$.

We have now defined abstractly what is meant by a Riemann surface and have shown that the Riemann surface of an analytic function (used to make the function single-valued) is just a Riemann surface in this abstract sense. The question now arises as to whether every abstract Riemann surface can be realized as (is conformally equivalent to) a Riemann surface of some analytic function. One of the principal results in this book is a proof that indeed every compact abstract Riemann surface can be realized as the Riemann surface of some algebraic function.

Problems

1. Describe the Riemann surface of the algebraic functions

$$\text{(a)} \quad w^3 - 1 - z = 0, \qquad \text{(b)} \quad z - w - \frac{1}{w} = 0.$$

2. Describe the Riemann surface of the function $w = \log z$. Show that it is topologically the finite complex plane.

The following series of problems leads to the nature of the Riemann surface of an arbitrary algebraic function (see Knopp, Ref. 27, Chap. V).

3. Let $G(z, w) = a_0(z) + a_1(z)w + \cdots + a_m(z)w^m = 0$, the $a_i(z)$ being polynomials in z, define the algebraic function $w = f(z)$. Assume that $G(z, w)$ is irreducible; that is, $G(z, w) \not\equiv G_1(z, w)G_2(z, w)$, where G_1 and G_2 are of positive degree in w. For each $z = z_0$, (except for a finite number of points, called critical points) we have an mth-degree polynomial in w which has m distinct roots: $w_0^{(1)}, w_0^{(2)}, \ldots, w_0^{(m)}$. The critical points $c_1, c_2, \ldots, c_r$ occur when $a_m(z_0) = 0$ or when $G(z_0, w)$ has a multiple root, i.e., when the discriminant, which is itself a polynomial in z, vanishes. Prove that the m roots depend continuously on the point z. That is, show that when $a_m(z_0) \neq 0$ and w_0 is a ν-fold root of $G(z_0, w) = 0$, then given any sufficiently small positive ϵ, there exists a $\delta = \delta(\epsilon, z_0)$ such that for each z in $|z - z_0| < \delta$, $G(z, w) = 0$ has precisely ν distinct roots in $|w - w_0| < \epsilon$.

4. If, in addition to $a_m(z_0) \neq 0$, we require that the m roots are distinct, then in $|z - z_0| < \delta$, m distinct continuous single-valued functions $f_1(z), f_2(z), \ldots, f_m(z)$ are determined with $G(z, f_i(z)) \equiv 0$. Show that $f_i(z)$ is a regular analytic function of z in $|z - z_0| < \delta$; that is, $f'(z)$ exists at each point in $|z - z_0| < \delta$.

5. We shall denote by $P_i(z - z_0)$, $i = 1, 2, \ldots, m$, the m distinct function elements found in problem 4. Show that each of these can be continued analytically throughout the whole plane with the critical points $c_1, c_2, \ldots, c_r$ removed. If a non-self-intersecting polygonal path L is drawn, connecting the critical points $c_1, c_2, \ldots, c_r$ and ∞, then m distinct single-valued analytic functions $F_1(z), F_2(z), \ldots, F_m(z)$ are determined in the z-plane cut along L.

6. Show that the singularities of the functions $F_i(z)$ at the critical points are all poles or algebraic branch points.

7. Show that by analytic continuation over suitable paths crossing the cut L, each $F_i(z)$ can be continued into any other $F_k(z)$. Thus the Riemann surface of the algebraic function $w = f(z)$ is precisely an m-sheeted covering of the sphere with only a finite number of algebraic branch points. Show that this surface is compact.

CHAPTER 4

COVERING MANIFOLDS

4–1 Covering manifolds. Let M represent a two-dimensional manifold. A *covering manifold M^* of M* is another two-dimensional manifold together with a continuous mapping f of M^* into M such that if for any $P_0^* \in M^*$ we write $f(P_0^*) = P_0 \in M$, then

1. there exists a local parameter $x^* + iy^* = z^* = \Phi^*(P^*)$, $\Phi^*(P_0^*) = 0$, about P_0^*, and
2. there exists a local parameter $x + iy = z = \Phi(P)$, $\Phi(P_0) = 0$, about P_0, such that
3. when represented in terms of z and z^*, f becomes $z = z^{*n}$ in a neighborhood of $z^* = 0$ for some positive integer n.†

We call P_0 the *projection* of P_0^* on M. P_0^* is said to *lie over* P_0, and the mapping f is the *projection* of M^* into M.

Since the mapping $z = z^{*n}$ is n-to-one, while Φ^* and Φ are locally one-to-one, we note that in the neighborhood of P_0^* there are n points corresponding to each point near P_0. Thus the number n is characteristic for a given pair of points P_0^* and P_0, only one such number being possible at each pair of corresponding points. If n is greater than one, we call the point P_0^* a *branch point of order $n - 1$ of M^* with respect to M*. If $n = 1$, P_0^* is called a *regular point*.

In the mapping $z^{*n} = z$, each point $z_1^* \neq 0$ has a neighborhood (not including $z^* = 0$) which is mapped one-to-one and continuously onto a neighborhood of z_1^{*n} (in other words, we restrict ourselves to one branch of the function $z^{*n} = z$). Thus each point in the deleted neighborhood of a branch point P_0^* is a regular point and branch points are *isolated* points on M^*. If the covering manifold M^* has no branch points, we call it *smooth*.

Any manifold M is trivially its own smooth covering manifold with the identity mapping as the projection mapping. A less trivial example of a covering manifold is obtained when we let M^* be the infinite strip

$$0 < x < 1, \qquad -\infty < y < \infty,$$

---

†We have given here the definition of a (branched) covering manifold of a two-dimensional manifold. For a generalization of this notion to covering manifolds of n-dimensional manifolds, see Seifert and Threlfall, Ref. 44.

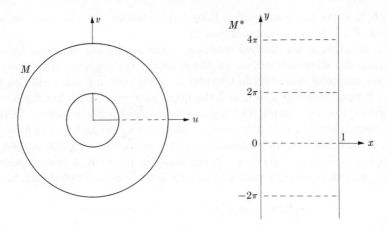

FIGURE 4–1.

and M be the annulus $1 < r < e$ in the (u, v)-plane where $r \cos \theta = u$, $r \sin \theta = v$; here we use the relative topology from $\mathcal{E}^2$ in both cases (Fig. 4–1). The projection mapping can be taken as $r = e^x$, $\theta = y$. This mapping is locally one-to-one in the strip M^*, making each rectangle $0 < x < 1$, $2\pi k \leq y < 2\pi(k+1)$ correspond one-to-one to the annulus M. At each point of M^* we can choose as local parameter $z^* = e^{x+iy}$, and at the corresponding point of M we use as local parameter $z = re^{i\theta}$. Then the projection mapping f expressed in terms of the local parameters becomes $z = z^*$ and

each point is a regular point. Thus M^* is a smooth covering manifold of M. It may be pictured topologically by imagining the strip M^* wound around to form an ascending helicoid over the annulus M, and the mapping f would be the ordinary projection of the helicoid down on the annulus. In this sense, M^* literally covers M (Fig. 4–2). In this covering surface of the annulus, an infinite number of points on M^* "lie over" each point of M. We obtain a different covering surface of M if we consider only the N rectangles $0 < x < 1$, $2\pi k \leq y \leq 2\pi(k+1)$, $k = 0, 1, \ldots, N-1$, with the end $y = 2\pi N$ identified with the end

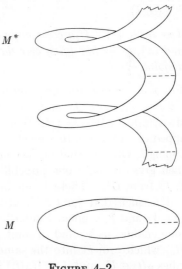

FIGURE 4–2.

$y = 0$, and the same projection mapping as before. In this case, only N points of M^* lie over each point of M.

An example of a branched covering of the z-sphere is obtained by considering the Riemann surface of the function $\sqrt{z}$ together with the projection mapping described in Chapter 3. This covering manifold has two branch points, one at $z = 0$ and the other at $z = \infty$, each having $n = 2$. There are exactly two points lying over each point of the z-sphere. In fact, the Riemann surface of any analytic function as defined in Chapter 3 is just a branched covering manifold of the z-sphere, using the projection mapping $(a, S(\sqrt[k]{z - a})) \to a$. If the analytic function A is an algebraic function, this covering manifold has only a finite number of sheets, for if

$$a_0(z)w^n + a_1(z)w^{n-1} + \cdots + a_n(z) = 0$$

determines w as an algebraic function of z, then there are in general n different function elements determined for each z. The sphere is a compact surface and the n-sheeted branched covering corresponding to an algebraic function is also a compact manifold, as we saw in problem 7 at the end of Chapter 3.

The curve $C^* = (\alpha^*, I)$ on M^* is a continuous mapping α^* of the unit interval I into M^*. If we project C^* onto the base manifold M using the projection mapping f, we obtain a curve $C = (\alpha, I)$ on M, where $\alpha(t) = f(\alpha^*(t))$. We may now ask the converse question: given a curve (α, I) on M, with $\alpha(0) = P_0$, and a point P_0^* on M^* such that $f(P_0^*) = P_0$, does there exist a curve (α^*, I) with $\alpha^*(0) = P_0^*$ which projects into (α, I)? If so, we say that we have *continued* the curve (α^*, I) from P_0^* over the curve (α, I).

THEOREM 4–1. *If a covering manifold M^* is smooth, two curves (α_1^*, I) and (α_2^*, I) on M^* lying over the same curve (α, I) either coincide or are disjoint.*

For if I_1 represents the subinterval of I for which $\alpha_1^*(t) = \alpha_2^*(t)$, and $I_2 = I - I_1$, both I_1 and I_2 are open relative to I; indeed, if $t_0 \in I_1$ and $\alpha_1^*(t_0) = \alpha_2^*(t_0) = Q^*$, then a whole neighborhood U^* of Q^* is mapped one-to-one onto a neighborhood U of $\alpha(t_0) = Q$ by the projection mapping f. Observe that in the neighborhood of any point Q^*, the mapping f then gives us only one possibility for continuing the curve (α_1^*, I) or (α_2^*, I) from Q^*. There is an interval $V: t_0 - \delta < t < t_0 + \delta$, $\delta > 0$, about t_0 such that for $t \in V$, $\alpha(t) \in U$. Thus $f^{-1}(\alpha(t)) = \alpha_1^*(t) = \alpha_2^*(t)$ for $t \in V$, and I_1 is open. Similarly, if $t_0 \in I_2$, the fact that f is locally one-to-one enables us to find disjoint neighborhoods U_1^* of $\alpha_1^*(t_0)$ and U_2^* of $\alpha_2^*(t_0)$ which project into the same neighborhood U of $\alpha(t_0)$. Then $t \in V$ implies $\alpha(t) \in U$, and if $f^{-1}(\alpha(t)) = \alpha_1^*(t)$ is continued from $\alpha_1^*(t_0)$, then

$\alpha_1^*(t)$ is in U_1^*, while if $f^{-1}(\alpha(t)) = \alpha_2^*(t)$ is continued from $\alpha_2^*(t_0)$, then $\alpha_2^*(t)$ is in U_2^*, so all $t \in V$ are in I_2. Therefore I has been divided into two disjoint open sets, which means that either I_1 or I_2 is empty, since I is connected. This proves our assertion and we see that *on a smooth covering manifold, continuation is unique.*

If the covering manifold is not smooth, the continuation of a curve at an n-fold branch point ($z^{*n} = z$) is not unique but can be carried out in n distinct ways. It may also be that continuation over a given curve is not possible; for starting at the point P_0^* lying over the initial point P_0 of the curve (α, I), there may be no curve lying over the whole of (α, I); instead, the covering manifold M^* may cover only part of (α, I), and our continuation leads us to the "boundary" of M^*. For example, consider the annulus $M: 1 < r < e$ in the (u, v)-plane ($u = r \cos \theta, v = r \sin \theta$) covered by the rectangle $M^*: 0 < x < 1, 0 < y < 3\pi$, with the projection mapping $r = e^x$, $\theta = y$. We take the curve (α, I) to be $\alpha(t) = 2e^{3\pi it/2}$ and try to continue over (α, I) from the point $(\log 2, 2\pi)$ of M^*. The continuation is possible only until $t = \frac{2}{3}$, when $\alpha^*(t) = (\log 2, 2\pi + \frac{3}{2}\pi t)$ meets the boundary point $(\log 2, 3\pi)$ of M^*.

When continuation over every curve is always possible, we say that M^* is an unlimited covering manifold of M. More precisely, M^* is an *unlimited covering manifold of M* if, given any curve (α, I) on M with $\alpha(0) = P_0$ and given any point P_0^* on M^* lying over P_0, then there is a curve (α^*, I) on M^* such that $\alpha^*(0) = P_0^*$ and $f(\alpha^*(t)) = \alpha(t)$ for all $t \in I$. We then have the following corollary of Theorem 4–1.

COROLLARY 4–1. *On a covering manifold which is both smooth and unlimited, continuation over any curve is always possible and unique.*

The covering manifolds of the annulus presented above are all examples of unlimited and smooth covering manifolds. In the first case of the infinite strip, each point of the annulus is covered by an infinite number of points $(x_0, y_0 + 2\pi k)$, $k = 0, \pm 1, \pm 2, \ldots$. In the second case of the strip of length $2\pi n$ with ends identified, each point of the annulus is covered by exactly n points. This property of covering each point of the base manifold the same number of times also applies to branched covering manifolds which are unlimited, as the following theorem shows.

THEOREM 4–2. *If M^* is an unlimited covering manifold of M, every point of M is covered the same number of times provided a branch point of order $n - 1$ is counted n times.*

We shall consider the set of points E_n on M which are covered at least n times, and prove first that E_n is open. Suppose that the point P_0 is in E_n; then we can certainly find n points P_i^*, $i = 1, 2, \ldots, n$ lying above P_0 (counting branch points multiply) and each P_i^* has a neighborhood U_i^*

which projects into a neighborhood U_i of P_0 under the projection mapping. If P_i^* is not a branch point, the projection is one-to-one and each point in U_i is covered once by U_i^*. If P_i^* is a branch point of order k, each point of U_i is covered k times by U_i^*. The intersection U of the sets U_i is again a neighborhood of P_0, and each point of U is covered n times by the points in the U_i^*; thus $U \subset E_n$ and E_n is open.

We can now show, however, that E_n is also closed or, what is the same thing, that $\widetilde{E}_n = M - E$ is open. If $P_0 \in \widetilde{E}_n$, P_0 is covered at most $n - 1$ times, say by P_i^*, $i = 1, 2, \ldots, k$, $k \leq n - 1$. Again let U_i^* be a neighborhood of P_i^* which projects into the neighborhood U_i of P_0 under the projection mapping of the form $z = z^{*m}$. Let

$$U = \bigcap_{i=1}^{k} U_i = U_1 \cap U_2 \cap \cdots \cap U_k$$

and, finally, let K be a parametric disk $|z| < r$ with center at P_0 and lying entirely inside of U. Then there are at least k points lying above each point $Q \in K$, these k points lying in the sets U_i^*, since each P_i^* was counted the proper number of times to account for the branching. These are the only points lying over Q, for if Q^* is any point lying over $Q \in K$, we can draw a radial line L in K from P_0 to Q and continue over L from Q^* to one of the points P_j^* lying over P_0, since M^* is unlimited. Then Q^* lies in the neighborhood U_j^* of P_j^* and is one of the k points already accounted for. Thus there are at most $k \leq (n - 1)$ points lying over each point K and $\widetilde{E}_n$ is open, or E_n is closed.

Since M is connected, E_n is either the whole of M or is empty. If there is an integer n such that the set E_n is nonempty but E_{n+1} is empty, each point of M is covered exactly n times. Otherwise M^* covers each point of M an infinite number of times.

4–2 Monodromy theorem. From now on we shall restrict ourselves to smooth and unlimited covering manifolds M^*. If each point of M is covered n times, we say that M^* has n sheets. We have already pointed out that two curves lying over the same curve either are entirely disjoint or coincide. If we consider two curves C_1 and C_2 on M, both of which join P_0 to P_1, we may fix a point P_0^* lying over P_0 and continue over both C_1 and C_2 from P_0^* to obtain two (uniquely defined) curves C_1^* and C_2^*. The end points of C_1^* and C_2^* shall be denoted by P_1^* and P_2^*, respectively. We ask whether $P_1^* = P_2^*$, so that both continuations lead to the same end point. The answer to this question is intimately connected with the notion of homotopic deformation of curves.

If $C_1 = (\alpha_1, I)$ and $C_2 = (\alpha_2, I)$ are two curves on M each joining the points P_0 and P_1, we say that C_1 is homotopic to C_2 if C_1 can be "deformed continuously" into C_2, a notion which we shall now properly define. Each point $\alpha_1(t)$ on C_1 moves along a continuous curve to $\alpha_2(t)$. This curve can be represented in terms of a parameter u as $\varphi(t, u)$, $0 \leq u \leq 1$. We now ask that φ be a continuous function of both variables t and u, giving us a curve joining P_0 to P_1 for each fixed value of u. These curves give us the desired continuous deformation of C_1 into C_2. Therefore, we say that C_1 is *homotopic* to C_2 if there exists a continuous mapping φ of the square $I \times I$ into M such that

$$\varphi(t, 0) = \alpha_1(t), \qquad t \in I,$$
$$\varphi(t, 1) = \alpha_2(t), \qquad t \in I,$$
$$\varphi(0, u) = P_0, \qquad u \in I,$$
$$\varphi(1, u) = P_1, \qquad u \in I.$$

We shall denote the fact that C_1 is homotopic to C_2 by writing $C_1 \approx C_2$. We call φ a *deformation* of C_1 into C_2.

THEOREM 4–3.   *Let $C_1 = (\alpha, I)$ be a curve on M and $C_2 = (\beta, I)$ be another curve on M such that there is a continuous function g from I to I with $g(0) = 0$, $g(1) = 1$, and $\alpha(t) = \beta(g(t))$. Then $C_1 \approx C_2$.*

The two curves have the same carrier on M, and we may look upon β as a different parametrization of the curve α. To prove the theorem, we observe that $\varphi(t, u) = \beta(ut + (1 - u)g(t))$ gives us the desired deformation of C_1 into C_2; for φ is continuous from $I \times I$ to M and $\varphi(t, 0) = \beta(g(t)) = \alpha(t)$, $\varphi(t, 1) = \beta(t)$, $\varphi(0, u) = \beta(0) = \alpha(0)$,   and $\varphi(1, u) = \beta(1) = \alpha(1)$.

As an illustration of the notion of homotopy of curves, take an annulus $1 < |z| < 3$ and let C_1 be any curve lying entirely in Im $z \geq 0$ and in the annulus and joining $z = 2$ to $z = -2$. If C_2 is another such curve $C_1 \approx C_2$, but if C_2 lies in Im $z \leq 0$ and in the annulus and joins $z = 2$ to $z = -2$, then C_1 is not homotopic to C_2, since C_1 cannot be deformed into C_2 without crossing the inner boundary $|z| = 1$.

We now return to the question of whether two continuations starting at the same point on M^* lead to the same end point. The answer is embodied in the following theorem, called the *monodromy theorem*:

THEOREM 4–4.   *Hypotheses:*
   (1) *M^* is a smooth unlimited covering manifold of M.*
   (2) *$C_0 = (\alpha_0, I)$ and $C_1 = (\alpha_1, I)$ are two curves on M with $\alpha_0(0) = \alpha_1(0) = P_0$ and $\alpha_0(1) = \alpha_1(1) = P_1$.*
   (3) *$C_0 \approx C_1$.*
   (4) *P_0^* is a point of M^* lying over P_0.*
   (5) *$C_0^* = (\alpha_1^*, I)$ is a continuation from P_0^* over C_0.*
   (6) *$C_1^* = (\alpha_1^*, I)$ is a continuation from P_0^* over C_1.*

Conclusion: $C_0^* \approx C_1^*$ and $\alpha_0^*(1) = \alpha_1^*(1)$.

Since $C_0 \approx C_1$, there is a continuous deformation of C_1 into C_2 effected by the continuous function φ mapping $I \times I \to M$, with $\varphi(t, 0) = \alpha_0(t)$, $\varphi(t, 1) = \alpha_1(t)$, $\varphi(0, u) = P_0$ and $\varphi(1, u) = P_1$. For each fixed value of $u \in I$, $\varphi(t, u)$ defines a curve C_u on M. Let $C_u^* = (\varphi^*(t, u), I)$ be the curve on M^* obtained by continuation from P_0^* over C_u. The function $\varphi^*(t, u)$ thus defined is from $I \times I$ to M^* and has $\varphi^*(t, 0) = \alpha_0^*(t)$, $\varphi^*(t, 1) = \alpha_1^*(t)$, and $\varphi^*(0, u) = P_0^*$. Our theorem will be proved if we show that φ^* is continuous in $I \times I$ and that $\varphi^*(1, u)$ is a constant. To accomplish this, let E be the subset of I consisting of values t_0 such that $\varphi^*(t, u)$ is continuous in the rectangle $0 \leq t < t_0$, $0 \leq u \leq 1$. Since $\varphi^*(0, u) = P_0^*$ for all u, $\varphi^*(0, u)$ is continuous in $0 \leq u \leq 1$, and we shall say that $t_0 = 0$ belongs to E. Thus E is not empty, and a proof that E is both open and closed will then give us $E = I$.

To show that E is closed, we shall show that its complement $\widetilde{E} = I - E$ is open. If $t_1 \in \widetilde{E}_1$, all $t > t_1$ are also in $\widetilde{E}$ by definition and $\varphi^*(t, u)$ has a discontinuity in the rectangle $0 \leq t < t_1$, $0 \leq u \leq 1$. Let (t_2, u_2) be a point of discontinuity in this rectangle, so that $t_2 < t_1$. Then all t in the strip $t_2 < t \leq 1$ belong to $\widetilde{E}$ and $\widetilde{E}$ is open relative to I.

To show that E iself is open, let $t_1 \in E$. Then all $t < t_1$ are also in E, by definition. We shall show that $\varphi^*(t, u)$ is also continuous in a small strip to the right of $t = t_1$, that is, there is a positive number η such that $\varphi^*(t, u)$ is continuous in $t_1 \leq t < t + \eta$, $0 \leq u \leq 1$. Let (t_1, u_1) be any point on the line $t = t_1$ and $Q^* = \varphi^*(t_1, u_1)$. We shall prove the continuity of $\varphi^*(t, u)$ in a whole neighborhood of (t_1, u_1). Let U^* be a neighborhood of Q^* on M^* which projects one-to-one and bicontinuously into a neighborhood U of Q on S using the projection mapping f on M^* onto M. From the continuity of the mapping $\varphi(t, u)$, we deduce the existence of a square Δ: $t_1 - \delta < t < t_1 + \delta$, $u_1 - \delta < u < u_1 + \delta$, $\delta > 0$, about (t_1, u_1), which is mapped entirely into U by $\varphi(t, u)$. Let t_2 be any value of t such that $t_1 - \delta < t_2 < t_1$. The function φ^* is continuous for all $t < t_1$; in particular, for $t = t_2$, $0 \leq u \leq 1$. Thus there is an $\epsilon(0 < \epsilon < \delta)$ such that the image of the segment $L: t = t_2$, $u_1 - \epsilon < u < u_1 + \epsilon$, under the mapping φ^* is inside of U^* and φ^* is continuous in the whole strip $t \leq t_2$, $u_1 - \epsilon < u \leq u_1 + \epsilon$. The function $f^{-1}(\varphi(t, u))$ is continuous in Δ, agrees with $\varphi^*(t, u)$ on L, and for fixed u gives us a continuation over the part of the curve C_u in U. Since continuation is unique, $\varphi^*(t, u) \equiv f^{-1}(\varphi(t, u))$ in Δ and is hence a continuous function in Δ. For each u on the line $t = t_1$, we may perform the same construction to get a square Δ_u: $t_1 - \delta_u < t < t_1 + \delta_u$, $u_1 - \delta_u < u < u_1 + \delta_u$, in which $\varphi^*(t, u)$ is continuous. A finite number of these squares covers the line $t = t_1$, $0 \leq u \leq 1$, and if we set $\eta = $ minimum δ_u for this finite number of squares, we get a strip $t_1 - \eta < t < t_1 + \eta$, $0 \leq u \leq 1$, entirely covered by these squares and in which $\varphi^*(t, u)$ is continuous. Thus all $t < t_1 + \eta$ are in E and E is open, proving that $E = I$ and $\varphi^*(t, u)$ is a continuous mapping for $0 \leq t < 1$, $0 \leq u \leq 1$.

The proof that φ^* is also continuous for $t = 1$, $0 \leq u \leq 1$, is accomplished in the same fashion. Let U^* be a neighborhood of $\varphi^*(1, u_1)$ which projects one-to-one onto a neighborhood U of $\varphi(1, u_1)$ on M. Thus for some $\delta > 0$, the rectangle Δ: $1 - \delta < t \leq 1$, $u_1 - \delta < u < u_1 + \delta$ maps into U by φ. For any value t_2 such that $1 - \delta < t_2 < 1$, the function $\varphi^*(t, u)$ is continuous by what we proved above. Thus there is an $\epsilon (0 < \epsilon < \delta)$ such that the image of the segment L: $t = t_2$, $u_1 - \epsilon < u < u_1 + \epsilon$ under φ^* is made of U^*, and φ^* is continuous in the strip $t \leq t_2, u_1 - \epsilon < u < u_1 + \epsilon$. The function $f^{-1}(\varphi(t, u))$ is continuous in Δ, is equal to $\varphi^*(t, u)$ on L, and for fixed u gives us a continuation over the part of the curve C_u in U. Since the continuation is unique, $\varphi^*(t, u) \equiv f^{-1}(\varphi(t, u))$ in Δ and φ^* is continuous in Δ, and hence at $(1, u_1)$. Thus φ^* is continuous in all of $I \times I$.

The function $\varphi^*(1, u)$ is a continuous function of u in $0 \leq u \leq 1$ and all values must project under the projection mapping f into the same point P_1. Since the points that lie above P_1 are isolated points, the continuous function $\varphi^*(1, u)$ must assume a constant value and $\varphi^*(1, u) = P_1^*$. Thus we have proved that $\alpha_0^*(1) = \alpha_1^*(1) = P_1^*$ and $C_0^* \approx C_1^*$.

4–3 Fundamental group. Since homotopy plays such a fundamental role in the study of covering manifolds, we shall investigate this notion more extensively. We have already introduced the multiplication of two curves if the end point of one is the initial point of the other; that is, if $C_1 = (\alpha, I)$ and $C_2 = (\beta, I)$ with $\alpha(1) = \beta(0)$, then $C_1 C_2 = (\gamma, I)$, where

$$\gamma(t) = \begin{cases} \alpha(2t), & 0 \leq t \leq \frac{1}{2}, \\ \beta(2t - 1), & \frac{1}{2} \leq t \leq 1. \end{cases}$$

We shall let $\mathbf{1} = (\beta, I)$ denote the constant curve in which $\beta(t) \equiv P_0$ for all $t \in I$ (here P_0 can be any point of M). If $C = (\alpha, I)$ and $\alpha(1) = P_1$, and if $\mathbf{1} = (\beta, I)$ is the constant curve $\beta(t) \equiv P_1$, then $C\mathbf{1} \approx C$; for $C\mathbf{1}$ is merely a reparametrization of C. Similarly, if $\mathbf{1} = (\beta, I)$, where $\beta(t) \equiv \alpha(0)$, then $\mathbf{1}C \approx C$. Finally, we have defined C^{-1} to be the curve (β, I), where $\beta(t) = \alpha(1 - t)$. We have $CC^{-1} \approx \mathbf{1}$; for $CC^{-1} = (\gamma, I)$ where

$$\gamma(t) = \begin{cases} \alpha(2t), & 0 \leq t \leq \frac{1}{2}, \\ \beta(2t - 1) = \alpha(2 - 2t), & \frac{1}{2} \leq t \leq 1. \end{cases}$$

Then the homotopic deformation

$$\varphi(t, u) = \begin{cases} \alpha(2t(1 - u)), & 0 \leq t \leq \frac{1}{2}, \ 0 \leq u \leq 1, \\ \alpha(2(1 - t)(1 - u)), & \frac{1}{2} \leq t \leq 1, \ 0 \leq u \leq 1, \end{cases}$$

deforms CC^{-1} continuously into a constant curve. It actually shrinks the curve CC^{-1} continuously down to the point $\alpha(0)$.

The multiplication of curves defined above is applicable not to all pairs of curves on M but only to those pairs for which the end point of one and the initial point of the other coincide. To make multiplication possible for all pairs of curves under consideration, we shall now restrict ourselves to the set of curves beginning and ending at the same point, that is, curves (α, I) with $\alpha(0) = \alpha(1) = P_0$. Because of the parametrization of the curves through P_0, the multiplication here defined is not associative. If $C_1 = (\alpha_1, I)$, $C_2 = (\alpha_2, I)$, and $C_3 = (\alpha_3, I)$, then in $C_1C_2 = (\beta, I)$ the interval $[0, \frac{1}{2}]$ maps into C_1 and $[\frac{1}{2}, 1]$ into C_2. Then in $(C_1C_2)C_3$, $[0, \frac{1}{4}]$ maps into C_1, $[\frac{1}{4}, \frac{1}{2}]$ maps into C_2, and $[\frac{1}{2}, 1]$ maps into C_3. On the other hand, in $C_1(C_2C_3)$, $[0, \frac{1}{2}]$ maps into C_1, $[\frac{1}{2}, \frac{3}{4}]$ maps into C_2, and $[\frac{3}{4}, 1]$ maps into C_3. Thus $(C_1C_2)C_3 \neq C_1(C_2C_3)$. However, since they differ only in parametrization, they are homotopic to each other. We shall denote the collection of curves through P_0 with this multiplication as $F(P_0)$. The constant curve (α, I) with $\alpha(t) \equiv P_0$ is denoted by $\mathbf{1}$.

The homotopy relation between two curves, $C_1 \approx C_2$, is an equivalence relation; for (a) $C \approx C$ by the identity deformation $\varphi(t, u) = \alpha(t)$ where $C = (\alpha, I)$; (b) $C_1 \approx C_2$ implies $C_2 \approx C_1$, since if $\varphi(t, u)$ deforms C_1 into C_2 then $\varphi(t, 1 - u)$ deforms C_2 into C_1; and (c) $C_1 \approx C_2$, $C_2 \approx C_3$ implies $C_1 \approx C_3$, for if $\varphi_1(t, u)$ deforms C_1 into C_2 and $\varphi_2(t, u)$ deforms C_2 into C_3, then

$$\varphi(t, u) = \begin{cases} \varphi_1(t, 2u), & 0 \leq u \leq \frac{1}{2}, \\ \varphi_2(t, 2u - 1), & \frac{1}{2} \leq u \leq 1, \end{cases}$$

deforms C_1 into C_3. Thus $F(P_0)$ is divided into equivalence classes by the homotopy relation. We shall denote the class of curves homotopic to C by $\mathcal{C}$.

We shall prove that if $C_1 \approx D_1$ and $C_2 \approx D_2$, then $C_1C_2 \approx D_1D_2$. Indeed, if $\varphi_1(t, u)$ deforms C_1 into D_1 and $\varphi_2(t, u)$ deforms C_2 into D_2, then

$$\varphi(t, u) = \begin{cases} \varphi_1(2t, u), & 0 \leq t \leq \frac{1}{2}, \\ \varphi_2(2t - 1, u), & \frac{1}{2} \leq t \leq 1, \end{cases}$$

deforms C_1C_2 into D_1D_2. Furthermore, if $C \approx D$, then $C^{-1} \approx D^{-1}$; for if $\varphi(t, u)$ deforms C into D, then $\varphi(1 - t, u)$ deforms C^{-1} into D^{-1}. Thus we may form the multiplication of homotopy classes $\mathcal{C}$ and $\mathcal{D}$ by selecting any representative C in $\mathcal{C}$ and D in $\mathcal{D}$ and setting $\mathcal{C}\mathcal{D}$ = homotopy class of CD. Furthermore, if we denote by $\mathcal{I}$ the class of the constant curve $\mathbf{1}$, then $\mathcal{I}$ is the identity in the multiplication of classes $\mathcal{C}\mathcal{I} = \mathcal{C}$ and $\mathcal{I}\mathcal{C} = \mathcal{C}$. These equivalence classes of homotopic curves with the prescribed multiplication and identity element form a group which we call the *fundamental group* $\mathfrak{F}(P_0)$ relative to P_0. We call P_0 the *base point* of the group $\mathfrak{F}(P_0)$.

It appears as though the fundamental group depends upon the point P_0 selected as the initial and terminal point of all curves in $F(P_0)$. This is not true, for *if another point P_1 is selected as base point, the resulting group $\mathfrak{F}(P_1)$ is isomorphic to $\mathfrak{F}(P_0)$.* (We shall denote group isomorphism by $\cong$.) Since M is arcwise connected, we can find a curve J going from P_0 to P_1. To each class of curves $\mathfrak{C}$ in $\mathfrak{F}(P_0)$, we can associate the class of curves $\mathfrak{J}^{-1}\mathfrak{C}\mathfrak{J}$ in $\mathfrak{F}(P_1)$. This is a homomorphism of $\mathfrak{F}(P_0)$ into $\mathfrak{F}(P_1)$; for if $\mathfrak{C}$ and $\mathfrak{D}$ are in $\mathfrak{F}(P_0)$, then $(J^{-1}CJ)(J^{-1}DJ) \approx J^{-1}C1DJ \approx J^{-1}(CD)J$, and in terms of the homotopy classes $(\mathfrak{J}^{-1}\mathfrak{C}\mathfrak{J})(\mathfrak{J}^{-1}\mathfrak{D}\mathfrak{J}) = \mathfrak{J}^{-1}\mathfrak{C}\mathfrak{D}\mathfrak{J}$. This homomorphism is one-to-one onto $\mathfrak{F}(P_1)$, since to each class of curves $\mathfrak{D} \in \mathfrak{F}(P_1)$ the inverse homomorphism $\mathfrak{D} \to \mathfrak{J}\mathfrak{D}\mathfrak{J}^{-1}$ assigns an element of $\mathfrak{F}(P_0)$.

The isomorphism $\mathfrak{F}(P_0) \to \mathfrak{F}(P_1)$ depends upon the curve J joining P_0 to P_1, for if another curve J_1 joining P_0 to P_1 is used, a different mapping $\mathfrak{F}(P_0) \to \mathfrak{F}(P_1)$ is obtained. If $P_0 = P_1$, $J \in F(P_0)$ and $\mathfrak{C} \to \mathfrak{J}^{-1}\mathfrak{C}\mathfrak{J}$ defines an automorphism of the fundamental groups. Since $\mathfrak{F}(P_0) \cong \mathfrak{F}(P_1)$ for all points $P_1 \in M$, we can denote the abstract group $\mathfrak{F}(P_0)$ simply by $\mathfrak{F}$ and call it the *fundamental group of M.*

A curve is homotopic to the identity curve 1 of $F(P_0)$ if it can be deformed continuously to a point (constant curve). This is just the notion usually used to define simple connectivity of a region. Thus we shall make the following definition. *A manifold is called simply connected if its fundamental group consists only of the identity element $\mathfrak{I}$.* Thus every closed curve in a simply connected region can be shrunk continuously to a point. The disk $|z| < 1$, for example, is simply connected; for consider the set $F(0)$ of closed curves with $z = 0$ as initial and terminal point. If $C = (\alpha, I) \in F(0)$, then $\varphi(t, u) = \alpha(t)(1 - u)$ is a deformation of C into the identity curve $1 = (\beta, I)$, $\beta(t) \equiv 0$.

THEOREM 4–5. *The fundamental group of M is a topological invariant; that is, if M is homeomorphic to M', then the fundamental group $\mathfrak{F}$ of M is isomorphic to the fundamental group $\mathfrak{F}'$ of M'.*

Suppose that f is a homeomorphism of M onto M'. Then each closed curve $C = (\alpha, I)$ on M is mapped into a closed curve $f(C) = (f \circ \alpha, I)$ on M'. If $\varphi: I \times I \to M$ is a homotopic deformation of C_1 into C_2 on M, then $f \circ \varphi$ is a homotopic deformation of $f(C_1)$ into $f(C_2)$, so that curves in the same homotopy class on M map into homotopic curves on M'. Finally, if C_1 and C_2 are closed curves on M through P_0, then

$$f(C_1 C_2^{-1}) = f(C_1)f(C_2)^{-1},$$

where $f(C_1)$ and $f(C_2)$ are closed curves on M' through $P_0' = f(P_0)$. Thus

f defines a homomorphism of $\mathfrak{F}(P_0)$ on M into $\mathfrak{F}'(P_0')$ on M', and hence a homomorphism of $\mathfrak{F}$ info $\mathfrak{F}'$. Since the f mapping M onto M' is one-to-one, it has an inverse mapping f^{-1} for which $f^{-1}(C') = (f^{-1} \circ \alpha', I)$ for each curve $C' = (\alpha', I)$ on M'. Thus f defines an isomorphism of the fundamental groups; $\mathfrak{F} \cong \mathfrak{F}'$.

COROLLARY 4–2. *Simple connectivity is a topological invariant.*

Let M^* be a smooth unlimited covering manifold of M. Fix a point $P^* \in M^*$ lying above $P \in M$, and let $K(P^*)$ represent the set of curves in $F(P)$ which are projections of closed curves on M^* through P^*. Then $C \in K(P^*)$ if and only if continuation over C from P^* always leads back to P^*. The monodromy theorem tells us that if $C \approx D$, continuation over C and over D leads to the same end point, so that if $C \in K(P^*)$, D is also in $K(P^*)$. Thus if $C \in K(P^*)$, each of the class of curves $\mathcal{C}$ homotopic to C is also in $K(P^*)$, and if we denote by $\mathcal{K}(P^*)$ the collection of classes of homotopic curves in $K(P^*)$, that is, $\mathcal{C} \in \mathcal{K}(P^*)$ if $C \in K(P^*)$, C being a representative curve in $\mathcal{C}$, we can prove that $\mathcal{K}(P^*)$ is a subgroup of $\mathfrak{F}(P) = \mathfrak{F}$ by noting that if $C \in K(P^*)$ and $D \in K(P^*)$, then continuation over CD^{-1} starting at P^* also leads back to P^* and $CD^{-1} \in K(P^*)$. Thus the smooth unlimited covering manifold M^* and the point $P^* \in M^*$ determine a subgroup $\mathcal{K}(P^*)$ of the fundamental group $\mathfrak{F}$ of M.

There may be more than one point of M^* lying above $P \in M$. Let us denote the points (not necessarily countable) on M^* which lie above P by $P_1^*, P_2^*, \ldots$. To each of these points corresponds the subgroup $\mathcal{K}(P_1^*)$, $\mathcal{K}(P_2^*), \ldots$ of $\mathfrak{F}$. We shall now prove the following important theorem relating covering manifold and subgroups of the fundamental group.

THEOREM 4–6. *Let M^* be a smooth unlimited covering manifold of M. The homotopy classes of all closed curves from $P \in M$ which are projections of closed curves from $P^* \in M^*$ over P, form a subgroup $\mathcal{K}(P^*)$ of the fundamental group $\mathfrak{F}$ of M. For different points P_i^* over P, the groups $\mathcal{K}(P_i^*)$ form a complete set of conjugate subgroups of $\mathfrak{F}$ and, conversely, each complete set of conjugate subgroups of $\mathfrak{F}$ corresponds to a smooth unlimited covering manifold of M.*

First let P_i^* and P_j^* be two points of M^* lying over $P \in M$. Join P_i^* to P_j^* by a curve J^* on S which projects into the closed curve J on M. Then the mapping $\mathcal{C} \rightarrow \mathcal{J}\mathcal{C}\mathcal{J}^{-1}$ from $\mathcal{K}(P_j^*)$ to $\mathcal{K}(P_i^*)$ defines an inner automorphism of $\mathfrak{F}$ which carries $\mathcal{K}(P_j^*)$ onto $\mathcal{K}(P_i^*)$. Thus $\mathcal{K}(P_j^*)$ and $\mathcal{K}(P_i^*)$ are conjugate subgroups of $\mathfrak{F}$.

If we fix the point P_1^* over P, each homotopy class of closed curves $\mathcal{J}$ determines a unique point P_i^* over P obtained by continuing over $J \in \mathcal{J}$ from P_i^*. Then every subgroup of $\mathfrak{F}$ which is conjugate to $\mathcal{K}(P_1^*)$ is obtained as a $\mathcal{K}(P_i^*)$, proving that we get a complete set of conjugate subgroups in this manner.

To prove the last part of the theorem, let $\mathcal{K}$ be a subgroup of $\mathcal{F}$. Fix a point Q on M. We shall now construct a covering manifold M^* of M which will correspond to the subgroup $\mathcal{K}$ of $\mathcal{F}$. As a point of M^*, we consider the equivalence class consisting of pairs (P, C), where P is a point on M and C is a curve that joins Q to P. Two pairs (P_1, C_1) and (P_2, C_2) will be identified as the same point of M^* if (1) $P_1 = P_2$ and (2) $\mathcal{C}_1\mathcal{C}_2{}^{-1} \in \mathcal{K}$, where $C_1 \in \mathcal{C}_1$ and $C_2 \in \mathcal{C}_2$. It is easily verified that this is actually an equivalence relation.

We introduce a topology in M^* as follows. Let N be a disk about $P_0 \in M$ in one system of local coordinates, say, $|z| < 1$. An open disk about (P_0, C_0) on M^* is to consist of all points (P, C) such that $P \in N$ and $C = C_0 J$, where J is any curve lying in N and joining P_0 to P. Since N is simply connected, the point (P, C) is determined independently of which curve J we select in N; for if J_1 and J_2 are two such curves from P_0 to P in N, $J_1 J_2^{-1}$ is a closed curve homotopic to 1, so $C_0 J_1 \approx C_0 J_2$ and $(\mathcal{C}_0\mathcal{J}_1)(\mathcal{C}_0\mathcal{J}_2)^{-1} = \mathcal{J} \in \mathcal{K}$.

A set V of M^* is defined to be open if each point of V is contained in an open disk contained entirely in V. In particular, the open disk itself is an open set. This definition of open sets satisfies the axioms for a Hausdorff space; for example, we shall demonstrate the separation axiom 5. If (P_1, C_1) and (P_2, C_2) are two points of M^*, the case $P_1 \neq P_2$ is easily disposed of by using disjoint parametric disks N_1 and N_2 about P_1 and P_2, respectively. If $P_1 = P_2$, we must have $\mathcal{C}_1\mathcal{C}_2{}^{-1}$ not in $\mathcal{K}$. Consider the open local coordinate disk N about P_1 and let V_1 be the set of all points $(P, C_1 J)$ and V_2 the set of all points $(P, C_2 J)$, where $P \in N$ and J joins P_1 to P within N. Then V_1 and V_2 are disjoint open sets; for if $(q_1, C_1 J_1) \in V_1$ and $(q_2, C_2 J_2) \in V_2$, and $(q_1, C_1 J_1) = (q_2, C_2 J_2)$, we have $q_1 = q_2$ and $(\mathcal{C}_1\mathcal{J}_1)(\mathcal{C}_2\mathcal{J}_2)^{-1} \in \mathcal{K}$. Since $J_1 J_2^{-1} \approx 1$, however, $\mathcal{C}_1\mathcal{J}_1(\mathcal{C}_2\mathcal{J}_2)^{-1} = \mathcal{C}_1\mathcal{J}_1\mathcal{J}_2^{-1}\mathcal{C}_2^{-1} = \mathcal{C}_1\mathcal{C}_2^{-1}$, which is not in $\mathcal{K}$: a contradiction telling us that V_1 and V_2 are disjoint.

M^* is arcwise connected; for if (P_1, C_1) and (P_2, C_2) are two points of M^*, $C_1 = (\alpha_1, I)$ and $C_2 = (\alpha_2, I)$ are curves joining Q to P_1 and P_2, respectively. Then $C_1^{-1}C_2 = (\gamma, t)$ is a curve joining P_1 to P_2, where

$$\gamma(t) = \begin{cases} \alpha_1(1 - 2t), & 0 \leq t \leq \tfrac{1}{2}, \\ \alpha_2(2t - 1), & \tfrac{1}{2} \leq t \leq 1. \end{cases}$$

Let $C_\tau = (\beta_\tau, I)$ where

$$\beta_\tau(t) = \begin{cases} \alpha_1(t(1 - 2\tau)), & 0 \leq \tau \leq \tfrac{1}{2}, \ 0 \leq t \leq 1, \\ \alpha_2(t(2\tau - 1)), & \tfrac{1}{2} \leq \tau \leq 1, \ 0 \leq t \leq 1. \end{cases}$$

Then the mapping $\tau \to (\gamma(\tau), C_\tau)$ from I to M^* defines a curve on M^* joining (P_1, C_1) to (P_2, C_2).

The mapping $f: (P, C) \to P$ associates to each point $(P, C) \in M^*$ the point $P \in M$ in such a way that each point (P, C) has about it an open disk which is mapped one-to-one and bicontinuously onto an open disk about $P \in M$. This mapping f may be used to carry the local coordinates on M up to M^*, making M^* a manifold and, moreover, a smooth unlimited covering manifold of M.

Finally, M^* corresponds to the subgroup $\mathcal{K}$ of the fundamental group $\mathcal{F}$. Indeed, let $Q^* = (Q, \mathbf{1})$ where $\mathbf{1}$ is the constant curve. Starting at Q^*, continue over a closed curve C beginning at Q. This continuation leads to the point (Q, C) on M^* and $(Q, C) = (Q, \mathbf{1})$ if and only if $\mathcal{C} \in \mathcal{K}$. Thus M^* corresponds to $\mathcal{K}$ and we obtain subgroups of $\mathcal{F}$ which are conjugate to $\mathcal{K}$ if we begin with another point over Q.

To show that the manifold M^* is actually determined by the class of conjugate subgroups in $\mathcal{F}$, we shall show that if $\mathcal{K}_1$ and $\mathcal{K}_2$ are conjugate subgroups of $\mathcal{F}$, they correspond to the same surface M^* in the following sense. If $\mathcal{K}_1$ corresponds to M_1^* and $\mathcal{K}_2$ to M_2^*, we shall define a homeomorphism h of M_1^* onto M_2^* in terms of which the projection mappings f_1 of M_1^* onto M and f_2 of M_2^* onto M can be written as $f_1(P_1^*) = f_2(h(P_1^*))$ for all $P_1^* \in M_1^*$. Since $\mathcal{K}_1$ and $\mathcal{K}_2$ are conjugate subgroups, there is a closed curve J such that $\mathcal{K}_2 = \mathcal{J}\mathcal{K}_1\mathcal{J}^{-1}$. Thus let h map the point $P_1^* = (P, C)$ on M_1^* into the point $P_2^* = (P, JC)$ on M_2^*. We must show that h is well defined on M_1^* in that it does not depend upon the curve C used to represent P_1^*. If C_1 and C_2 both define the same point P_1^* on M_1^*, then $\mathcal{C}_1\mathcal{C}_2^{-1} \in \mathcal{K}_1$. We must show that JC_1 and JC_2 define the same point on M_2^*, that is, $(\mathcal{J}\mathcal{C}_1)(\mathcal{J}\mathcal{C}_2)^{-1} \in \mathcal{K}_2$. This is true because $(\mathcal{J}\mathcal{C}_1)(\mathcal{J}\mathcal{C}_2)^{-1} = \mathcal{J}\mathcal{C}_1\mathcal{C}_2^{-1}\mathcal{J}^{-1} \in \mathcal{K}_2$ if $\mathcal{C}_1\mathcal{C}_2^{-1} \in \mathcal{K}_1$. Thus h determines P_2^* uniquely in terms of P_1^*. This mapping h gives us the desired homeomorphism of M_1^* onto M_2^* and shows that the same covering surface corresponds to the complete class of conjugate subgroups of $\mathcal{F}$, completing the proof of the theorem.

The fundamental group $\mathcal{F}$ always contains the two trivial subgroups: $\mathcal{I}$, which is the subgroup consisting of the identity class alone, and $\mathcal{F}$ itself. The covering manifold corresponding to $\mathcal{F}$ is the manifold M itself, using the identity mapping as the projection mapping. To the identity subgroup $\mathcal{I}$ corresponds the *universal covering manifold* $\hat{M}$ of M. Thus a curve is closed on the universal covering manifold of M if and only if its projection is homotopic to a point. Consequently, each point of M is covered as many times by $\hat{M}$ as there are different homotopy classes in $\mathcal{F}$.

THEOREM 4–7. *A manifold M is simply connected if and only if its only smooth unlimited covering manifold is M itself (or if and only if every such covering manifold of M has only one sheet).*

Let the simply connected manifold M have a covering manifold M^* with the points P_1^* and P_2^* lying over a given point P. If C^* joins P_1^* to P_2^*, its projection C is a closed curve on M and hence $C \approx 1$. But by the monodromy theorem, continuation over C leads back to the same point, so $P_1^* = P_2^*$ and M^* has only one sheet. Conversely, if $\mathfrak{F} \neq \mathfrak{g}$ the universal covering manifold $\hat{M}$ has more than one sheet.

COROLLARY 4–3. *If G is a simply connected region of the extended complex plane, and if analytic continuation of a function element $P(z - a)$, $a \in G$, is possible over all paths in G (thus leading to no singular point in G), then the analytic function A in G obtained by continuation of $P(z - a)$ is single-valued in G.*

The Riemann surface of A is a smooth unlimited covering surface of G and hence has only one sheet. Thus A is single-valued. On an arbitrary simply connected manifold, we can go through the same type of argument (constructing a covering surface) using complex-valued continuous functions instead of analytic functions and arrive at the result that continuous functions on simply connected manifolds must be single-valued.

COROLLARY 4–4. *The complement of a simply connected region G of the sphere (extended complex plane) has at most one component.*

Assume that the complement $\mathbf{C}G$ of G contains more than one component. The point at infinity can be in at most one of these components, so that at least one component, say A, is bounded. Let $B = \mathbf{C}G - A$. We select two points: $a \in A$ and $b \in B$. The sets A and B are closed disjoint subsets of the extended plane, so they have a shortest distance $\rho > 0$ which may be infinite. We now cover the plane with a net of squares σ by drawing horizontal and vertical lines such that the distance between successive parallel sides is $\delta < \rho/3$. We may do this in such a way that a lies at the center of one of the squares, say σ_1. Let σ_i, $i = 1, 2, \ldots, N$, denote the closed squares σ which meet A, and let γ_i denote the boundary of σ_i oriented counterclockwise. If we let γ denote the boundary of $\Sigma = \cup_{i=1}^N \sigma_i$, also oriented counterclockwise, γ is a closed polygonal path composed of horizontal and vertical line segments. We now show that γ lies in G. Since each point of γ is within the distance $\delta < \rho/3$ from A, γ does not meet B. If a point c on an edge of a square σ_i is in A, then all the squares which meet in c belong to Σ, and hence c is an interior point of Σ. Thus γ lies in G.

We next consider the function $f(z) = \log\left[(z - a)/(z - b)\right]$ in G. Since its only singularities are at a and b (both not in G), corollary 4–3 tells us that f is single-valued in G. But let us compute the change in value $\Delta_\gamma f$ of f around γ. This is given by

$$\Delta_\gamma f = \int_\gamma \frac{1}{z-a}\, dz - \int_\gamma \frac{1}{z-b}\, dz.$$

We may compute each integral by noting that each edge of σ_i interior to Σ appears oppositely oriented in two adjacent squares of Σ. Thus integration over γ and $\sum_{i=1}^N \gamma_i$ gives the same result, and we have

$$\Delta_\gamma f = \sum_{i=1}^N \int_{\gamma_i} \frac{1}{z-a}\, dz - \sum_{i=1}^N \int_{\gamma_i} \frac{1}{z-b}\, dz.$$

Since b is outside every square σ_i,

$$\int_{\gamma_i} (z-b)^{-1}\, dz = 0,\ i = 1, 2, \ldots, N.$$

Likewise,

$$\int_{\gamma_i} (z-a)^{-1}\, dz = 0,\ i = 2, 3, \ldots, N,$$

while

$$\int_{\gamma_1} (z-a)^{-1}\, dz = 2\pi i.$$

Thus $\Delta_\gamma f = 2\pi i$, and f is not single-valued in G. This contradiction confirms the fact that the complement of G consists of at most one component.

THEOREM 4–8. *Let M have the fundamental group $\mathfrak{F}$. Let M^* be a covering manifold of M corresponding to the subgroup $\mathfrak{K}$ of $\mathfrak{F}$. Then the fundamental group $\mathfrak{F}^*$ of M^* is isomorphic to $\mathfrak{K}$.*

Each closed curve on M^* projects into a curve in K, whereas each curve in K is the image of some closed curve on M^*. If C_1^* and C_2^* represent the same element in $\mathfrak{F}^*$, $C_1^* \approx C^*$ and their projections C_1 and C_2 are also homotopic, since the projection mapping is continuous, so that C_1 and C_2 represent the same element in $\mathfrak{K}$. Conversely, if $C_1 \approx C_2$, then $C_1^* \approx C_2^*$, by the monodromy theorem. This one-to-one correspondence defines an isomorphism between $\mathfrak{F}^*$ and $\mathfrak{K}$.

COROLLARY 4–5. *The universal covering manifold $\hat{M}$ of a manifold M is simply connected.*

For $\hat{M}$ corresponds to $\mathscr{I}$ and hence its fundamental group $\hat{\mathfrak{F}} \approx \mathscr{I}$, making $\hat{M}$ simply connected.

Let M_1^* and M_2^* be covering manifolds of M with projection mappings f_1 and f_2, respectively. Suppose, moreover, that M_2^* is also a covering manifold of M_1^* with projection mapping h. We can go from M_2^* to M via two routes, first, by way of f_2 and, second, by way of $f_1 \circ h$, where $f_1 \circ h(P_2^*) = f_1(h(P_2^*))$ for $P_2^* \in M_2^*$. If $f_2 = f_1 \circ h$, then we say that M_2^* is a larger covering manifold than M_1^*. For some $P_2^* \in M_2^*$, let M_2^* correspond to $\mathcal{K}_2 = \mathcal{K}_2(P_2^*)$, and for $P_1^* = h(P_2^*)$, let M_1^* correspond to $\mathcal{K}_1 = \mathcal{K}_1(P_1^*)$. A closed curve on M_2^* certainly projects into a closed curve on M_1^* and hence on M; thus $\mathcal{K}_2 \subset \mathcal{K}_1$. If we apply this to $\hat{M}$, the universal covering manifold of M, $\mathcal{K} = \mathcal{I}$ and any larger covering would necessarily correspond to a subgroup of $\mathcal{I}$ and hence to $\mathcal{I}$ itself. This tells us that there is no covering manifold larger than the universal covering manifold. In this sense, *the universal covering manifold is the largest covering manifold of M.*

We shall now introduce several notions that will be useful later. A closed curve $C = (\alpha, I)$ is called *simple* if $\alpha(t) = \alpha(t')$ implies that $|t - t'| = 0$ or 1. The simple closed curve $C = (\alpha, I)$ is said to *locally separate* M if each point $\alpha(t)$ has a neighborhood N about it such that $N - |C|$ is composed of two disjoint components. Furthermore, we say that C *separates* M if $M - |C|$ is composed of two or more disjoint components. The manifold M is called *schlichtartig* if each simple closed curve that locally separates M also separates M.

THEOREM 4–9. *Every simply connected manifold is schlichtartig.*

Assume that there is a simple closed curve C on M which separates locally but such that $M - |C|$ is connected. Then $M - |C|$ is arcwise connected and we proceed to define a smooth, unlimited two-sheeted covering manifold M^* of M. Take two replicas of M, say M_1 and M_2, and let C_1 be the replica of C on M_1 and C_2 the replica of C on M_2. The point P on M not on C now appears as the point P_1^* on M_1 and P_2^* on M_2. A local coordinate disk N of P on M appears as a parametric disk N_1^* of P_1^* on M_1 and N_2^* of P_2^* on M_2, each of which is homeomorphic to an N and hence to a disk in $\mathcal{E}^2$. Any point $P \in |C|$ has a neighborhood N which is separated into two parts by C. Call one of these parts N' and the other N''. On M_1, we have the components N_1' and N_1'' on the two sides of C_1, and on M_2 we have the components N_2' and N_2'' on the two sides of C_2. We join N_1' to N_2'' over the edges of C, and above P on $|C|$ we get a point P_1^*. Then we join N_1'' to N_2' over the edges of C and get a point P_2^* over P on $|C|$. A neighborhood of P_1^* consists of N_1', N_2'', and points lying over C, while a neighborhood of P_2^* consists of N_1'', N_2', and points over C. Each of these is homeomorphic to the neighborhood N about P on $|C|$. Thus over each point of M lie two points P_1^* and P_2^* which, together with the neighborhoods defined above, give us a manifold M^* covering M, once we show that M^* is connected. But this is clear, since $M_1 - |C_1|$ and $M_2 - |C_2|$ are each arcwise connected and any point of $M_1 - |C_1|$ can be joined to any point of $M_2 - |C_2|$ by an arc crossing over the curves lying over C. But this two-sheeted covering surface cannot exist over a simply connected manifold, so M is schlichtartig.

4–4 Covering transformations.

A *covering transformation* of a smooth unlimited covering manifold M^* is a homeomorphism of M^* onto itself which maps each point P^* over P into another point lying over the same point P. Thus a covering transformation merely interchanges points having the same projection on M. *The covering transformation h which maps P_1^* into P_2^* is unique.* We show, to substantiate this statement, that $P_1^* \to P_2^*$ completely determines h. Let P^* be an arbitrary point on M^*, let C_1^* be a curve from P_1^* to P^*. C_1^* lies over the curve C on M. When P_1^* transforms into P_2^*, C_1^* goes into a curve C_2^* on M^* which starts at P_2^* and also lies over C. Thus the end point of C_2^* must be the uniquely defined image of P^* determining h completely. The set of covering transformations of M^* clearly forms a group under the operation of composition of mappings.

The group of covering transformations of M^* is called *transitive* if there is a transformation of the group which carries any point P_1^* over P into any other prescribed point P_2^* over P. We now prove

THEOREM 4–10. *The group of covering transformations of M^* is transitive if and only if the subgroup $\mathcal{K}$ of $\mathcal{F}$ corresponding to M^* is a normal subgroup of $\mathcal{F}$. In this case, the group of covering transformations is isomorphic to $\mathcal{F}/\mathcal{K}$.*

We first note that $\mathcal{K}$ is normal in $\mathcal{F}$ if and only if for each curve $C \in F(P_0)$ all curves in M^* lying over C are simultaneously closed or are simultaneously not closed. For if C_i^* is a curve lying over C which passes through P_i^* above P_0, C_i^* is closed (or not closed) according to whether $\mathcal{C}$ does (or does not) belong to $\mathcal{K}(P_i^*)$. If all the conjugate $\mathcal{K}(P_i^*)$ are equal to $\mathcal{K}$ (as is the case when $\mathcal{K}$ is normal in $\mathcal{F}$) then either $C \in K(P_i^*)$ for all P_i^* over P and all C_i^* are closed, or C does not belong to some $K(P_i^*)$, in which case all C_i^* are not closed. If $\mathcal{K}(P_1^*) \neq \mathcal{K}(P_2^*)$, then there is a path $C \in K(P_1^*)$ but not in $K(P_2^*)$. Then C_1^* is closed and C_2^* is not closed.

Now if $\mathcal{K}$ is not normal in $\mathcal{F}$, there is a closed curve C_1^* and a curve C_2^* which is not closed, both projecting into C. Then the covering transformation h carries P_1^* (over P_0), through which C_1^* passes, into P_2^* (over P_0) through which C_2^* passes. This transformation must carry C_1^* into C_2^*, and since h is a homeomorphism, it carries closed curves into closed curves, which shows that no such h can exist.

On the other hand, if $\mathcal{K}$ is normal, we can find a covering transformation taking P_1^* into any other point P_2^* lying over the same point P_0. We have seen that any point P^* on M^* can be written in the form $P^* = (P, C)$, where P is the projection of P^* and C is the projection of the curve from

P_1^* to P^*, P_1^* lying over P_0. We have $(P, C_1) = (Q, C_2)$ if and only if $P = Q$ and $\mathcal{C}_1\mathcal{C}_2^{-1} \in \mathcal{K}$. Now let J^* be a path from P_1^* to P_2^*, lying over P_0, which projects into J. We define a mapping h_J of M^* onto itself by $h_J(P, C) = (P, JC)$. The mapping h_J is continuous, and we shall prove that it is also one-to-one. If $(P, JC) = (Q, JC_1)$, we know that $P = Q$ and $\mathcal{J}\mathcal{C}(\mathcal{J}\mathcal{C}_1)^{-1} = \mathcal{J}\mathcal{C}\mathcal{C}_1^{-1}\mathcal{J}^{-1} \in \mathcal{K}$, or $\mathcal{C}\mathcal{C}_1^{-1} \in \mathcal{J}^{-1}\mathcal{K}\mathcal{J} = \mathcal{K}$, since $\mathcal{K}$ is normal. Thus h_J is one-to-one and its inverse $h_J^{-1} = h_{J^{-1}}$ is also continuous. Finally, $P_1^* = (P_0, 1)$ and $P_2^* = (P_0, J)$, so that $h_J(P_0, 1) = (P_0, J)$, giving us the desired covering transformation.

Each covering transformation of M^* can be written as h_J for some closed curve J. Then h_{J_1} and h_{J_2} give the same covering transformation if $(P, J_1C) = (P, J_2C)$ or if $\mathcal{J}_1\mathcal{C}(\mathcal{J}_2\mathcal{C})^{-1} \in \mathcal{K}$. But $(J_1C)(J_2C)^{-1} = J_1CC^{-1}J_2^{-1} = J_1J_2$, so $h_{J_1} = h_{J_2}$ if and only if $\mathcal{J}_1\mathcal{J}_2^{-1} \in \mathcal{K}$. Thus there is a one-to-one correspondence between covering transformations and cosets of $\mathcal{K}$. Also, $h_{J_1} \circ h_{J_2} = h_{J_1J_2}$, so the group of covering transformations is isomorphic to the group of cosets of $\mathcal{K}$ and hence to $\mathcal{F}/\mathcal{K}$.

The universal covering manifold $\hat{M}$ of M corresponds to the normal subgroup $\mathcal{J}$ of $\mathcal{F}$. Thus the covering transformations of $\hat{M}$ form a transitive group which is isomorphic to $\mathcal{F}/\mathcal{J} = \mathcal{F}$.

We close this chapter with the remark that if M is a Riemann surface, any smooth unlimited covering manifold M^* of M also has a natural analytic structure. To any point $P^* \in M^*$ corresponds a local uniformizing parameter z^* which can be expressed in terms of the local parameter z about the projection P of P^* as $z^* = z$, using the projection mapping. If the parametric disks about P^* and Q^* (with local parameters z^* and ζ^*, respectively) intersect, the common part projects into a region of M in which z is an analytic function of ζ. Since $z = z^*$ and $\zeta = \zeta^*$, z^* is also an analytic function of ζ^*, and we have an analytic structure on M^*, making it a Riemann surface which we shall call a *covering surface* of M. The covering transformations of a covering surface M^* are conformal mappings of M^* onto itself. Furthermore, the projection mapping of M^* onto M is a conformal mapping. These remarks, moreover, need not be restricted to smooth unlimited coverings of a Riemann surface, since it is clear that any covering manifold of a Riemann surface has a natural analytic structure and the projection mapping is an analytic mapping of the covering manifold into the surface.

PROBLEMS

1. Let G be a simply connected region on a Riemann surface and let f be a regular analytic function in G. Prove that f is single-valued by showing that if f were multiple-valued it would be possible to construct a multiply sheeted smooth unlimited covering manifold of G.

2. Describe the fundamental group and the universal covering manifold of the annulus. Describe the subgroups of $\mathfrak{F}$, the corresponding covering manifolds, and their groups of covering transformations.

3. The torus of Fig. 1–29 is topologically equivalent to the rectangle of Fig. 1–30 with the opposite sides identified. For each point z in the z-plane, there exists one and only one pair of integers m and n such that $T(z) = z + 2mpi + 2n\pi$ lies in the rectangle $-p < y \leq p$, $-\pi < x \leq \pi$. Let $M*$ be the whole finite z-plane and let f be the mapping which takes z into the point of the torus corresponding to $T(z)$. Show that $M*$ is the universal covering surface of the torus and describe its group of covering transformations.

4. Carry out a study similar to that of problem 3 for the cylinder $\xi^2 + \eta^2 = 1$, $-\infty < \zeta < \infty$, using the fact that it is mapped topologically onto the infinite strip $0 \leq x \leq 2\pi$, $-\infty < y < \infty$, by the mapping $(x, y) = (\tan^{-1}(\eta/\xi), \zeta)$.

CHAPTER 5

COMBINATORIAL TOPOLOGY

In Chapter 2, we studied the properties of manifolds from a "local" point of view. We were primarily interested in what happened in a neighborhood of some point of the manifold, and we found properties common to all manifolds. In our further study of Riemann surfaces, we shall be interested in the nature of functions which are harmonic or analytic on the whole surface. This study will require a knowledge of the properties of the manifold "in the large," or the "global" properties of the manifold. We shall be interested in those properties which can be used to distinguish different manifolds. The most basic of these properties are the ones which determine whether two manifolds are topologically equivalent, i.e., whether there exists a homeomorphism of one of the manifolds onto the other. It is with this in mind that we now continue the study of the topology of manifolds.

5–1 Triangulation. We shall begin by assigning new names to familiar geometrical figures in the euclidean plane $\mathcal{E}^2$:

$$\text{euclidean 0-simplex} = \text{point,}$$
$$\text{euclidean 1-simplex} = \text{closed line segment,}$$
$$\text{euclidean 2-simplex} = \text{closed triangle.}†$$

By an *n-simplex* s^n, $n = 0, 1, 2$, *on a manifold* M is understood a euclidean *n*-simplex e^n and a one-to-one bicontinuous mapping φ of e^n into M. We shall write $s^n = [e^n, \varphi]$ for this concept and call the image of e^n under φ the *carrier* of s^n and denote it by $|s^n|$; that is, $\varphi(e^n) = |s^n|$. We say that a point P belongs to s^n when $P \in |s^n|$. The images of the edges and vertices of e^2 are called *edges* and *vertices* of $s^2 = [e^2, \varphi]$, while s^2 itself is called a *triangle* on M. Each edge of s^2 is a 1-simplex and each vertex of s^2 is a 0-simplex when one restricts the mapping φ to that edge or vertex of e^2.

---

† The concept of simplex is easily generalized to *n*-dimensions. A euclidean *n*-simplex is the convex set of euclidean *r*-space ($r \geq n$) spanned by $n + 1$ points, no k of which lie in a $(k - 2)$-dimensional hyperplane. The notion of triangulated manifold also generalizes to *n*-dimensions and most of the material in this chapter has its rather obvious extension to *n*-dimensions. For a good introduction to *n*-dimensional combinatorial topology, the reader is referred to Seifert and Threlfall (Ref. 44).

Let us now suppose that a collection Δ of triangles (2-simplexes) is defined on M such that each point P of M belongs to at least one triangle in Δ and

(i) if P belongs to a triangle s^2 of Δ but is not on an edge of s^2, then s^2 is the only triangle containing P and $|s^2|$ is a neighborhood of P;

(ii) if P belongs to an edge s^1 of a triangle s_1^2 in Δ but P is not a vertex of s_1^2, then there is exactly one other triangle s_2^2 in Δ such that $|s_1^2| \cap |s_2^2| = |s^1|$, s_1^2 and s_2^2 are the only triangles containing P, and $|s_1^2| \cup |s_2^2|$ is a neighborhood of P;

(iii) if P is a vertex of s_1^2, there is a finite number of triangles s_1^2, $s_2^2, \ldots, s_k^2$, each having P as a vertex, such that each successive pair of triangles s_j^2, s_{j+1}^2 have only one edge in common, s_k^2 has one edge in common with s_1^2, while $s_1^2, s_2^2, \ldots, s_k^2$ are the only triangles containing P, and $|s_1^2| \cup |s_2^2| \cup \cdots \cup |s_k^2|$ forms a neighborhood of P. The triangles $s_1^2, s_2^2, \ldots, s_k^2$ are said to form a *star* of triangles in Δ.

Note that in each case, (i), (ii), or (iii), P is contained in an open set which meets only a finite number of triangles in Δ.

If the above conditions are satisfied, Δ is called a *triangulation* of M, and M is called a *triangulated manifold*. When a triangulation of M does exist, we say that M is *triangulable*. We then define a *surface* to be a triangulable manifold.

Not all two-dimensional manifolds are triangulable. We shall prove presently that every triangulable manifold has a countable base. Therefore the Prüfer example of a manifold without countable base is also an example of a nontriangulable manifold. We shall later prove that every Riemann surface is triangulable (Chapter 9) and hence justify the use of the word "surface." The letter S will henceforth be used to denote a surface, and if a particular triangulation Δ is to be distinguished on S, we shall denote the triangulated surface by S_Δ.

We shall now prove several properties of triangulations.

THEOREM 5–1. *Any compact set on a triangulated surface S_Δ meets only a finite number of the triangles in Δ.*

Suppose that the contrary were true; then a compact set K meets an infinite number of triangles in Δ. We may select one point of K interior to each of these triangles. According to the compactness of K, this set of points has a cluster point P_0 in K which has the property that any open set containing P_0 meets an infinite number of the triangles in the given set. But according to the definition of triangulation, the point P_0 is contained in an open set which meets only a finite number of the triangles and hence only a finite number of the points in the set, which is a contradiction.

We see now that any triangulation of a compact surface must contain only a finite number of triangles. Conversely, since each triangle is a compact set and the union of a finite number of compact sets is compact, any surface with a finite triangulation is compact. Therefore, we have proved the following theorem.

THEOREM 5–2. *A surface is compact if and only if it has a finite triangulation.*

It is traditional in the study of Riemann surfaces to call a compact surface a *closed* surface and a noncompact surface an *open* surface. We shall frequently use these designations.

A *(simple) chain* of triangles is a finite collection of triangles $s_1, s_2, \ldots, s_n$, of which each pair of successive triangles has a common edge. We say that s_1 and s_n are *joined* by this chain.

THEOREM 5–3. *In S_Δ, each pair of triangles s and s' can be joined by a simple chain of triangles in Δ.*

Let P and P' be any two points interior to s and s', respectively. Since S is arcwise connected, P and P' may be joined by an arc C whose carrier is compact and meets only a finite number of triangles in Δ. In going from P to P' along C, let P_1 be the last point of intersection of C with s. If P_1 is not a vertex of s, then P_1 lies on an edge of only one other triangle in Δ, which we shall call s_1, the second triangle in the desired chain. If P_1 is a vertex of s, the star about P_1 consists of triangles $s, s_1, s_2, \ldots, s_n$. Let P_2 be the last point of intersection of C with this star; P_2 is not on s, since P_1 was the last intersection of C with s. Take s_k to be the first triangle of the star on which P_2 lies. Then let the desired chain start with $s, s_1, s_2, \ldots, s_k$. We repeat this process, using P_2 in place of P_1, and so on, to build up a chain of triangles. This chain does not return to any triangle already used, since we always choose the last point of intersection of C with the triangles already selected. The process terminates after a finite number of steps, since C meets only a finite number of triangles in going from s to s'.

THEOREM 5–4. *There is only a countable (or a finite) number of triangles in any triangulation of a surface.*

Choose an arbitrary triangle s_1 in a triangulation Δ. Adjoin to s_1 the finite number of triangles $s_2, s_3, \ldots, s_{n_1}$ which meet s_1. Next adjoin the finite number of new triangles $s_{n_1+1}, s_{n_1+2}, \ldots, s_{n_2}$ which meet those already selected. Proceeding in this manner, we exhaust all the triangles in Δ in either a finite or a countable number of steps, since each triangle in Δ can be joined to s_1 by a finite chain and hence is included after a finite number of steps.

Since each triangle is a compact set on S, it may be covered by a finite number of parametric disks. Then the fact that there is only a countable number of triangles means that S must have a countable base. Thus we have proved the following theorem.

THEOREM 5–5. *Every surface has a countable base.*

A few examples of surfaces will now be given:

(1) The sphere can be triangulated into eight spherical triangles by drawing the following great circles: equator, 0°-meridian, 90°-meridian, 180°-meridian, 270°-meridian (Fig. 5–1).

(2) To triangulate the torus, we consider it as a rectangle with opposite edges identified. Figure 5–2 shows a triangulation of the torus into 18 triangles.

(3) The previous two examples were both compact surfaces with finite triangulations. The euclidean plane is an example of a noncompact (open) surface, which can be triangulated by drawing the lines $x = n$, $y = n$, $y = x + n$, where $n = 0, \pm1, \pm2, \ldots$ (Fig. 5–3).

(4) The open square $0 < x < 1$, $0 < y < 1$, is also an open surface which can be triangulated as follows. Draw the lines $x = \frac{1}{3}$, $x = \frac{2}{3}$, $y = \frac{1}{3}, y = \frac{2}{3}$. In the center square (the one not having an edge in common with the original square), draw the diagonal having positive slope. Then draw the lines $x = \frac{1}{6}$, $x = \frac{5}{6}$, $y = \frac{1}{6}$, $y = \frac{5}{6}$. In each rectangle not having an edge in common with the original square, draw the diagonal having positive slope. Continue this process until the square is filled out with a countable number of triangles (Fig. 5–4).

(5) Another interesting example of an open surface is the Moebius band. If we take a rectangular strip of paper and paste the two narrow ends together, we obtain a cylinder. If we twist the paper once before pasting the ends together, we obtain a Moebius band. The Moebius band is equivalent topologically to a rectangle with one pair of opposite ends identified in such a way that a point P on one edge corresponds to the point P' lying at the opposite end of a line through the center of the rectangle. Figure 5–5 shows a triangulation of the Moebius band.

(6) The projective plane Π is the final example of a surface to be given here. A point in the projective plane is an equivalence class of triples of real numbers (x_1, x_2, x_3) not all zero; two triples (x_1, x_2, x_3) and (y_1, y_2, y_3) represent the same point if $x_1 : x_2 : x_3 = y_1 : y_2 : y_3$. We make Π into a topological space if we say that an ϵ-neighborhood about the point (a_1, a_2, a_3) consists of all points (x_1, x_2, x_3) satisfying

$$\frac{(x_1a_2 - x_2a_1)^2 + (x_2a_3 - x_3a_2)^2 + (x_3a_1 - x_1a_3)^2}{(x_1^2 + x_2^2 + x_3^2)(a_1^2 + a_2^2 + a_3^2)} < \epsilon^2.$$

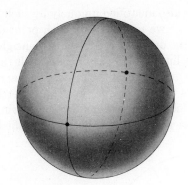

FIGURE 5–1.

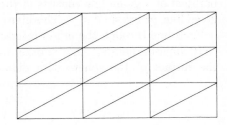

FIGURE 5–2.

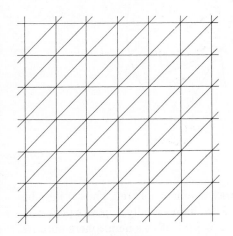

FIGURE 5–3.

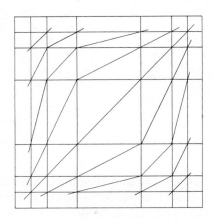

FIGURE 5–4.

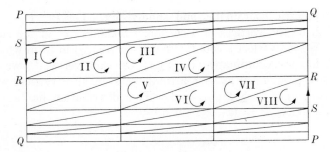

FIGURE 5–5.

Since each line through the origin in $\mathcal{E}^3$ is also identified uniquely by such a triple of real numbers (direction numbers), we may identify each point of the projective plane with a line through the origin in $\mathcal{E}^3$. Then the ϵ-neighborhood of a given line consists of those lines making an angle θ with the given line, where $\sin \theta < \epsilon$. This gives us one model of the projective plane.

Each line through the origin intersects the unit sphere in two diametrically opposite points. Thus another model of Π is obtained by considering the surface of the sphere with diametrically opposite points identified.

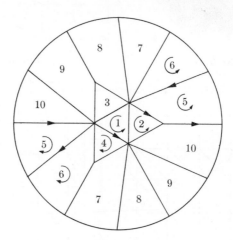

FIGURE 5–6.

This may be simplified if we throw away one hemisphere. Thus Π may be realized topologically as a hemisphere with diametrically opposite points on the equatorial circle identified. If we now project this hemisphere onto its equatorial plane, the final model of Π is a circular disk with diametrically opposite points on its circumference identified. Figure 5–6 shows a triangulation of the projective plane into ten triangles.

5–2 Barycentric coordinates and subdivision. Let $P_0, P_1, \ldots, P_n$, $n = 0, 1, 2$, be the vertices of a euclidean n-simplex e^n in the euclidean plane $\mathcal{E}^2$. We may select a coordinate system (x_1, x_2) in $\mathcal{E}^2$ in which each vertex P_k has the coordinates (x_{1k}, x_{2k}). On each vertex P_k we place a non-negative point mass μ_k with a total mass on all n vertices equal to a unit mass; $\mu_k \geq 0$, $\sum_{k=0}^{n} \mu_k = 1$. This distribution has a centroid (center of gravity) $P = (x_1, x_2)$ given by

$$x_j = \sum_{k=0}^{n} \mu_k x_{jk}, \qquad j = 1, 2. \tag{1}$$

The numbers $\mu_0, \mu_1, \ldots, \mu_n$ are called the *barycentric coordinates of the point P in e^n* (see, for example, Seifert and Threlfall, Ref. 44, p. 36). If we change the coordinates in the plane to a new system (y_1, y_2), not necessarily rectangular, by an affine transformation

$$y_i = \sum_{j=1}^{2} a_{ij}x_j + b_i, \qquad i = 1, 2,$$

equation (1) becomes

$$y_i = \sum_{j=1}^{2} a_{ij}x_j + b_i = \sum_{j=1}^{2} a_{ij} \sum_{k=0}^{n} \mu_k x_{jk} + b_i$$

$$= \sum_{k=0}^{n} \mu_k \left[\sum_{j=1}^{2} a_{ij}x_{jk} + b_i \right] = \sum_{k=0}^{n} \mu_k y_{ik},$$

which shows that the centroid again has the same barycentric coordinates. We may choose the new affine coordinates (y_1, y_2) in a special way so that the origin is at P_0 and the vertex P_k has the coordinates $y_{jk} = 0$ if $j \neq k$ and $y_{kk} = 1$. Then $y_1, \ldots, y_n$ form a coordinate system in the n-dimensional subspace of $\mathcal{E}^2$ containing e^n with $\overline{P_0 P_k}$ as a unit basis vector. If $n < 2$, the point P in e^n has coordinates $y_j = 0$ if $j > n$, and $y_j = \sum_{k=0}^{n} \mu_k y_{jk} = \mu_j, j \leq n$. Thus these affine coordinates $y_1, \ldots, y_n$ of a point P in e^n are the same as the barycentric coordinates $\mu_1, \ldots, \mu_n$.

A *barycentric (simplicial) mapping* of an n-simplex e_1^n onto an r-simplex e_2^r, $r \leq n$, is a mapping which

(1) takes each vertex of e_1^n into a vertex of e_2^r,
(2) makes each vertex of e_2^r the image of at least one vertex of e_1^n, and
(3) if the masses $\mu_1, \ldots, \mu_n$ are placed at the vertices of e_1^n and the same masses are placed at the image vertices in e_2^r, the centroids correspond in e_1^n and e_2^r.

This defines the mapping at each point of e_1^n. If $r < n$, we call the mapping *degenerate*; in this case at least two vertices of e_1^n map into the same vertex of e_2^r. If $r = n$, the mapping is a homeomorphism.

THEOREM 5–6. *For euclidean simplexes e_1^n and e_2^r of dimensions n and r, respectively, the barycentric mapping of e_1^n onto e_2^r is accomplished by an affine transformation of the n-dimensional subspace of $\mathcal{E}^2$ containing e_1^n onto the r-dimensional subspace containing e_2^r.*

Let $x_1, \ldots, x_n$ be a set of affine coordinates in the subspace of e_1^n, and $y_1, \ldots, y_r$ be a set in e_2^r. Let $x_{1k}, \ldots, x_{nk}$ be the coordinates of the vertex P_k, $k = 0, 1, \ldots, n$, of e_1^n, and $y_{1k}, \ldots, y_{rk}$ the coordinates of P_k', the image of P_k in e_2^r. If we put masses $\mu_0, \ldots, \mu_n$ on the $P_0, \ldots, P_n$, the center of gravity P will be at the point with coordinates

$$x_i = \sum_{k=0}^{n} \mu_k x_{ik}, \qquad i = 1, \ldots, n, \tag{2}$$

and the image P' of P will have coordinates

$$y_j = \sum_{k=0}^{n} \mu_k y_{jk}, \qquad j = 1, \ldots, r. \tag{3}$$

Since the vectors $\overline{P_0P_k}$, $k = 1, \ldots, n$, are linearly independent, equations (2) can be solved for the μ_k in terms of the x_i, and then these values for μ_k may be substituted into (3) to give a system of equations of the form

$$y_j = \sum_{i=1}^{n} a_{ji} x_i, \qquad j = 1, \ldots, r.$$

This is the desired affine transformation of the subspace of e_1^n onto the subspace of e_2^r.

In a euclidean n-simplex e^n, the point having equal barycentric coordinates will be called the *midpoint* of the simplex. In a 2-simplex, the vertices have barycentric coordinates $(1, 0, 0)$, $(0, 1, 0)$, and $(0, 0, 1)$. The points which have one coordinate equal to zero lie on the edge opposite the vertex which has on it zero mass. Thus $(\mu_0, \mu_1, 0)$ lies on the edge $\overline{P_0P_1}$ and has barycentric coordinates (μ_0, μ_1) when we consider $\overline{P_0P_1}$ as a 1-simplex.

The locus of points for which $\mu_0 = \mu_1$ is the median line from P_2 to the edge $\overline{P_0P_1}$. In general, in e^n the locus of points for which any two of the barycentric coordinates are equal divides the n-simplex into $(n + 1)!$ n-simplexes called the *barycentric subdivision* of the n-simplex e^n. In the case of a 0-simplex the barycentric subdivision is exactly the same 0-simplex. For the 1-simplex e^1, the midpoint is the only point with equal barycentric coordinates, and this divides the line segment e^1 into two equal segments. The 2-simplex is divided into six triangles by the three medians. By the diameter of a triangle, we shall mean the length of its longest side. The medians intersect $\frac{2}{3}$ of the way from a vertex to the midpoint of the opposite side of a triangle, so the diameter of a triangle in the subdivision is at most $\frac{2}{3}$ the diameter of the original triangle. If we barycentrically subdivide each triangle of the once subdivided triangle, we obtain a second barycentric subdivision (Fig. 5–7). Repeating this subdivision process N times leads to the Nth barycentric subdivision of the n-simplex, in which the diameter of each triangle is at most $(\frac{2}{3})^N$ times the diameter of the original triangle.

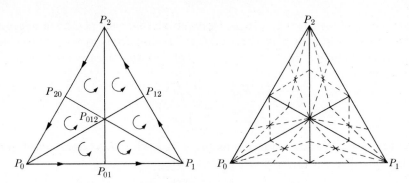

FIGURE 5–7.

Let S be a surface with a triangulation Δ. For each $s_j^2 = [e_j^2,\ \varphi_j] \in \Delta$, φ_j is a homeomorphism mapping a euclidean triangle e_j^2 into s_j^2. We may assign barycentric coordinates to each point P of s_j^2 by giving P the same coordinates that $\varphi_j^{-1}(P)$ has in e_j^2. This defines an affine structure in each s_j^2 in Δ. A point P belonging to only one triangle s_j^2 in Δ has a single set of barycentric coordinates in s_j^2. On the other hand, a point P lying on a common edge s^1 of s_j^2 and s_k^2 has one set of barycentric coordinates induced in s^1 from s_j^2 and another set from s_k^2. We shall now prove the following theorem.

THEOREM 5–7. *For a triangulation* $\Delta = \{s_j^2\}$, $s_j^2 = [e_j^2,\ \varphi_j]$ *of a surface* S, *it is possible to pick a set of mappings* φ_j *so that the coordinates of a point* P *on each edge are the same in both of the triangles containing* P.

This set of barycentric coordinates will be called *normal (barycentric) coordinates* on S. The existence of a set of normal coordinates on S shows that each adjacent pair of triangles in Δ is homeomorphic to an adjacent pair of euclidean triangles, and that each star of triangles in Δ is homeomorphic to a star of euclidean triangles in $\mathcal{E}^2$.

To obtain the normal coordinates on S, select an arbitrary triangle $s_1^2 = [e_1^2,\ \varphi_1]$ in Δ with vertices P_0, P_1, P_2. Since barycentric coordinates are affine invariants, we may take e_1^2 to be an equilateral triangle with vertices p_0, p_1, p_2 corresponding to P_0, P_1, P_2, respectively. Now let $s_2^2 = [e_2^2,\ \varphi_2]$ be the triangle in Δ that has the edge $\overline{P_1 P_2}$ in common with s_1^2, and the point P_3 as its third vertex. We already have the barycentric coordinates defined on $\overline{P_1 P_2}$ considered as the image of $\overline{p_0 p_1}$ under φ_1. We must extend these to coordinates in the rest of s_2^2. Let p_1, p_2, p_3 be the equilateral triangle having the edge $p_1 p_2$ in common with e_1^2. We may also take the triangle $e_2^2 = \varphi_2^{-1}(s_2^2)$ to be an equilateral triangle with vertices p_1', p_2', p_3' corresponding to P_1, P_2, P_3, respectively. The mapping $\varphi_2^{-1} \circ \varphi_1$ is a homeomorphism of $\overline{p_1 p_2}$ onto $\overline{p_1' p_2'}$. This is extended to a homeomorphism χ of $p_1p_2p_3$ onto $p_1'p_2'p_3'$ by requiring that each point q of $p_1p_2p_3$ map into $q' = \chi(q)$ in $p_1'p_2'p_3'$ as follows: The line from p_3 to q intersects p_1p_2 in the point p. Then $p' = \varphi_2^{-1} \circ \varphi_1(p)$ and we determine the point q' such that

$$\frac{\overline{p_3'q'}}{\overline{p_3'p'}} = \frac{\overline{p_3q}}{\overline{p_3p}} .$$

(See Fig. 5–8.) We now define the mapping $\psi_{1,2}$, which is a homeomorphism of the rhombus $p_0p_1p_2p_3$ onto $|s_1^2| \cup |s_2^2|$, as

$$\psi_{1,2}(p) = \begin{cases} \varphi_1(p), & \text{if } p \in p_0p_1p_2, \\ \varphi_2 \circ \chi(p), & \text{if } p \in p_1p_2p_3. \end{cases}$$

We now use $\psi_{1,2}$ to carry the barycentric coordinates in $p_0p_1p_2p_3$ onto $|s_1^2| \cup |s_2^2|$. These coordinates agree with those previously assigned in s_1^2 and are now continued into s_2^2; we take these as the normal coordinates in s_1^2 and s_2^2.

We can use exactly the same methods to define the normal coordinates in the other triangles meeting s_1^2, then in those triangles meeting triangles already handled, and so on until Δ is exhausted. If we come to a triangle with more than one edge in common with triangles already treated, we note that the mapping χ leaves the barycentric coordinates on the sides $\overline{p_1p_3}$ and $\overline{p_2p_3}$ unchanged. Thus we repeat this process once for each side on which normal coordinates have already been defined, the result being the normal coordinates in all of Δ.

Now let T be a star of triangles in Δ and t be a euclidean star having the same number of triangles. T is mapped homeomorphically onto t when each point $P \in T$ with normal coordinates (μ_0, μ_1, μ_2) is taken into the point p having the same barycentric coordinates (μ_0, μ_1, μ_2) in the corresponding triangle of t.

Each triangle of Δ can now be barycentrically subdivided (in the normal coordinates). This gives us a barycentric subdivision Δ_1 of Δ. In the normal coordinates, each edge of

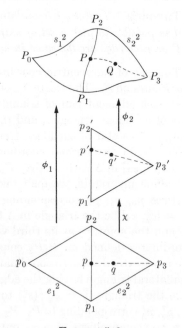

FIGURE 5–8.

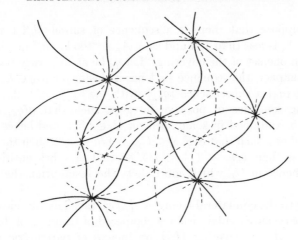

FIGURE 5–9.

a triangle has a well-defined midpoint, so the triangles in Δ_1 fit together properly to give a new triangulation of S. In Fig. 5–9 the solid lines represent triangles in Δ, whereas the dotted lines and solid lines together represent the triangles in Δ_1.

If M is a manifold on which we do not have a triangulation, the same construction as that presented above may be used to show that in any chain of triangles T on M, we may introduce barycentric coordinates which agree on common edges. These coordinates will again be called normal barycentric coordinates on T. Each point of T can be surrounded by a parametric disk, the totality of which forms a covering of T by open sets. If s_1^2 and s_2^2 are two adjacent triangles in T, the normal barycentric coordinates define a homeomorphism of $|s_1^2| \cup |s_2^2|$ onto two adjacent equilateral euclidean triangles e_1^2 and e_2^2. The open disks covering $|s_1^2| \cup |s_2^2|$ map into open sets $\{U_i\}$ relative to $e_1^2 \cup e_2^2$ which cover $e_1^2 \cup e_2^2$. The set $e_1^2 \cup e_2^2$ is a compact subset of $\mathcal{E}^2$ and hence is a compact metric space in which the distance $d(p, q)$ between two points p and q is taken as the ordinary euclidean distance.

Recall that in an arbitrary metric space E, the set of points $p \in E$ satisfying the relation $d(p, q) < \rho$ for some given point $q \in E$ and positive number ρ is called a *spherical neighborhood of radius ρ about q* and is denoted by $S(q, \rho)$. If A is a subset of E, the *diameter of A* is defined to be the least upper bound of $d(p, q)$ for all $p \in A$, $q \in A$. We then have the following lemma.

LEMMA 5–1.   *In a compact metric space E, to each open covering $\{U_i\}$ corresponds a positive number δ (called the Lebesgue number of the covering $\{U_i\}$) such that any subset of E of diameter less than δ lies entirely within one set of $\{U_i\}$.*

Indeed, suppose that there is a sequence of subsets $\{A_i\}$ where the diameter of A_n is less than $1/n$ and each A_n is "too large," i.e., is not contained within one set of the covering. Let q_n be an arbitrary point in A_n. Since E is compact, the sequence $\{q_n\}$ has a cluster point $q \in E$. We may extract from $\{q_n\}$ a subsequence $\{q_{n_k}\}$, with the n_k, $k = 1, 2, \ldots$, being an increasing sequence of positive integers, such that $d(q_{n_k}, q) < 1/k$. The point q is contained in some open set $U_j \in \{U_i\}$, and hence there is a positive number ρ such that $S(q, \rho) \subseteq U_j$. If $1/k < \rho/2$, then the diameter of A_{n_k} is less than $1/n < 1/k < \rho/2$, so that A_{n_k} lies entirely within $S(q, \rho)$ and hence in U_j, which contradicts the assumption that A_{n_k} was too large.

Returning to the equilateral triangles $e_1^2 \cup e_2^2$, each having sides of length σ, the Nth barycentric subdivision is composed of triangles of diameter at most $(\frac{2}{3})^N \sigma$. If the covering $\{U_i\}$ by images of parametric disks has Lebesgue number δ, we can choose N large enough so that $(\frac{2}{3})^N \sigma < \delta/2$. Then each adjacent pair of triangles in the Nth barycentric subdivision lies entirely within a single set of the covering $\{U_i\}$, and the image in the Nth barycentric subdivision of $|s_1^2| \cup |s_2^2|$ lies entirely within one parametric disk. Since there is only a finite number of different adjacent pairs of triangles in T, we may use the largest N and get an Nth barycentric subdivision Δ_N of T such that each adjacent pair of triangles in Δ_N lies entirely within a single parametric disk. We have now proved the following theorem.

THEOREM 5–8. *Corresponding to any finite chain T of triangles on M, there is an integer N such that any adjacent pair of triangles in the Nth barycentric subdivision of T lie in the same parametric disk.*

5–3 Orientability. An n-simplex s^n, $n = 0, 1, 2$, on a manifold M is said to be *oriented* if its $n + 1$ vertices are specified in a definite order. We shall say that two orders of the vertices define the same orientation in s^n if one can be obtained from the other by an even permutation (cyclic interchange) of the vertices. If $n > 0$, a given simplex s^n then has two possible orientations; if we denote the simplex with one orientation as s^n, then the same simplex with the other (opposite) orientation will be denoted by $-s^n$. For example, the 1-simplex with vertices P_0 and P_1 has the two orientations $\langle P_0, P_1 \rangle$ and $\langle P_1, P_0 \rangle$, where we use the brackets $\langle \ \rangle$ to denote the simplex having the given vertices in the order specified in the brackets. A 2-simplex with vertices P_0, P_1, P_2 has the two orientations

$$\langle P_0, P_1, P_2 \rangle = \langle P_1, P_2, P_0 \rangle = \langle P_2, P_0, P_1 \rangle$$

and

$$\langle P_2, P_1, P_0 \rangle = \langle P_1, P_0, P_2 \rangle = \langle P_0, P_2, P_1 \rangle.$$

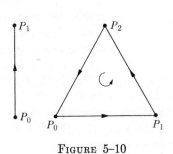

FIGURE 5–10　　　　　　　　　　　FIGURE 5–11.

For convenience, we shall also say that the 0-simplex with one vertex P_0 has two orientations, denoted by $\langle P_0 \rangle$ and $-\langle P_0 \rangle$.

We observe from Fig. 5–10 that an orientation of a 2-simplex *induces* an orientation in each of the 1-simplexes forming its edges. For example, the orientation $\langle P_0, P_1, P_2 \rangle$ induces the orientations $\langle P_0, P_1 \rangle$, $\langle P_1, P_2 \rangle$, $\langle P_2, P_0 \rangle$ in its three edges. Two adjacent oriented triangles are said to be oriented *coherently* if they induce opposite orientation in their common edge (Fig. 5–11).

A simple chain of triangles s_1^2, s_2^2, ..., s_n^2, $n > 2$, is called *closed* if s_1^2 and s_n^2 have a common edge. A closed chain of triangles is said to be coherently oriented if each triangle is oriented in such a way that each adjacent pair of triangles is coherently oriented. A manifold is *orientable* if every simple closed chain of triangles on the manifold can be coherently oriented. A manifold that is not orientable is called *nonorientable*.

The sphere, plane, and square are examples of orientable manifolds and, in fact, we shall prove later that every Riemann surface is orientable. But first we ask whether there are such things as nonorientable manifolds. The Moebius band and the projective plane give us the desired examples of nonorientable manifolds. In the Moebius band of Fig. 5–5, the chain I, II, ..., VIII is a closed chain, since I and VIII have the edge $\overline{RS}$ in common. If we assign the indicated orientation in I, the edge $\overline{RS}$ is oriented as $\langle S, R \rangle$. If we now assign the coherent orientation in II, then in III, etc., we are led to the indicated orientation of VIII, which again induces the orientation $\langle S, R \rangle$ in the edge $\overline{RS}$. Thus we have found a closed chain which cannot be coherently oriented. Similarly in the projective plane (Fig. 5–6), the closed chain 1, 2, 5, 6, 4 cannot be coherently oriented.

If $\langle P_0, P_1 \rangle$ is an oriented 1-simplex, its barycentric subdivision consists of the two oriented 1-simplexes $\langle P_0, P_{01} \rangle$ and $-\langle P_1, P_{01} \rangle$, where P_{01} is the midpoint of $\langle P_0, P_1 \rangle$. Furthermore, if we take an unoriented 1-simplex s^1 with vertices P_0, P_1, and assign an orientation in one of the two 1-simplexes in its subdivision, then an orientation is determined in s^1; for example, $\langle P_0, P_{01} \rangle$ determines $\langle P_0, P_1 \rangle$ and $-\langle P_0, P_{01} \rangle$ determines

$-\langle P_0, P_1\rangle$. In the oriented 2-simplex $\langle P_0, P_1, P_2\rangle$, we shall designate the midpoint of the edge $\langle P_j, P_k\rangle$ by P_{jk} and the midpoint (centroid) of $\langle P_0, P_1, P_2\rangle$ by P_{012}. Then the barycentric subdivision consists of the six oriented 2-simplexes $\langle P_0, P_{01}, P_{012}\rangle$, $-\langle P_1, P_{01}, P_{012}\rangle$, $\langle P_1, P_{12}, P_{012}\rangle$, $-\langle P_2, P_{12}, P_{012}\rangle$, $\langle P_2, P_{20}, P_{012}\rangle$, $-\langle P_0, P_{20}, P_{012}\rangle$. Thus if $\langle P_0, P_1, P_2\rangle$ is an oriented 2-simplex with barycenter P and if we let $P_{ij} = P_{ji}$ be the barycenter of the edge $\langle P_i, P_j\rangle$, then the barycentric subdivision of $\langle P_0, P_1, P_2\rangle$ consists of the six triangles of the form $\epsilon_{i,j,k}\langle P_i, P_{ij}, P_{ijk}\rangle$, where $\epsilon_{i,j,k} = 1$ (or -1) if i, j, k is an even (or odd) permutation of $0, 1, 2$. Observe that these six triangles form a coherently oriented closed chain (Fig. 5–7). In an unoriented triangle s^2 with vertices P_0, P_1, P_2, the specification of the orientation of an edge determines an orientation of the triangle; for example, $\langle P_0, P_1\rangle$ determines $\langle P_0, P_1, P_2\rangle$ as the orientation of s^2. Let s_1^2 and s_2^2 be two adjacent unoriented triangles, s_1^2 having vertices P_0, P_1, P_2 and s_2^2 having vertices P_1, P_2, P_3, the edge $\overline{P_1 P_2}$ being held in common. Using normal coordinates in the pair of triangles s_1^2 and s_2^2, we subdivide them barycentrically, and then coherently orient the chain of six triangles forming the subdivision of each. Now suppose that each edge of the subdivision lying on $\overline{P_1 P_2}$ receives opposite orientations from the two triangles of the subdivision, so that the closed chain of all twelve triangles is coherently oriented. Then the edge $\overline{P_1 P_2}$ receives opposite orientation from each pair of triangles of the subdivision having a common edge along $\overline{P_1 P_2}$, and coherent orientations are thus defined in s_1^2 and s_2^2. Therefore we have proved the following theorem.

THEOREM 5–9. *A coherent orientation in a barycentric subdivision of two adjacent triangles defines a coherent orientation in the original two triangles.*

To prove the orientability of every Riemann surface, we shall study some properties of plane curves. If $C = (\alpha, I)$ is a closed curve in $\mathcal{E}^2$ and Q is a point not on C, we may draw a ray from Q to the point $\alpha(t)$, $t \in I$, and let ν represent an "angle function" satisfying the following conditions:

(a) ν is a single-valued continuous function of t for $t \in I$, and

(b) for each $t \in I$, $\nu(t)$ is equal to one of the determinations of the polar angle θ of the ray from Q to $\alpha(t)$.

To construct such an angle function ν, we observe that $|C|$ has a minimum distance $\delta > 0$ from Q. Subdivide I into $0 = t_0 < t_1 < \cdots < t_m = 1$ [let I_k represent the subinterval $t_k \leq t \leq t_{k+1}$ and $C_k = (\alpha, I_k)$] such that for any t', $t'' \in I_k$, the distance between $\alpha(t')$ and $\alpha(t'')$ is less than δ. Then each arc C_k lies entirely in a quarter-plane determined by a pair of perpendicular lines through Q. If we determine $\nu(t')$ for a single value t' in I_k, then a single-valued continuous function ν exists satisfying (b) and never differing from $\nu(t')$ by more than $\pi/2$ radians. If we arbitrarily select $\nu(0)$ according to (b), $\nu(t)$ is uniquely determined in I_0 and hence at the starting point of I_1. Continuing in this way, we define ν on I satisfying (a) and (b).

A consequence of (b) is that $\nu(1) = \nu(0) + 2\pi n$, where n is an integer. We know from (b) that if we had used a different angle function ν' satisfying (a) and (b), $\nu'(t) - \nu(t) = k(t) \cdot 2\pi$, where $k(t)$ is an integer. Since ν' and ν are continuous, k is also continuous, and being an integer, k must be a constant and $\nu'(t) - \nu(t) = 2\pi k$. Therefore

$$\nu'(1) - \nu'(0) = \nu(1) - \nu(0) = 2\pi n,$$

and the number n is independent of the angle function used. We call n the *order* of the point Q with respect to the curve C, and introduce the notation $\circ(Q, C)$ for this order.

If Q_1 and Q_2 are two points of $\mathcal{E}^2$ not on C which can be joined by an arc A having no points in common with the curve C, then $\circ(Q_1, C) = \circ(Q_2, C)$. For the angle function $\nu(t)$ depends continuously on Q, and since $\circ(Q, C) = (1/2\pi)[\nu(1) - \nu(0)]$ is always an integer, it must be a constant along the arc A.

If the curve $C = (\alpha, I)$ is homotopically deformed into a curve $C' = (\alpha', I)$ in such a way that Q is not crossed during the deformation, then $\circ(Q, C) = \circ(Q, C')$. [Precisely, we ask that when the deformation is given by $\varphi: I \times I \to \mathcal{E}^2$ with $\varphi(t, 0) = \alpha(t)$, $\varphi(t, 1) = \alpha'(t)$, then $Q \notin \varphi(I, I)$.] For, indeed, the change in the angle function $\nu(t)$ is continuous as C is deformed, and since $(1/2\pi)[\nu(1) - \nu(0)] = \circ(Q, C)$ is always an integer, it must be a constant. Therefore if G is a region in $\mathcal{E}^2$ with $Q \in G$, and C and C' are in the same homotopy class in the manifold $G - Q$, then $\circ(Q, C) = \circ(Q, C')$. We now show that if G is simply connected the converse is also true.

THEOREM 5–10. *For a simply connected region G, the homotopy class in $G - Q$ which contains a curve C is characterized by $\circ(Q, C)$, so that $C \approx C'$ in $G - Q$ if and only if $\circ(Q, C) = \circ(Q, C')$.*

If Q has coordinate $z_0 = x_0 + iy_0$, a disk $|z - z_0| \le \rho$ lies in G, and we shall denote by K its circumference $|z - z_0| = \rho$ oriented counterclockwise; $K = (\beta, I)$ where $\beta(t) = \rho e^{2\pi it}$. Let $C = (\alpha, I)$ be an arbitrary closed curve in $G - Q$. The point $\alpha(0)$ can be joined to $\beta(0) = z_0 + \rho$ by an arc $A = (\gamma, I)$ in $G - Q$. Then $A^{-1}CA$ represents an element of the fundamental group $\mathcal{F}$ of $G - Q$ relative to the point $\beta(0)$, and since G is simply connected, $A^{-1}CA$ may be deformed in G to the point $\beta(0)$. Furthermore, $A^{-1}CA \approx C$ in $G - Q$; for if we define $A_u = (\gamma_u, I)$, where $\gamma_u(t) = \gamma(u + t(1 - u))$, then the curve $A_u^{-1}CA_u$ varies in $G - Q$ continuously from $A^{-1}CA$ to C. Let $\varphi: I \times I \to G$ deform $A^{-1}CA = (\alpha_1, I)$ into $\beta(0)$ so that $\varphi(t, 0) = \alpha_1(t)$, $\varphi(t, 1) = \beta(0)$. We define a new deformation $\psi: I \times I \to G - Q$ of $A^{-1}CA$ into a curve C' lying in $|z - z_0| \leq \rho$. For any t such that $|\alpha_1(t) - z_0| \leq \rho$, we set $\psi(t, u) = \alpha_1(t)$ for all $u \in I$. For a value of t such that $|\alpha_1(t) - z_0| > \rho$, we observe that as u goes from 0 to 1, $\varphi(t, u)$ changes continuously from $\alpha_1(t)$ to $z_0 + \rho$; thus there is a first value of u, say u_1, for which

$$|\varphi(t, u) - z_0| = \rho.$$

We define

$$\psi(t, u) = \begin{cases} \varphi(t, u), & 0 \leq u < u_1, \\ \varphi(t, u_1), & u_1 \leq u \leq 1. \end{cases}$$

Let $C' = (\alpha', I)$, where $\alpha'(t) = \psi(t, 1)$; C' is a closed curve lying in $|z - z_0| \leq \rho$ and $C' \approx A^{-1}CA \approx C$ in $G - Q$, so that $\circ(Q, C) = \circ(Q, C')$.

Subdivide C' into arcs $C'_j = (\alpha', I_j)$, $j = 0, 1, \ldots, m - 1$, as before, so that $|\nu(t') - \nu(t'')| < \pi/2$ for t', $t'' \in I_j$. Let K_j represent the arc on $|z - z_0| = \rho$ defined by (β_j, I_j), where

$$\beta_j(t) = \rho e^{i\psi_j(t)} \quad \text{and} \quad \psi_j(t) = \frac{(t - t_j)\nu(t_{j+1}) + (t_{j+1} - t)\nu(t_j)}{t_{j+1} - t_j}, \quad \text{for } t \in I_j.$$

The line segment from $\beta_j(t)$ to $\alpha'(t)$, $t \in I_j$, does not pass through Q, since C'_j and K_j both lie in an angle of $\pi/2$ at Q. Hence we may define a deformation φ_j of C'_j into K_j which does not pass through Q as follows:

$$\varphi_j(t, u) = u\beta_j(t) + (1 - u)\alpha'(t), \qquad t \in I_j.$$

Since

$$2\pi \circ (Q, C) = \nu(1) - \nu(0) = \sum_{j=0}^{m-1} [\nu(t_{j+1}) - \nu(t_j)]$$

$$= \sum_{j=0}^{m-1} [\psi_j(t_{j+1}) - \psi_j(t_j)],$$

the curve $K_0 K_1 \ldots K_{m-1} = K^n$, where $n = \circ(Q, C)$. Furthermore, $C' = C'_0 C'_1 \ldots C'_{m-1}$, and since $C'_j \approx K_j$, we conclude that $C' \approx K^n$ in $G - Q$. Therefore $C \approx K^n$ in $G - Q$, where $n = \circ(Q, C)$. If $\circ(Q, C_1) = \circ(Q, C_2) = n$, then $C_1 \approx K^n$, $C_2 \approx K^n$, and we conclude that $C_1 \approx C_2$. If $C_1 \approx K^n$ and $C_2 \approx K^m$, then $C_1 C_2 \approx K^{n+m}$, so that K forms a basis for the fundamental group $\mathfrak{F}(G - Q)$ of $G - Q$, and $\mathfrak{F}(G - Q)$ is isomorphic to the additive group of integers.

If G is a simply connected region in $\mathcal{E}^2$, $\mathfrak{F}(G) \cong \mathcal{J}$, and if G is homeomorphic to $G' \subset \mathcal{E}^2$, then (by Theorem 4-5) $\mathfrak{F}(G') \cong \mathfrak{F}(G) \cong \mathcal{J}$, so

G' is also simply connected. Furthermore, if $Q \in G$ maps into $Q' \in G'$, $\mathfrak{F}(G - Q) \cong \mathfrak{F}(G' - Q')$. Let K' be a circle about Q' in G'; then K' oriented counterclockwise forms a basis for $\mathfrak{F}(G' - Q')$ and $\circ(Q', K') = 1$. The circle K maps into a closed curve $f(K)$ which is also a generator of $\mathfrak{F}(G' - Q')$, since $\mathfrak{F}(G' - Q') \cong \mathfrak{F}(G - Q)$, so that $\circ(Q', f(K)) = \pm 1$. Moreover, for any closed curve C in $G - Q$, $\circ(Q', f(C)) = \circ(Q', f(K)) \circ (Q, C)$. This is easily verified by noticing that if $n = \circ(Q, C)$, then $C \approx K^n$ and $f(C) \approx f(K^n) \approx f(K)^n$. But then $\circ(Q', f(C)) = \circ(Q', [f(K)]^n) = n[\circ(Q', f(K))] = \circ(Q, C) \circ (Q', f(K))$, as we said. If $\circ(Q', f(K)) = +1$, we say that the mapping f *preserves the sense of rotation* at Q, in which case $\circ(Q', f(C)) = \circ(Q, C)$ for all C in $G - Q$.

The order of Q with respect to K is also given by

$$\circ(Q, K) = \frac{1}{2\pi} \Delta_k \arg (z - z_0) = \frac{1}{2\pi i} \int_K d \log (z - z_0)$$

$$= \frac{1}{2\pi i} \int_K \frac{dz}{z - z_0} = 1,$$

where z_0 is the coordinate of Q. Under a conformal homeomorphism $w = f(z)$ of G onto G', K goes into a curve $f(K)$ and the order of Q' with respect to $f(K)$ is given by

$$\circ(Q', f(K)) = \frac{1}{2\pi} \Delta_{f(K)} \arg (w - w_0) = \frac{1}{2\pi i} \int_{f(K)} \frac{dw}{w - w_0}$$

$$= \frac{1}{2\pi i} \int_K \frac{f'(z)\, dz}{f(z) - f(z_0)}.$$

This integral can be evaluated by the residue theorem and is equal to the residue of $f'(z)/(f(z) - f(z_0))$ at $z = z_0$, which is

$$\lim_{z \to z_0} \frac{z - z_0}{f(z) - f(z_0)} f'(z_0) = \frac{f'(z_0)}{f'(z_0)} = +1.$$

Since Q is an arbitrary point of G, we conclude that *conformal homeomorphisms preserve the sense of rotation at all points of G*. This enables us to define the order of a point Q on a Riemann surface S with respect to a curve C lying entirely within one local parametric disk containing Q. We merely treat C as a plane curve in this parametric disk and compute $\circ(Q, C)$; if a different parameter is used, the disks are related conformally and the sense of rotation is preserved.

Let T be an arbitrary closed chain of triangles on a Riemann surface S. We may subdivide T barycentrically N times until each pair of adjacent triangles in the Nth subdivision T_N lies entirely within one parametric disk. Each triangle s^2 of T_N is a homeomorphic image of a euclidean equilateral triangle e^2; the boundary of e^2 may be parametrized to be a closed curve which imparts an order ± 1 to any point interior to e^2, the sign depending upon the parametrization. Therefore, the boundary of s^2 is also a closed curve C on S which imparts to any point in s^2 order ± 1 depending upon the parametrization of C. We now specify that the boundary of each triangle of T_N be parametrized to impart order $+1$ to each of its interior points. This parametrization of the boundary of each s^2 in T_N specifies an order of the vertices of s^2 and hence an orientation of s^2 which we call the *positive orientation*. We shall prove that this is a coherent orientation of T_N and thereby defines a coherent orientation in T.

If s_1^2 and s_2^2 are two adjacent triangles in T_N, they are contained in a parametric disk D. Let s_1^2 have vertices P_0, P_1, P_2, and s_2^2 have vertices P_1, P_2, P_3, so that the edge $\overline{P_1 P_2}$ is held in common. Suppose that s_1^2 has $\langle P_0, P_1, P_2 \rangle$ as its positive orientation. The edge $\overline{P_1 P_2}$ can be deformed homotopically into the curve composed of the two edges $\overline{P_1 P_3} \cdot \overline{P_3 P_2}$, the deformation taking place in $|s_2^2|$. Then the curve C composed of the segments $\overline{P_2 P_0} \cdot \overline{P_0 P_1} \cdot \overline{P_1 P_3} \cdot \overline{P_3 P_2}$ imparts order $+1$ to any point Q_1 interior to s_1^2. We can join Q_1 to Q_2 interior to $|s_2^2|$ by a curve interior to $|s_1^2| \cup |s_2^2|$, so that Q_2 also has order $+1$ with respect to C. We next deform the curve $\overline{P_2 P_0} \cdot \overline{P_0 P_1}$ homotopically into $\overline{P_2 P_1}$ in $|s_1^2|$. Then the closed curve $\overline{P_2 P_1} \cdot \overline{P_1 P_3} \cdot \overline{P_3 P_2}$ imparts order $+1$ to Q_2, so that the triangle $\langle P_2, P_1, P_3 \rangle$ has positive orientation. The edge $\overline{P_1 P_2}$ therefore has opposite orientations in the positive orientations of s_1^2 and s_2^2. This completes the proof of the following important theorem.

THEOREM 5–11. *Every Riemann surface is orientable.*

We now return to the case of an arbitrary surface S on which a triangulation Δ is given.

THEOREM 5–12. *If S is orientable, it is possible to assign an orientation to each triangle of Δ in such a way that each adjacent pair of triangles is coherently oriented.*

To demonstrate this possibility, we select one triangle in Δ arbitrarily, say s_0^2, and assign to s_0^2 an orientation. Then we assign coherent orientations to all triangles in Δ having an edge in common with s_0^2. We next assign coherent orientations in all triangles having an edge in common with those already oriented. If, in this way, we come upon a triangle s^2 having two edges in common with those already oriented, we can find two different chains of triangles leading from s_0^2 to s^2, in which all triangles except s^2 are oriented. This gives us a closed chain of triangles from which a simple closed chain containing s^2 may be extracted. Since S is orientable, this simple closed chain of triangles may be oriented coherently, so that s^2 may be assigned an orientation which is coherent with those of both of its neighbors. Since all triangles in Δ can be connected to s_0^2 by a finite chain of triangles, this process ultimately includes each triangle of Δ and hence a coherent orientation is prescribed in all of Δ.

In Chapter 9, we shall prove that every Riemann surface is triangulable, and thus justify the use of the word "surface." We have also seen that every Riemann surface is orientable. These two properties actually characterize a class of Riemann surfaces.

THEOREM 5–13. *If an arbitrary manifold M is given which is both triangulable and orientable, it is possible to define an analytic structure on M which makes M into a Riemann surface.*

We must show that a collection of coordinate neighborhoods can be defined on M in which overlapping neighborhoods induce conformal mappings in the coordinate planes.† Suppose that the orientable surface S has the triangulation Δ in which a coherent orientation has been assigned, as well as normal barycentric coordinates. Fix an equilateral triangle e^2 in $\mathcal{E}^2$, and map each triangle s^2 of Δ barycentrically onto e^2 in such a way that the orientation of s^2 carries over into the positive orientation of e^2. These mappings define coordinates in a neighborhood of each point lying interior to a triangle of Δ.

If a point P lies on an edge of a triangle $s_1^2 \in \Delta$ but is not a vertex, then there is another triangle $s_2^2 \in \Delta$ which also has P on its edge. We then map $|s_1^2| \cup |s_2^2|$ barycentrically onto the union of the two adjacent equilateral triangles e_1^2 and e_2^2 with the orientations of s_1^2 and s_2^2 going into the positive orientations of e_1^2 and e_2^2. The point P is mapped into a point $p \in e_1^2 \cap e_2^2$. We then take as coordinates about P the coordinates of the corresponding points about p. About any point in either e_1^2 or e_2^2, these coordinates are analytic functions of those previously defined, for the affine mapping of one equilateral triangle onto another is conformal, actually being a similarity transformation of $\mathcal{E}^2$ and hence an entire linear transformation.

There remains only the case when P is a vertex at which n triangles s_1^2, $s_2^2, \ldots, s_n^2$ of Δ meet. We first map s_1^2 barycentrically onto an equilateral triangle e_1^2 in $\mathcal{E}^2$ whose vertex corresponding to P is at the origin. (Here and in the following mappings, we make the orientations of s_i^2 go into the positive orientation of e_i^2.) We next map s_2^2 barycentrically onto the equi-

---

†This theorem was first proved by Stoilow (Ref. 44, p. 77). Another proof was given by Heins (Ref. 22, p. 951). The proof presented here was suggested by M. Rosenlicht.

lateral triangle e_2^2 having the vertex corresponding to P at the origin and the edge corresponding to $|s_1^2| \cap |s_2^2|$ in common with e_1^2. We continue in this way, mapping s_i^2 barycentrically onto the equilateral triangle e_i^2 with the vertex corresponding to P at the origin and the edge corresponding to $|s_{i-1}^2| \cap |s_i^2|$ in common with e_{i-1}^2. The chain of triangles $e_1^2, e_2^2, \ldots, e_n^2$ will cover a neighborhood of the origin once completely only if $n = 6$. Otherwise, we perform the mapping $\zeta = z^{6/n}$ and the image of the chain of triangles forms a neighborhood of the origin in the ζ-plane. We use, as local coordinates about P, the coordinates of the corresponding points in the ζ-plane. Since the mapping $\zeta = z^{6/n}$ is conformal in the deleted neighborhood of $z = 0$, these coordinates are analytic functions of those previously defined, and give us an analytic structure on S. Since the analytic structure which we may put on M is not unique, we see that each orientable triangulable manifold corresponds to a class of Riemann surfaces.

5–4 Differentiable and analytic curves. In $\mathcal{E}^2$, a curve $C = (\alpha, I)$ is called differentiable if $z = \alpha(t) = \alpha_1(t) + i\alpha_2(t)$ has a continuous first derivative with respect to the real variable $t \in I$, and $d\alpha/dt \neq 0$. This leads us to say that a curve $C = (\alpha, I)$ on a Riemann surface S is *differentiable* if

(a) in terms of a local parameter $z = \varphi(P)$ about any point $P_0 = \alpha(t_0)$ on C the function $f(t) = \varphi(\alpha(t))$ has a continuous derivative with respect to t in an interval about t_0, and

(b) $f'(t_0) \neq 0$. (At $t_0 = 0$ or 1, we use one-sided derivatives.)

This definition is invariant with respect to coordinate changes on S; for if $w = \psi(P)$ is another local parameter about P_0, then $w = \psi(\varphi^{-1}(z)) = w(z)$ is an analytic function of z and $w'(z) \neq 0$. For $g(t) = \psi(\alpha(t))$ we have $g'(t) = w'(z)f'(t)$, so that $g'(t)$ is continuous and does not vanish. If C is a closed curve on S, we can periodically extend the definition of α to $-\infty < t < \infty$ by specifying that $\alpha(t + 1) = \alpha(t)$. The closed curve C is then differentiable if the conditions (a) and (b) hold for $-\infty < t < \infty$.

In a similar fashion, we say that a curve $C = (\alpha, I)$ on S is *analytic* if

(a') in terms of a local parameter $z = \varphi(P)$ about any point $P_0 = \alpha(t_0)$ on C the function $f(t) = \varphi(\alpha(t))$ is an analytic function of the real variable t in an interval about t_0; that is, $f(t) = \sum_{n=0}^{\infty} a_n(t - t_0)^n$ converges about t_0, and

(b') $a_1 = f'(t_0) \neq 0$.

If C is a closed curve, we again extend α to $-\infty < t < \infty$ by specifying that $\alpha(t + 1) = \alpha(t)$, and we say that C is analytic if (a') and (b') hold at all points of $-\infty < t < \infty$. Since coordinate changes are conformal mappings, this definition is invariant on S.

If the series $\sum_{n=0}^{\infty} a_n(t - t_0)^n$ converges for $|t - t_0| < \delta, \quad \delta > 0$, it converges for complex $\tau = t + is$ in the disk $D: |\tau - t_0| < \delta$. Thus the function $f(t) = \varphi(\alpha(t))$ is extended to be analytic in the disk D in the complex τ-plane, and since $f'(t_0) \neq 0$ we may choose δ small enough so that f is a one-to-one conformal mapping of D into a neighborhood of $z_0 = \varphi(P_0)$ in the z-plane. We may therefore use $\tau = f^{-1}(\varphi(P))$ as a local parameter about P_0 in terms of which an arc of C in the vicinity of P_0 is a segment of the real axis. A curve $C = (\alpha, I)$ is called *piecewise analytic* if $C = C_1 C_2 \ldots C_n$, where $C_k = (\alpha, I_k)$, I_k being the interval $t_{k-1} \leq t \leq t_k$, $0 = t_0 < t_1 < \ldots < t_n = 1$, and each C_k is an analytic curve. One similarly defines a *piecewise differentiable* curve to be one in which the arcs $C_1, C_2, \ldots, C_n$ are differentiable curves.

THEOREM 5–14. *Every simple closed piecewise analytic curve on a Riemann surface S locally separates.*

If a point P_0 on C is not an end point of analytic arcs, we may take as a separated neighborhood about P_0 a parametric disk in which C appears as a diameter. If P_0 is an end point of analytic arcs C_k and C_{k+1}, we may take a parametric disk $D: |z| < 1$ about P_0 in which C_k appears as the radial line from 0 to 1 and C_{k+1} as an analytic arc emanating from the center. If $z = \varphi(P)$ is the local parameter in D with $\varphi(P_0) = 0$, then the part of C_{k+1} in D is given by $z = f(t) = \varphi(\alpha(t))$, $t_k \leq t \leq t'_{k-1} \leq t_{k+1}$, where $f(t)$ is an analytic function of t with $f(t_k) = 0$. The function $|f(t)|$ increases for t in an interval $t_k \leq t \leq t'$. We then let ρ_0 be the minimum of $|f(t)|$ for $t \geq t'$. We may take as a separated neighborhood of P_0 any disk $|z| < \rho$, so long as $\rho < \rho_0$. For in $|z| < \rho_0$, C_k has the polar equation $\theta = h(r)$, where $z = re^{i\theta}$ and h is uniquely determined by $0 < h < 2\pi$. C_k divides the disk $|z| < \rho$ into the two disjoint nonempty open sets A_1 and A_2, where A_1 consists of those points $re^{i\theta}$ with $0 < r < \rho$, $0 < \theta < h(r)$, and A_2 consists of those points $re^{i\theta}$ with $0 < r < \rho$, $h(r) < \theta < 2\pi$. This completes the proof.

A simple closed curve $C = (\alpha, I)$ on S is said to have *two sides* (or is *two-sided*) if there is a region G on S with $|C| \subset G$ such that $G - |C|$ consists of two disjoint nonempty regions. Otherwise C is called *one-sided*. That one-sided curves do exist on some surfaces is illustrated on the Moebius band in Fig. 5–12, in which the vertical ends are identified as

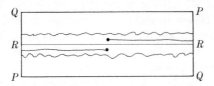

FIGURE 5–12.

indicated. The horizontal line $\overline{RR}$ joining the midpoints of the vertical edges is a closed curve C and any region containing C remains connected when C is removed.

THEOREM 5–15. *On a Riemann surface S, every simple closed piecewise analytic curve C is two-sided.*

Every point of C is the center of a parametric disk which is separated by C. Since $|C|$ is compact, a finite number of these, say $U_1, U_2, \ldots, U_n$, suffice to cover $|C|$. It is possible to find another covering of $|C|$ by parametric disks $V_1, V_2, \ldots, V_n$ with $\overline{V}_k \subset U_k$. Indeed, if $|C_1|$ represents the part of $|C|$ in U_1 but not in any other U_k, $k = 2, 3, \ldots, n$, then $|C_1|$ is compact, and $|C_1| \subset U_1$. If $z_1 = \varphi_1(P)$ is a local parameter in U_1, then the disk $|z_1| < 1 - \epsilon$ contains $|C_1|$ if ϵ is sufficiently small but positive. We select the disk $|z_1| < 1 - \epsilon$ as the set V_1 and note that $V_1, U_2, \ldots, U_n$ is also a covering of $|C|$. Now assume that $V_1, V_2, \ldots, V_j$ have been defined so that $\overline{V}_k \subset U_k$ and $V_1, V_2, \ldots, V_j, U_{j+1}, \ldots, U_n$ forms a covering of $|C|$. We let $|C_{j+1}|$ represent the part of C in U_{j+1} but not in any V_k, $k = 1, \ldots, j$, or U_k, $k = j + 2, \ldots, n$. Since $|C_{j+1}|$ is compact and lies interior to U_{j+1}, we may use the local parameter z_{j+1} in U_{j+1} to define a disk V_{j+1}: $|z_{j+1}| < 1 - \epsilon$, where ϵ is small enough so that $|C_{j+1}| \subset V_{j+1}$. Then $V_1, V_2, \ldots, V_{j+1}, U_{j+2}, \ldots, U_n$ forms a covering of $|C|$. This inductively defines the desired sets $V_1, V_2, \ldots, V_n$.

We next seek a new finite covering of C by parametric disks each of which is separated by C and having the additional property that if two of these disks overlap, they lie in the same set U_k of the original covering of $|C|$. Given an arbitrary point P_0 on C, P_0 is interior to certain sets V_k, $k \in K$, and is on the boundary of other sets V_k, $k \in K'$, where K and K' are index sets consisting of integers selected from $1, 2, \ldots, n$. If P_0 is on the boundary of the set V_k, $k \in K'$, then P_0 is interior to U_k, since $\overline{V}_k \subset U_k$. The set

$$N = \left(\bigcap_{k \in K} V_k \right) \cap \left(\bigcap_{k \in K'} U_k \right) - \left(\bigcup_{j \notin K \cup K'} \overline{V}_j \right)$$

forms a neighborhood of P_0, and we may take a parametric disk W about P_0 which is separated by C and which is contained in N. Since $|C|$ is compact, a finite number of the sets W, say $W_1, W_2, \ldots, W_m$, cover C. Now suppose that W_i and W_j have a point P in common. The disk W_i has its center on C and hence in some V_k; thus, by definition, $W_i \subset V_k$ and $P \in V_k$. But whenever the set W_j contains a point in V_k, the whole set W_j is contained in U_k by definition. Thus both W_i and W_j are contained in the same disk U_k, which is what we wanted.

Let $G = \cup_{i=1}^m W_i$; we shall show that the region G which clearly contains C is separated into disjoint nonempty regions when C is removed.

Each of the disks U_i (or W_i) is separated into two parts by C. At each point of C in U_i (or W_i) at which C is analytic, C has a tangent vector oriented toward the direction of increasing parameter along C. Therefore if $C = (\alpha, I)$, and $z = \varphi(P)$ is a local parameter in U_i (or W_i), then $z = \varphi(\alpha(t)) = f(t)$ is the equation of C in the disk and the direction of the tangent is given by $\arg df/dt$. The part of U_i (or W_i) in the direction of the normal to C directed toward $[\arg (df/dt)] - \pi/2$ is said to be on the right side of C, whereas the part of U_i (or W_i) on the side of the normal directed toward $[\arg (df/dt)] + \pi/2$ is on the left side of C. (Even if local parameters are changed, these designations remain the same, since coordinate changes are conformal and the senses of the angles are preserved.) Clearly, if $W_i \subset U_i$, the right side of C in W_i lies in the right side of C in U_i. Let W_i^+ be the part of W_i to the right of C and W_i^- the part of W_i to the left of C, and denote $G^+ = \cup_{i=1}^m W_i^+$ and $G^- = \cup_{i=1}^m W_i^-$. Then $G^+ \cup G^- = G - |C|$, and we shall prove that $G^+ \cap G^- = \phi$. Indeed, if $P \in G^+ \cap G^-$, then $P \in W_i^+$ and $P \in W_j^-$ for some i and j. Since W_i and W_j have a point P in common, they both lie in the same U_k. Therefore in U_k, P is on both the left and the right sides of C; but this is impossible, since U_k was divided into two disjoint parts by C, one on the left and the other on the right of C. This completes the proof that C has two sides.

We close this section with another property of analytic curves. If $C_1 = (\alpha, I)$ and $C_2 = (\beta, I)$ are closed analytic curves which have an infinite number of points in common, then the carriers of C_1 and C_2 are the same; $|C_1| = |C_2|$. Indeed, $|C_1|$ and $|C_2|$ are compact sets and the points of intersection must have a point of accumulation $P_0 = \alpha(t_0) = \beta(\tau_0)$. We then can find a sequence of points of intersection $\{P_n\}$ with $P_n \to P_0$, $P_n = \alpha(t_n) = \beta(\tau_n)$, $t_n \to t_0 \in I$ and $\tau_n \to \tau_0 \in I$. We take as parameters about P_0 the $z = t + is$ and $\zeta = \tau + i\sigma$, so that in the z-plane C_1 lies along the real axis, and in the ζ-plane C_2 lies along the real axis. We have a conformal mapping $\zeta = f(z)$ which has the property that $\operatorname{Im} f(t_n) = 0$ for $n = 1, 2, \ldots$ such that $t_n \to t_0$. If $f(z) = \sum_{n=0}^{\infty} (a_n + ib_n)(z - z_0)^n$, then $f(t) = \sum_{n=0}^{\infty} (a_n + ib_n)(t - t_0)^n$ and $\operatorname{Im} f(t) = \sum_{n=0}^{\infty} b_n(t - t_0)^n$. Since $\operatorname{Im} f(t_n) = 0$ on a sequence having t_0 as a limit point, $b_n = 0$ for $n = 0, 1, 2, \ldots$, and $\operatorname{Im} f(t) \equiv 0$, or $f(z)$ maps the real axis into the real axis. Thus in a neighborhood of P_0, the carriers of C_1 and C_2 coincide. By a process of analytic continuation, they coincide at all points.

5–5 Normal forms of compact orientable surfaces. In dealing with topological questions about surfaces, it is convenient to be able to visualize a model which is homeomorphic to the surface in question rather than to proceed abstractly. Such models help our intuitive understanding of the problems we attack and give a fuller meaning to the results. For compact surfaces, such models are easily found. These models will be called *normal forms* and will have the property that every compact orientable surface will be homeomorphic to one and only one normal form.†

The first project we undertake will be to "flatten out" a given compact orientable surface S. Fix a triangulation Δ of S with a coherent orientation and normal barycentric coordinates. This triangulation contains only a finite number of triangles, since S is compact. Map one of these triangles, say s_1^2, barycentrically onto a euclidean triangle e_1^2. Then select a triangle s_2^2 adjacent to s_1^2 and map it barycentrically onto a euclidean triangle e_2^2 adjacent to e_1^2 along the corresponding edge. The coherent orientations of s_1^2 and s_2^2 assign an orientation in the boundary of the polygon $|s_1^2| \cup |s_2^2|$ and hence in the boundary of the polygon $e_1^2 \cup e_2^2$ (see Fig. 5–13). The polygon $e_1^2 \cup e_2^2$ may be mapped topologically into a square with edges going into edges, and this square will be considered as $e_1^2 \cup e_2^2$ from here on. We next select a triangle s_3^2 having an edge in common with either s_1^2 or s_2^2 and map it barycentrically onto a euclidean triangle e_3^2 adjacent to the corresponding edge of e_1^2 or e_2^2 and selected so that it does not overlap e_1^2 or e_2^2. The coherent orientations of these three triangles again assign an orientation to the boundary of the polygon $e_1^2 \cup e_2^2 \cup e_3^2$. The polygon $e_1^2 \cup e_2^2 \cup e_3^2$ may be mapped topologically into a regular pentagon with edges going into edges, and this pentagon will be considered as $e_1^2 \cup e_2^2 \cup e_3^2$ from here on. This process is repeated until all the triangles of Δ have been used, each time taking care not to overlap the triangles already selected.

We then find ourselves with a plane regular polygon Π having a given orientation in its boundary induced by the orientations in the individual triangles of S_Δ. We shall call this orientation the positive direction of traversing the boundary of Π.

Let Δ be made up of n triangles; it is easily proved by induction on n that Π has $n + 2$ sides. Since each edge belongs to exactly two triangles in Δ, exactly two edges of Π correspond to the same edge in Δ. Thus Π has an even number of sides. A topological model of S_Δ is now

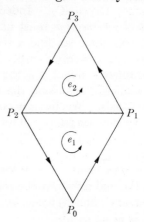

FIGURE 5–13.

---

†The treatment here follows Lefschetz (Ref. 31, pp. 73–80) and Seifert and Threlfall (Ref. 44, pp. 130–140). There is a gap (on page 78, line 3) in the proof presented by Lefschetz. The proofs presented in both references are for any compact surfaces, but we shall consider here only orientable compact surfaces.

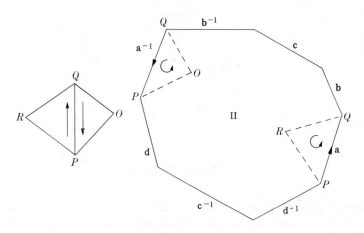

FIGURE 5–14.

obtained by properly identifying (pasting together) the pairs of sides of Π.

Let $s^1 = \langle p, q \rangle$ be an edge of Δ which corresponds to two edges of Π. The vertex p of s^1 then corresponds to two vertices of Π, both of which we label P; similarly, q corresponds to two vertices of Π, which we call Q. In going around the boundary of Π in the positive direction, we encounter the edge $\overline{PQ}$ once (in which we first cross P and then Q) and encounter the edge $\overline{QP}$ once; for the two triangles in Δ having $\overline{pq}$ as an edge induce opposite orientations in $\overline{pq}$. If we label the edge $\overline{PQ}$ with the letter **a**, then we use $\mathbf{a}^{-1}$ to designate QP (Fig. 5–14). In this way, we associate a letter with each edge of Π. We obtain a *symbol* for Π by writing these letters in the order in which they are encountered going around the boundary of Π in the positive direction. The symbol for the polygon in Fig. 5–14 is $\mathbf{a\,b\,c\,b^{-1}\,a^{-1}\,d\,c^{-1}\,d^{-1}}$.

If the polygon Π is now cut into two polygons along a line joining two of its vertices, and if the two parts are then again attached along a pair of identified edges with equivalent points corresponding to each other, and if the two edges of the cut are identified, we obtain a new polygon Π′ with pairs of sides identified. The two polygons Π and Π′ both represent the same surface S, for the identification of points was not changed in this process. With this observation, we begin the simplification of Π.

First, a cyclic interchange of the letters in the symbol for Π leads to another symbol for the same polygon Π. If the letters $\mathbf{a\,a^{-1}}$ appear in the symbol as adjacent edges of Π, and if the symbol has at least one other letter (hence at least four letters altogether) then the letters $\mathbf{a\,a^{-1}}$ can be removed from the symbol to obtain a new symbol for Π. Figure 5–15

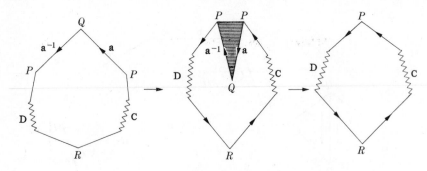

FIGURE 5–15.

illustrates this process and suffices as a proof. The two-sided polygon $\mathbf{a}\,\mathbf{a}^{-1}$ which we could not handle in this way is one of our normal forms. From now on, we may assume that Π has at least four sides.

We next transform Π into a polygon in which all the vertices correspond to the same point on S. Designate a certain vertex of Π by P and also label P all other vertices of Π which correspond to the same point on S as does P. The points so labeled form a class of equivalent vertices. If there is an edge $\mathbf{a}$ of Π with one vertex unlabeled, we label it Q, together with all other vertices of Π equivalent to Q, to obtain a second equivalence class of vertices. We now show how to reduce the number of Q vertices by 1 and thereby increase the number of P vertices by 1. Let $\mathbf{a} = \overline{PQ}$ and let $\mathbf{b}$ denote the edge of Π which has the vertex Q in common with $\mathbf{a}$. We know that $\mathbf{b}$ is not $\mathbf{a}^{-1}$, for if it were, we would have had $\mathbf{a}\,\mathbf{a}^{-1}$, which was already suppressed. We join the other vertex R of $\mathbf{b}$ (R may be P or Q) to the vertex P of $\mathbf{a}$ by a diagonal $\mathbf{c}$ to form the triangle Δ with edges $\mathbf{a}$, $\mathbf{b}$, $\mathbf{c}$. Cut Δ out of Π along $\mathbf{c}$ and then attach Δ to the rest of Π along the edge $\mathbf{b}$ of Δ and $\mathbf{b}^{-1}$ of the rest of Π to form a new polygon Π' with the same number of edges as Π. Whereas Δ was previously attached along $\overline{PR}$ in Π, exposing the vertex Q, it is now attached along RQ in Π', exposing the vertex P. Thus Π' has one more P vertex and one less Q vertex than did Π. Continuing in this manner, we obtain a polygon in which all vertices are equivalent and denoted by P.

A pair of edges $\mathbf{a}$ and $\mathbf{b}$ are called *linked* if they appear in the symbol in the following order

$$\ldots \mathbf{a} \ldots \mathbf{b} \ldots \mathbf{a}^{-1} \ldots \mathbf{b}^{-1} \ldots \qquad (1)$$

We show now that each edge of Π (with all vertices equivalent) is linked with some other edge. If this is not true, there must be an edge $\mathbf{c}$ such that all the letters between $\mathbf{c}$ and $\mathbf{c}^{-1}$ are identified among themselves, so that the inverse of any one of them does not lie outside the letters in $\mathbf{c} \ldots \mathbf{c}^{-1}$.

Then select a point on the edge **c** not the vertex P and join it by a line segment **d** in Π to the equivalent point on $\mathbf{c}^{-1}$. This line divides Π into two parts Π_1 and Π_2 which have P and the points on **d** identified. But one vertex P of **c** lies in Π_1 and the other vertex P lies in Π_2, which is impossible since P would not have a euclidean neighborhood in the surface. Thus each edge of Π is linked with another. By the process shown in Fig. 5–16, Π can be transformed so that the linked pair (1) is brought together in the sequence $\mathbf{c}\,\mathbf{d}\,\mathbf{c}^{-1}\,\mathbf{d}^{-1}$. The further combination of linked pairs does not destroy those already combined, so that we finally obtain the sought-after normal form.

THEOREM 5–16. *The normal form of a compact orientable surface is a polygon with symbol*

(a) $\mathbf{a}\,\mathbf{a}^{-1}$, *or*

(b) $\mathbf{a}_1\,\mathbf{b}_1\,\mathbf{a}_1^{-1}\,\mathbf{b}_1^{-1}\,\mathbf{a}_2\,\mathbf{b}_2\,\mathbf{a}_2^{-1}\,\mathbf{b}_2^{-1}\ldots\mathbf{a}_g\,\mathbf{b}_g\,\mathbf{a}_g^{-1}\,\mathbf{b}_g^{-1}$.

In case (a) we say that the normal form has *genus zero*, while in case (b) the normal form has *genus g*.

We have now obtained as the normal forms of compact orientable surfaces certain polygons with pairs of sides identified. A topological deformation can be used to make the normal form a regular convex polygon. What do these normal forms look like when we actually paste together the identified edges? Let us begin with the normal form of genus zero; pasting together the edges **a** and $\mathbf{a}^{-1}$ in Fig. 5–17, we get a surface which is topologically a sphere. It is convenient here to imagine the sphere made of rubber; then cutting it open along the dotted line a and flattening it out gives us the two-sided "polygon" which we have taken to be the normal form of genus zero.

The normal form of genus 1 is a quadrilateral $\mathbf{a}\,\mathbf{b}\,\mathbf{a}^{-1}\,\mathbf{b}^{-1}$ which is homeomorphic to the rectangle in Fig. 5–18. If we paste together the identified sides **a** and $\mathbf{a}^{-1}$, we obtain a cylinder with its two ends **b** and $\mathbf{b}^{-1}$ identified. Now pasting together the ends **b** and $\mathbf{b}^{-1}$, we get a torus as a model for the normal form of genus 1.

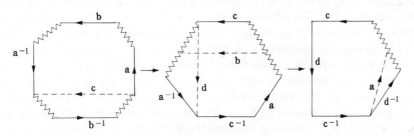

FIGURE 5–16.

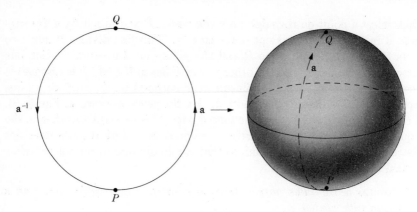

FIGURE 5–17.

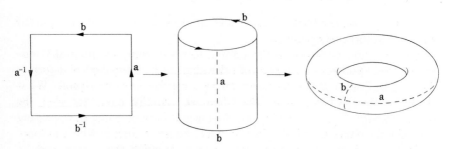

FIGURE 5–18.

The torus may be viewed topologically in yet another way. If we cut a disk out of the torus as shown in Fig. 5–19, we obtain a *handle*. The hole left after cutting out the disk is bounded by a curve **h** which may be made to pass through the point corresponding to the vertex P. In the rectangle $\mathbf{a\,b\,a^{-1}\,b^{-1}}$, this disk corresponds to the shaded hole in Fig. 5–20. If we now separate the curve **h** at P, the rectangle with a hole opens up into a pentagon (Fig. 5–21) with the symbol $\mathbf{a\,b\,a^{-1}\,b^{-1}\,h}$, which is the symbol of a handle. The disk which we cut out of the torus can be deformed into a sphere with a disk removed, the disk being bounded by the curve **h**. Thus the torus may be conceived as a sphere with a handle attached to it.

This leads us to the normal forms of higher genus. Out of the sphere let us cut g disks bounded by curves $\mathbf{h}_1, \mathbf{h}_2, \ldots, \mathbf{h}_g$ having only the point P in common. By flattening out the resulting surface, we obtain a g-sided polygon with the symbol $\mathbf{h}_1\,\mathbf{h}_2 \ldots \mathbf{h}_g$. If we attach to each $\mathbf{h}_k$ the handle $\mathbf{a}_k\,\mathbf{b}_k\,\mathbf{a}_k^{-1}\,\mathbf{b}_k^{-1}\,\mathbf{h}_k$ by pasting together the curves $\mathbf{h}_k$, we obtain the normal form of genus g.

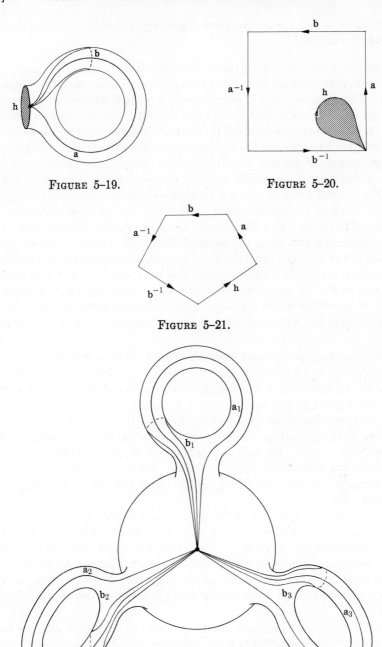

FIGURE 5–19.

FIGURE 5–20.

FIGURE 5–21.

FIGURE 5–22.

THEOREM 5–17. *The normal form of genus g is topologically a sphere with g handles attached.*

Figure 5–22 shows a sphere with three handles.

We have established that every compact orientable surface is homeomorphic to a normal form of genus g and hence to a sphere with g handles. The genus g completely determines the normal form, so that two triangulated surfaces are homeomorphic if their normal forms have the same genus. On the other hand, to find the normal form, we used a specific triangulation of the surface. If we had taken a different triangulation of the same surface, would we get the normal form of the same genus? In other words, can the normal form of genus g be mapped homeomorphically onto the normal form of a different genus? The answers to these questions are embodied in the fact that the genus of the normal form depends only upon the surface and not upon the triangulation used, so that homeomorphic normal forms have the same genus. This enables us to define the genus of a compact orientable surface as the genus of the normal form homeomorphic to it. To prove these assertions, we shall express the genus in terms of quantities which are topological invariants of the surface. These invariants are the Betti numbers, which are defined in the next section.

5–6 Homology groups and Betti numbers.† On the surface S with the triangulation Δ, we let $\pm s_1^n, \pm s_2^n, \ldots, \pm s_k^n, \ldots$ denote all oriented n-simplexes in Δ, $n = 0, 1, 2$. A (simplicial) n-*chain* c^n is an integer-valued function defined on the n-simplexes in Δ, taking on the value zero on all but a finite number of the simplexes in Δ and satisfying $c^n(-s^n) = -c^n(s^n)$. For two chains c_1^n and c_2^n, their sum $c_1^n + c_2^n$ is the function taking on the value $c_1^n(s^n) + c_2^n(s^n)$ for each n-simplex s^n in Δ. This addition operation gives us a group $C^n = C^n(S_\Delta)$ of n-chains. The zero (additive identity) of this group is the function taking on the value zero on all $s^n \in \Delta$, and is denoted by 0.

To each simplex $s_k^n \in \Delta$ is associated a special n-chain which takes on the value 1 on s_k^n, the value -1 on $-s_k^n$, and the value 0 on all s_j^n, $j \neq k$. We shall also denote this n-chain by s_k^n and in this sense consider the n-simplex s_k^n an n-chain. Then an arbitrary n-chain which assumes the value a_j on the n-simplex s_j^n can be written as $c^n = \sum_i a_i s_i^n$, the sum being over a finite number of terms, since only a finite number of the a_i are different

---

†In this chapter, it is desirable for the reader to be acquainted with the basic concepts of group theory such as group, subgroup, homomorphism, isomorphism, quotient (factor) group, etc. There are many good sources for this information; an excellent summary can be found in the first chapter of *Topological Groups* by Pontrjagen, Ref. 38. This material is also easily accessible in Birkhoff and MacLane, Ref. 10.

from zero. Thus each n-chain is a finite linear combination of n-simplexes with integral coefficients. If $c_1^n = \sum_i a_i s_i^n$ and $c_2^n = \sum_i b_i s_i^n$, then $c_1^n + c_2^n = \sum_i (a_i + b_i) s_i^n$.

The *boundary operator* ∂ is a homomorphism of C^n into C^{n-1}, which we shall proceed to define first on n-simplexes and then extend linearly to all chains. For the oriented 0-simplex $\langle P_0 \rangle$, we set $\partial \langle P_0 \rangle = 0$. The boundary of the oriented 1-simplex $\langle P_0, P_1 \rangle$ is the 0-chain $\partial \langle P_0, P_1 \rangle = \langle P_1 \rangle - \langle P_0 \rangle$. Finally, the oriented 2-simplex $\langle P_0, P_1, P_2 \rangle$ has as its boundary the 1-chain

$$\partial \langle P_0, P_1, P_2 \rangle = \langle P_1, P_2 \rangle - \langle P_0, P_2 \rangle + \langle P_0, P_1 \rangle.$$

The boundary of a 1- or 2-simplex as defined here corresponds to what we would ordinarily consider the boundary of a line segment or triangle, respectively, as seen in Fig. 5–10. We easily verify that the boundary of an oriented simplex is the same regardless of which representative of the orientation class is selected, so that ∂ is actually well defined on oriented simplexes. We also observe that for each s^n, $\partial(-s^n) = -\partial s^n$. The extension of ∂ to a chain $c^n = \sum_i a_i s_i^n$ is immediately accomplished by setting

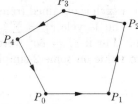

$$\partial c^n = \sum_i a_i\, \partial s_i^n.$$

Those n-chains c^n which satisfy $\partial c^n = 0$ are called (simplicial) *n-cycles* or *closed n-chains*. (The latter descriptive term is used because any closed

FIGURE 5–23.

polygonal path represented by the 1-chain $c^1 = \sum_{i=0}^{k-1} \langle P_i, P_{i+1} \rangle$, $P_k = P_0$, has $\partial c^1 = \sum_{i=0}^{k-1} \langle P_{i+1} \rangle - \langle P_i \rangle = 0$, since each $\langle P_i \rangle$ appears once with a plus sign and once with a minus sign, as in Fig. 5–23.) The n-cycles form the kernel of the homomorphism ∂ (i.e., those elements carried into 0) and hence form a subgroup of C^n, which we shall denote by Z^n.

An n-chain c^n which satisfies $c^n = \partial c^{n+1}$ for some $(n + 1)$-chain c^{n+1} is called an *n-boundary* or *exact n-chain*. As the homomorphic image of the group C^{n+1}, the collection of n-boundaries forms a group B^n which is a subgroup of C^n. We shall define $C^n = 0$ for $n > 2$, so that $B^2 = 0$. Moreover, B^n is also a subgroup of Z^n. To demonstrate this important fact, we must show that if $b^n = \partial c^{n+1}$, then $\partial b^n = 0$; or simply $\partial(\partial c^{n+1}) = 0$ for all c^{n+1}. Because of the linearity of the operator ∂, it is sufficient to demonstrate this for simplexes. For any 0-simplex s^0, we have $\partial s^0 = 0$, so that $\partial \partial s^0 = 0$ too. For $s^1 = \langle P_0, P_1 \rangle$, we have $\partial s' = \langle P_1 \rangle - \langle P_0 \rangle$

and $\partial\partial s^1 = \partial\langle P_1\rangle - \partial\langle P_0\rangle = 0$. Finally for $s^2 = \langle P_0, P_1, P_2\rangle$, we have $\partial s^2 = \langle P_1, P_2\rangle - \langle P_0, P_2\rangle + \langle P_0, P_1\rangle$, and

$$\partial\partial s^2 = [\langle P_2\rangle - \langle P_1\rangle] - [\langle P_2\rangle - \langle P_0\rangle] + [\langle P_1\rangle - \langle P_0\rangle] = 0,$$

since each $\langle P_i\rangle$ appears once with a plus sign and once with a minus sign. Geometrically, this says that the boundary of a triangle is a closed polygon.

The homomorphism ∂ which maps C^n onto B^{n-1} has Z^n as its kernel. Then B^{n-1} is isomorphic to the quotient group of C^n relative to Z^n or, symbolically,

$$B^{n-1} \cong \frac{C^n}{Z^n}.$$

We summarize these results in the following theorem.

THEOREM 5–18. *For any n-chain c^n we have $\partial\partial c^n = 0$, so that $B^n \subset Z^n$ and $B^{n-1} \cong C^n/Z^n$.*

We have seen that every boundary is a cycle; the converse is not true in general. For example, Fig. 5–24 indicates an infinite triangulation of an annulus which is obtained from a rectangle by identifying the left and right edges. The 1-cycle $c_1^1 = \sum_{i=1}^3 s_i^1$ is not the complete boundary of any 2-chain. For if $c_1^1 = \partial c^2$ were to hold, then c^2 would have to assume a nonzero value on some 2-simplex s^2 having s_1^1 as an edge. Then c^2 would

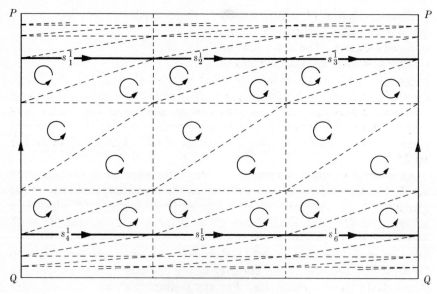

FIGURE 5–24.

have to assume the same value on every 2-simplex which is on the same side of s_1^1 as s^2 in order not to introduce some edge not in c_1^1 into ∂c^2. But this would mean that c^2 takes on a nonzero value on an infinite number of 2-simplexes, which is a contradiction, proving that c_1^1 is not a boundary. In the torus of Figs. 5–2 and 5–18, the edge **a** is a 1-cycle which does not bound.

The group B^n is a normal subgroup of Z^n (since C^n is commutative) and we may form the quotient group of Z^n relative to B^n. We call this group $H^n = Z^n/B^n$ the *n*th *simplicial homology group* of S_Δ. Any *n*-cycle z^n which is in B^n represents the zero element of H^n; we denote this fact by saying that any *n*-cycle z^n which is a boundary is *homologous to zero*, and we write $z^n \sim 0$. Two *n*-cycles z_1^n and z_2^n with $z_1^n - z_2^n \sim 0$ are in the same coset of Z^n relative to B^n and hence represent the same element of H^n; these are said to be *homologous*† and we write $z_1^n \sim z_2^n$. In the annulus in Fig. 5–24, the 1-cycle c_1^1 is homologous to the 1-cycle $c_2^1 = \sum_{i=4}^6 s_i^1$. For let c^2 represent the 2-chain assuming the value $+1$ on each of the 2-simplexes with arrows indicating their orientation, and value 0 on all others. Then $c_2^1 - c_1^1 = \partial c^2$, since each edge of a triangle in c^2, which is not in either c_1^1 or c_2^1, is an edge of exactly two triangles of c^2 and appears with opposite signs in the boundaries of these two triangles.

Let us now suppose that certain *n*-cycles z_i^n, $i = 1, 2, \ldots, b_n$, can be found satisfying the following two properties:

(a) The z_i^n, $i = 1, 2, \ldots, b_n$, are homologously linearly independent; i.e., any relationship $\sum_{i=1}^{b_n} a_i z_i^n \sim 0$ where the a_i are integers implies that all $a_i = 0$, $i = 1, 2, \ldots, b_n$.

(b) For every *n*-cycle z^n of Z^n, we have $z^n \sim \sum_{i=1}^{b_n} a_i z_i$, where the a_i are integers.

The number b_n is called the *n*th *Betti number* of the surface S_Δ. Since the Betti numbers are defined in terms of homology, we could also define them directly in terms of H^n. If we denote by $[z^n]$ the homology class of the cycle z^n, then $[z^n]$ is an element of H^n. If there are b_n elements of H^n, say $[z_i^n]$, $i = 1, 2, \ldots, b_n$, with the properties that

(a) $\sum_{i=1}^{b_n} a_i [z_i^n] = 0$, a_i integers implies $a_i = 0$, $i = 1, \ldots, b_n$, and

(b) each element $[z^n]$ of H^n can be written $[z^n] = \sum_{i=1}^{b_n} a_i [z_i^n]$,

then b_n is the *n*th Betti number of S_Δ, and the $[z_i]$ form a basis for H^n.

---

†Two chains c_1^n and c_2^n are said to be homologous if $c_1^n - c_2^n = \partial c^{n+1}$ for some $(n+1)$-chain c^{n+1}. In particular, $c_1^n \sim c_2^n$ implies that c_1^n and c_2^n have the same boundary, for $\partial c_1^n - \partial c_2^n = \partial \partial c^{n+1} = 0$. Thus the notion of homologous cycles can be carried over to chains having the same boundary.

In general, the homology groups do not have such a basis, so that Betti numbers are defined somewhat differently. A collection of elements $x_1, \ldots, x_n$ is said to generate an additive abelian group G if every element of G is a linear combination with integral coefficients of these $x_1, \ldots, x_n$. A group with one generator x whose elements are then $0, \pm x, \pm 2x, \ldots$, such that $nx = 0$ implies $x = 0$, is called a *free cyclic group*. A group with one generator x such that $kx = 0$, $k \neq 0$ and $x \neq 0$, whereas for any $0 < n < k$, $nx = 0$ implies $x = 0$, is called a *cyclic group of order k*. If $G_1, G_2, \ldots, G_n$ are subgroups of an additive abelian group G, then G is said to be the direct sum of these subgroups, written $G = G_1 + G_2 + \cdots + G_n$, if each element $x \in G$ can be written uniquely in the form $x = x_1 + x_2 + \cdots + x_n$, $x_i \in G_i$, $i = 1, \ldots, n$, in which the terms commute; that is, $x_i + x_j = x_j + x_i$. Then the structure of any additive abelian group G with a finite number of generators is obtained from the theorem saying that G is the direct sum of ρ cyclic groups of orders $c_1, c_2, \ldots, c_\rho$ and of b free cyclic groups. The numbers $c_1, \ldots, c_\rho$ are called the torsion coefficients of G, and b is called the Betti number of G. A proof of this theorem can be found in Seifert and Threlfall, (Ref. 42, Chap. 12) as well as in most textbooks on modern algebra. The homology group H^n is an additive abelian group and, if it is finitely generated, it can be represented as a direct sum of b_n free cyclic groups and of ρ cyclic groups of orders $c_1^n, c_2^n, \ldots, c_\rho^n$. If the torsion coefficients all vanish, the number b_n of free cyclic groups is the same as the Betti number of H^n defined at first. In the case of orientable surfaces, the torsion coefficients are always zero, which means that the original definition of Betti number is adequate.

5–7 Invariance of the homology groups.

It would appear from the definition of the nth homology group and the nth Betti number of S_Δ that they depend upon the triangulation Δ. It is indeed remarkable that if a different triangulation Δ' of S is used, the homology group $H^n(S_{\Delta'})$ is isomorphic to $H^n(S_\Delta)$ and consequently the Betti numbers are the same. Thus we shall see that the homology groups and the Betti numbers depend intrinsically upon the surface. Since a homeomorphism of a surface S onto another surface S' carries a triangulation Δ of S into a triangulation Δ' of S', preserving the relationships between simplexes, the homology groups $H^n(S'_{\Delta'})$ and $H^n(S_\Delta)$ are isomorphic, giving us the topological invariants which we seek.

For the groups H^0 and H^2 the proofs of invariance as well as the computation of the Betti numbers b_0 and b_2 are particularly easy, for we can associate these with topological invariants already studied. For H^1, the work is more difficult and will be done in the next section.

First of all, *since every surface is by definition connected, the Betti number $b_0 = 1$*. To see this, we observe that every 0-chain is a 0-cycle. Under what conditions is a 0-chain a boundary? Let $c^1 = \sum_j a_j s_j^1$ be a 1-chain; then $\partial c^1 = \sum_j a_j \partial s_j^1 = \sum_j a_j (s_j^0 - \bar{s}_j^0)$, where we have set $\partial s_j^1 = s_j^0 - \bar{s}_j^0$. We notice that the coefficient a_j appears in ∂c^1 once with a plus sign and once with a minus sign, so that the sum of all the coefficients in

∂c^1 is equal to zero. Thus a necessary condition for a 0-cycle to be a boundary is that the sum of coefficients of all the 0-simplexes be equal to 0. Therefore the 0-cycle consisting of the single (arbitrary) 0-simplex s^0 is not a boundary. We shall now show that any other 0-simplex s_1^0 is homologous to s^0. Since S is connected, the vertices s^0 and s_1^0 can be joined by a finite chain of edges of triangles in Δ. If we designate these edges successively by $s_1^1, s_2^1, \ldots, s_k^1$, and orient them in the direction traversed in going from s^0 to s_1^0, we have $\partial \sum_{j=1}^{k} s_j^1 = s_1^0 - s^0$. Thus $s_1^0 \sim s^0$, and we have proved that the homology class of s^0 forms a basis for the homology group H^0, and hence $b_0 = 1$.

Let us next assign a coherent orientation to the triangles in Δ. Let $c^2 = \sum_{j=1}^{N} a_j s_j^2$ be a 2-chain on S_Δ. If c^2 is a 2-cycle, either all the $a_j = 0$, in which case c^2 is the 2-cycle 0, or with each s_j^2 the three 2-simplexes having edges in common with s_j^2 must appear in c^2 with the same coefficient as has s_j^2. For in ∂c^2, each side s_k^1 of s_j^2 must appear with the coefficient $\pm a_j$, and the other 2-simplex of which s_k^1 is a side must also appear in c^2 so as to cancel the term $\pm a_j s_k^1$. The only way in which c^2 can contain all triangles adjacent to each of its members would be for c^2 to contain all the 2-simplexes in Δ with the same coefficient. If S is not compact, Δ contains an infinite number of triangles and c^2 could not contain only a finite number of these, so that *except for the 2-cycle 0 there are no 2-cycles on a noncompact orientable surface*, and $b_2 = 0$ in this case.

On the other hand, if S is compact, we must have $c^2 = a\sum_{j=1}^{N} s_j^2$ in order for c^2 to be a cycle, the summation extending over all the 2-simplexes in Δ. The chain $\bar{c}^2 = \sum_{j=1}^{N} s_j^2$ is a 2-cycle, since each 1-simplex in $\partial \bar{c}^2$ appears as an edge of two coherently oriented triangles. Also $\bar{c}^2$ is not homologous to 0, for $B^2 = 0$. Thus *the homology class of $\bar{c}^2$ forms a basis for the homology group H^2 of a compact orientable surface and $b_2 = 1$ in this case*. We summarize the results of this section in the following theorem.

THEOREM 5–19. *For any surface, $b_0 = 1$. For any compact orientable surface, $b_2 = 1$. For any noncompact orientable surface, $b_2 = 0$.*

5–8 Fundamental group and first homology group. We have now discussed two important groups of curves on a surface S_Δ: the fundamental group $\mathfrak{F}$ and the first homology group H^1. By its definition, H^1 appears to depend upon the triangulation Δ, whereas the definition of $\mathfrak{F}$ does not involve the triangulation. To establish the invariance of H^1 we shall exhibit a relationship between H^1 and $\mathfrak{F}$.

The fundamental group $\mathfrak{F}$ is not always commutative; that is, $C_1 C_2$ is not necessarily homotopic to $C_2 C_1$, or simply $C_1 C_2 C_1^{-1} C_2^{-1}$ is not homotopic to $\mathbf{1}$. Recalling the notation of Chapter 4, we denote the class of curves homotopic to the curve C by $\mathfrak{C}$, the latter representing an element of $\mathfrak{F}$. An element of the form $\mathcal{C}_1\mathcal{C}_2\mathcal{C}_1^{-1}\mathcal{C}_2^{-1}$ is called a *commutator*, and will be denoted by $[\mathcal{C}_1, \mathcal{C}_2]$. A group is commutative if and only if each commutator is equal to $\mathcal{I}$, the identity element of the group. The inverse $[\mathcal{C}_1, \mathcal{C}_2]^{-1} = \mathcal{C}_2\mathcal{C}_1\mathcal{C}_2^{-1}\mathcal{C}_1^{-1} = [\mathcal{C}_2, \mathcal{C}_1]$ is also a commutator, and the group generated by taking all possible products of commutators is called the *commutator subgroup* of $\mathcal{F}$ and is denoted by $[\mathcal{F}, \mathcal{F}]$. The commutator subgroup is a normal subgroup of $\mathcal{F}$, for $\mathcal{C}[\mathcal{C}_1, \mathcal{C}_2]\mathcal{C}^{-1} = [\mathcal{C}\mathcal{C}_1\mathcal{C}^{-1}, \mathcal{C}\mathcal{C}_2\mathcal{C}^{-1}]$. We may therefore form the factor group $\mathcal{F}/[\mathcal{F}, \mathcal{F}]$, which turns out to be a commutative group, since every commutator in $\mathcal{F}$ has been identified with the identity element. The group $\mathcal{F}/[\mathcal{F}, \mathcal{F}]$ is called the *abelianized fundamental group*.

Any element of $[\mathcal{F}, \mathcal{F}]$ may be written in the form $\cdots \mathcal{C}^{m_1} \cdots \mathcal{C}^{m_2} \cdots \mathcal{C}^{m_n} \cdots$, where each factor $\mathcal{C}$ occurs with a sum of exponents equal to zero. The converse is also true; for suppose an element $\mathcal{A} \in \mathcal{F}$ has this property and let each $\mathcal{C}^m$ be replaced by $\mathcal{C}\mathcal{C}\mathcal{C} \cdots \mathcal{C}$ written m times. Let ν be the number of factors in $\mathcal{A}$ when each term is written in this expanded form. We then have

$$\mathcal{A} = \mathcal{B}\mathcal{C} \cdots \mathcal{D}^{-1}\mathcal{F} \cdots \mathcal{E},$$

where $\mathcal{B}^{-1}$ does not appear in the sequence $\mathcal{B}\mathcal{C} \cdots \mathcal{D}$. Then

$$\mathcal{A} = \{\mathcal{B}(\mathcal{C} \cdots \mathcal{D})\mathcal{B}^{-1}(\mathcal{C} \cdots \mathcal{D})^{-1}\}(\mathcal{C} \cdots \mathcal{D})(\mathcal{F} \cdots \mathcal{E}).$$

The brace is a commutator and the second term in parentheses is like the original $\mathcal{A}$ except that it contains only $\nu - 2$ terms. Proceeding in this manner, we exhibit $\mathcal{A}$ as a product of commutators.

THEOREM 5-20. $H^1 \cong \mathcal{F}/[\mathcal{F}, \mathcal{F}],$

or, in words, the first homology group is isomorphic to the abelianized fundamental group.

Fix a vertex P_0 in the triangulation Δ, and let $s_i^1 = \langle P_i, P_{i+1}\rangle$, $i = 0, 1, \ldots, n - 1$, be 1-simplexes in Δ with $P_0 = P_n$. The 1-chain

$$\gamma^1 = \sum_{i=0}^{n-1} s_i^1 = \langle P_0, P_1\rangle + \langle P_1, P_2\rangle + \cdots + \langle P_{n-1}, P_0\rangle$$

forms a closed curve on S which begins and ends at P_0; such 1-cycles are called *elementary cycles* on S. *Any 1-cycle c^1 can be written as an integral linear combination of elementary cycles.* Indeed, suppose that $c^1 = \sum_{i=1}^{N} a_i s_i^1$. If $s_1^1 = \langle P_1, P_2\rangle$, the fact that $\partial c^1 = 0$ means P_2 is not in ∂c^1 and there must be a simplex $\langle P_2, P_3\rangle$ present in $c^1 - s_1^1$. Proceeding in this way, we obtain a sequence of simplexes $\langle P_1, P_2 \rangle$, $\langle P_2, P_3 \rangle$, ..., $\langle P_k, P_{k+1} \rangle$, ... present in c^1. Since c^1 contains only a finite number of simplexes, we must return to P_1, and there must be a sequence of the form $\langle P_1, P_2 \rangle$, $\langle P_2, P_3 \rangle$, ..., $\langle P_m, P_1 \rangle$ consisting of simplexes in c^1. Hence

$$\tilde{c}^1 = c^1 - a_1(\langle P_1, P_2 \rangle + \langle P_2, P_3 \rangle + \cdots + \langle P_m, P_1 \rangle)$$

is a cycle which does not contain s_1^1 and contains no simplexes which were not in c^1. We repeat this process on $\tilde{c}^1$ and again reduce the number of simplexes in $\tilde{c}^1$, and so on until we get a 1-cycle containing only one simplex s^1, which must be the 1-cycle $0s^1 = 0$, and we are finished. Now we join P_1 to P_0 by a polygonal path in Δ with successive vertices $Q_0 Q_1 Q_2 \ldots Q_n$, $Q_0 = P_0$ and $Q_n = P_1$. Let $\lambda(P_1) = \langle Q_0, Q_1 \rangle + \langle Q_1, Q_2 \rangle + \cdots + \langle Q_{n-1}, Q_n \rangle$, and rewrite each of the 1-cycles $\langle P_1, P_2 \rangle + \cdots + \langle P_m, P_1 \rangle$ as $\lambda(P_1) + \langle P_1, P_2 \rangle + \cdots + \langle P_m, P_1 \rangle - \lambda(P_1)$, which is an elementary cycle. The original 1-cycle c^1 is an integral linear combination of these.

Each 1-simplex s^1 is the homeomorphic image of the unit interval I by a mapping φ, so that it represents a curve $C = (\varphi, I)$, the parametrization taken so as to agree in direction with the orientation of s^1. If the 1-simplex $\langle P_i, P_{i+1} \rangle$ represents the curve C_i from P_i to P_{i+1}, then the elementary cycle $\gamma^1 = \langle P_0, P_1 \rangle + \cdots + \langle P_{n-1}, P_0 \rangle$ represents a closed curve through P_0 which we shall denote by $\Gamma(\gamma^1) = C_0 C_1 \ldots C_{n-1}$. Furthermore, each 1-cycle c^1 is an integral linear combination of elementary cycles, $c^1 = \sum_{i=1}^m \alpha_i \gamma_i^1$, and represents the closed curve

$$\Gamma(c^1) = \Gamma(\gamma_1^1)^{\alpha_1} \Gamma(\gamma_2^1)^{\alpha_2} \ldots \Gamma(\gamma_m^1)^{\alpha_m}.$$

When we say that a closed curve C is a 1-cycle, we shall mean that $C = \Gamma(c^1)$ for some 1-cycle c^1 in Δ.

LEMMA 5–2 (*Simplicial approximation*). *Any closed curve C through P_0 can be deformed homotopically into a 1-cycle in the triangulation Δ.*

We begin by "chopping" the curve C into small pieces, each of which is "near" some 1-simplex of Δ. For each vertex Q of Δ, let $\text{St}(Q)$ represent the interior of the union of those triangles having Q as a vertex, hence the star about Q. The open sets $\text{St}(Q)$ for all Q form an open covering of S. Assuming that $C = (\varphi, I)$, the sets $\varphi^{-1}[|C| \cap \text{St}(Q)]$ give us an open covering of I. Subdivide I by $0 = t_0 < t_1 < \cdots < t_k = 1$ such that each segment $t_i \leq t \leq t_{i+1}$ lies in one open set of this covering. (We need ask only that $t_{i+1} - t_i < \epsilon/2$, where ϵ is the Lebesgue number of the covering.) Let $\varphi(t_i) = P_i$ and denote by $\widehat{P_i P_{i+1}}$ the arc of C between P_i and P_{i+1}; we have $P_0 = P_k$. As usual, denote $t_i \leq t \leq t_{i+1}$ by I_i.

The arc $\widehat{P_iP_{i+1}}$ lies in some $\operatorname{St}(Q)$. To the point P_i, $i = 0, 1, \ldots, k - 1$, we associate a vertex Q_i such that $\widehat{P_iP_{i+1}}$ lies in $\operatorname{St}(Q_i)$. There may be several possible Q_i satisfying this condition, but once we select one of them, we keep it fixed throughout the discussion. Observe that P_0 is already a vertex of Δ, so the arc $\widehat{P_0P_1}$ must lie completely only in $\operatorname{St}(P_0)$, and $P_0 = Q_0$. Furthermore, the points Q_i, Q_{i+1} either coincide or are ends of a 1-simplex $\overline{Q_iQ_{i+1}}$ in Δ. To see this, we note that the arc $\widehat{P_iP_{i+1}}$ lies in both $\operatorname{St}(Q_i)$ and $\operatorname{St}(Q_{i+1})$, and two stars have a point in common only if they coincide or have the edge $\overline{Q_iQ_{i+1}}$ in common.

We next define the deformation of $\widehat{P_iP_{i+1}}$ into the 1-simplex $\overline{Q_iQ_{i+1}}$. Using normal barycentric coordinates on S in each star $\operatorname{St}(Q)$, we can speak of line segments in the star as the barycentric images of line segments in the euclidean star defining the coordinates, and also points on these segments dividing them in a given ratio. The ratio remains the same if the segment is viewed in a different star, for this merely effects an affine transformation of the euclidean star. Now each arc $\widehat{P_iP_{i+1}}$ and each edge $\overline{Q_iQ_{i+1}}$ lies in the closure of $\operatorname{St}(Q_i)$. Thus we may join each point P of $\widehat{P_iP_{i+1}}$ to any point Q on $\overline{Q_iQ_{i+1}}$ with a line segment in the closure of $\operatorname{St}(Q_i)$. The 1-simplex $\overline{Q_iQ_{i+1}}$ for which $Q_i \neq Q_{i+1}$ is defined by the homeomorphism $\psi_i(t)$ of an interval, say I_i, into S. The homotopic deformation $\Theta_i \colon I_i \times I \to S$ of $\widehat{P_iP_{i+1}}$ into $\overline{Q_iQ_{i+1}}$ is given by

(a) $\qquad \Theta_i(t, 0) = \varphi(t), \qquad t \in I_i,$

(b) $\qquad \Theta_i(t, 1) = \begin{cases} \psi_i(t), & \text{if } Q_i \neq Q_{i+1}, \quad t \in I_i, \\ Q_i, & \text{if } Q_i = Q_{i+1}, \quad t \in I_i, \end{cases}$

(c) $\Theta_i(t, s)$ is the point on the line segment from $\varphi(t)$ to $\Theta_i(t, 1)$ which divides that segment in the ratio s to $1 - s$, $0 \leq s \leq 1$, $t \in I_i$.

It is not difficult to verify the continuity of Θ_i. This deforms each arc $\widehat{P_iP_{i+1}}$ into a 1-simplex in such a way that $\Theta_i(t_{i+1}, s) = \Theta_{i+1}(t_{i+1}, s)$. If we define $\Theta(t, s) = \Theta_i(t, s)$ for $t \in I_i$, $i = 0, 1, \ldots, k - 1$, we obtain a homotopic deformation of C into the curve

$$\widetilde{C} = \overline{Q_0Q_1} \cdot \overline{Q_1Q_2} \ldots \overline{Q_{k-1}Q_0} = \prod_{i=0}^{k-1} \overline{Q_iQ_{i+1}}.$$

Those segments $\overline{Q_iQ_{i+1}}$ in which $Q_i = Q_{i+1}$ are constant curves, so that $\widetilde{C}$ is homotopic to

$$C^* = \prod_{i=0}^{k-1}{}' \ \overline{Q_iQ_{i+1}},$$

in which the prime in the product denotes that each segment for which $Q_i = Q_{i+1}$ is omitted. Then $C^* = \Gamma(\gamma^1)$, where $\gamma^1 = \epsilon_1 \langle Q_0, Q_1 \rangle + \epsilon_2 \langle Q_1, Q_2 \rangle + \cdots + \epsilon_k \langle Q_{k-1}, Q_0 \rangle$, $\epsilon_i = 1$ if $Q_{i-1} \neq Q_i$ and $\epsilon_i = 0$ if $Q_{i-1} = Q_i$. The 1-cycle γ^1 is just an elementary cycle on S_Δ through $P_0(=Q_0)$ and C is homotopic to $\Gamma(\gamma^1)$, as we wished to show.

It should be observed that if the original closed curve C has its carrier on a simplicial 1-cycle c^1 in Δ, then the 1-cycle $\Gamma(\gamma^1)$ to which C is homotopic is composed of simplexes in c^1. Furthermore, if a point $P' = \varphi(t')$ on C lies in a triangle s^2 of Δ, then $\Theta(t', s)$, $0 \leq s \leq 1$, lies in s^2 too. Thus the deformation was made only through simplexes which contain points of C.

To complete the proof that $H^1 \cong \mathfrak{F}/[\mathfrak{F}, \mathfrak{F}]$, we shall need the following relationship between homotopy and homology.

LEMMA 5–3. *A 1-cycle that is homotopic to a point is homologous to zero.*

This merely states the intuitively obvious fact that if a curve can be deformed to one of its points, then the curve forms the boundary of the area over which the deformation is made. That the converse is not true is demonstrated by the curve C on the double torus $(g = 2)$ in Fig. 5–25. Here C is the boundary of the half of the surface on either side, but C cannot be deformed to a point. This is an example of a curve in the commutator subgroup of $\mathfrak{F}$ which is not equal to the identity element, for on the normal form of genus 2 with the symbol $\mathbf{a_1 b_1 a_1^{-1} b_1^{-1} a_2 b_2 a_2^{-1} b_2^{-1}}$, the curve C is homotopic to $\mathbf{a_1 b_1 a_1^{-1} b_1^{-1}}$ (see Fig. 5–26). We shall now prove the above statement.

We have seen that the 1-cycle c^1 determines a curve $\Gamma(c^1)$ through P_0. Let $\Gamma(c^1) = (\varphi, I)$, with $\varphi(0) = \varphi(1) = P_0$. Since $\Gamma(c^1)$ is homotopic to a point, there is a continuous mapping Φ of $I \times I$ into S such that $\Phi(t, 0) = \varphi(t)$, $\Phi(t, 1) = P_0$. If we map $I \times I$ into the circle $D \colon |z| < 1$ by the mapping $z = (1 - s)e^{2\pi i t}$, we note that the edge $s = 0$ goes into

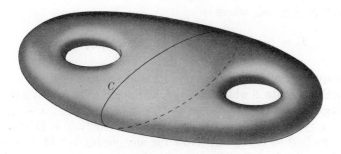

FIGURE 5–25.

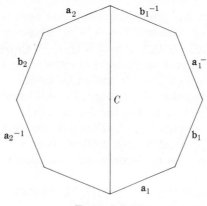

FIGURE 5–26.

$|z| = 1$ and $s = 1$ maps into the point $z = 0$. We can define a continuous mapping ψ of D into S by setting

$$\psi(z) = \psi[(1 - s)e^{2\pi i t}] = \Phi(t, s).$$

The vertices of the simplexes in c^1 give us a finite subdivision

$$0 = \theta_0 < \theta_1 < \cdots < \theta_{n-1} < \theta_n = 2\pi$$

of the circumference of $|z| = |re^{i\theta}| = 1$. We obtain a triangulation of the disk D by drawing the radial lines from $z = 0$ to $z = e^{i\theta_k}$, where $k = 0, 1, 2, \ldots, n - 1$. We introduce normal barycentric coordinates in this triangulation of D and barycentrically subdivide the triangulation enough times so that each closed star of triangles in the subdivision Λ maps into a set of S contained entirely within some open set $\text{St}(Q)$ in the star covering of S. This barycentric subdivision has introduced some new vertices on $|z| = 1$ between each pair $e^{i\theta_k}$ and $e^{i\theta_{k+1}}$. Let these be denoted by $e^{i\theta_{k,i}}, 0 \le j \le m_k$, where

$$\theta_k = \theta_{k,0} < \theta_{k,1} < \theta_{k,2} < \cdots < \theta_{k,m_k} = \theta_{k+1}.$$

The mapping ψ of D into S can now be modified to give a new continuous mapping Θ of D into S which maps each triangle σ^2 of Λ into a triangle s^2 of Δ. Begin by setting $\Theta(e^{i\theta_k}) = \psi(e^{i\theta_k})$, $k = 0, 1, \ldots, n - 1$. If $\theta_{k,j}$ satisfies $\theta_k \le \theta_{k,j} \le (\theta_k + \theta_{k+1})/2$, we set $\Theta(e^{i\theta_{k,i}}) = \Theta(e^{i\theta_k})$; otherwise set $\Theta(e^{i\theta_{k,i}}) = \Theta(e^{i\theta_{k+1}})$. Now for any vertex $re^{i\theta}$ of Λ, $r < 1$, we set $\Theta(re^{i\theta}) = Q$, where Q is the vertex at the center of the star $\text{St}(Q)$ which contains the image of the closed star about $re^{i\theta}$. This determination may not be unique, but once a determination is made we use it throughout the discussion. The mapping Θ is extended to any point $z = re^{i\theta}$, $r \le 1$, by noting that z lies in a triangle of Λ having vertices q_1, q_2, q_3. We set $\Theta(z) = P$, where P is that point of S in the triangle $\Theta(q_1)$, $\Theta(q_2)$, $\Theta(q_3)$ which has the same normal barycentric coordinates as does z in q_1, q_2, q_3. This defines a continuous mapping Θ of D into S, since the normal barycentric coordinates agree on common edges of triangles. (Note that some of the vertices $\Theta(q_1)$, $\Theta(q_2)$, $\Theta(q_3)$ may coincide to give a degenerate triangle on S.) The mapping Θ takes each triangle of Λ into a triangle (possibly degenerate) of Δ with edges going into edges. The image of each arc $e^{i\theta}$, $\theta_k \le \theta \le \theta_{k+1}$, covers the corresponding 1-simplex $\psi(e^{i\theta})$, $\theta_k \le \theta \le \theta_{k+1}$ just once.

The counterclockwise orientation of the circumference of D assigns a coherent orientation in each triangle q_1, q_2, q_3 of Λ. We may form the 2-simplex $\langle q_1, q_2, q_3 \rangle$ having the assigned orientation and also the 2-chain $\gamma^2 = \Sigma \langle q_1, q_2, q_3 \rangle$, in which each 2-simplex in Λ is counted once with coefficient $+1$ corresponding to the assigned orientation. Each edge σ^1 of a 2-simplex $\langle q_1, q_2, q_3 \rangle$ lying interior to D appears with opposite orientations in each of the two 2-simplexes meeting in σ^1, so that

$$\partial\gamma^2 = \sum_{k=0}^{n-1} \sum_{j=0}^{m_k-1} \langle e^{i\theta_k, i}, e^{i\theta_k, i+1} \rangle.$$

The orientation of $\langle q_1, q_2, q_3 \rangle$ induces an orientation $\langle Q_1, Q_2, Q_3 \rangle$ in the image simplex on S. We may then form the formal 2-chain $c^2 = \Sigma \langle Q_1, Q_2, Q_3 \rangle$ in which each simplex $\langle Q_1, Q_2, Q_3 \rangle$ is counted, as was the corresponding $\langle q_1, q_2, q_3 \rangle$ in γ^2. Then formally computing the boundary of c^2 by the usual rule $\partial\langle Q_1, Q_2, Q_3 \rangle = \langle Q_1, Q_2 \rangle - \langle Q_1, Q_3 \rangle + \langle Q_2, Q_3 \rangle$, we see that

$$\partial c^2 = \sum_{k=0}^{n-1} \sum_{j=0}^{m_k-1} \langle \Theta(e^{i\theta_k, i}), \Theta(e^{i\theta_k, i+1}) \rangle. \tag{1}$$

Unfortunately, neither c^2 nor the expression on the right side of (1) is a chain in Δ, for certain of the simplexes $\langle Q_1, Q_2, Q_3 \rangle$ or $\langle \Theta(e^{i\theta_k, i}), \Theta(e^{i\theta_k, i+1}) \rangle$ have two or more vertices equal (and are designated as degenerate). We begin by identifying with zero any 1-simplex $\langle P, P \rangle$ in which two vertices coincide. Then the boundary of any degenerate 2-simplex is zero, for if two vertices are equal, say $Q_1 = Q_2$, then

$$\partial\langle Q_1, Q_1, Q_3 \rangle = \langle Q_1, Q_1 \rangle - \langle Q_1, Q_3 \rangle + \langle Q_1, Q_3 \rangle = 0,$$

and if $Q_1 = Q_2 = Q_3$, then

$$\partial\langle Q_1, Q_1, Q_1\rangle = \langle Q_1, Q_1\rangle - \langle Q_1, Q_1\rangle + \langle Q_1, Q_1\rangle = 0.$$

Since a degenerate 2-simplex does not contribute to the boundary of a chain containing it, we shall also identify with zero all degenerate 2-simplexes. After this identification, c^2 becomes a 2-chain $\tilde{c}^2$ in Δ and $\tilde{c}^2$ has as its boundary the same nondegenerate 1-simplexes as does c^2. Under this identification, each 1-chain $\sum_{j=0}^{m_k-1}\langle \Theta(e^{i\theta_k}, i), \Theta(e^{i\theta_k}, i)\rangle$ becomes $\langle \Theta(e^{i\theta_k}), \Theta(e^{i\theta_k}+1)\rangle$ and

$$\sum_{k=0}^{n-1} \langle \Theta(e^{i\theta_k}), \Theta(e^{i\theta_k}+1)\rangle = c^1.$$

Thus $c^1 = \partial\tilde{c}^2$ and we have proved that $\Gamma(c^1) \approx 1$ implies $c^1 \sim 0$.

We are now in a position to prove $H^1 \cong \mathfrak{F}/[\mathfrak{F}, \mathfrak{F}]$. We define a homomorphism of $\mathfrak{F}$ into H^1 as follows. For any closed curve C_1 through P_0, we set $h(C_1)$ equal to a 1-cycle in Δ which is homotopic to C_1. For the curves C_1^{-1} and C_1C_2, we set

$$h(C_1^{-1}) = -h(C_1) \quad \text{and} \quad h(C_1C_2) = h(C_1) + h(C_2).$$

If $C_1 \approx C_2$, then $C_1C_2^{-1} \approx 1$ and $h(C_1C_2^{-1}) \sim 0$ or $h(C_1) \sim h(C_2)$. Thus h defines a homomorphism $\tilde{h}$ of $\mathfrak{F}(P_0)$ into H^1. This homomorphism is *onto*, since any 1-cycle c^1 is an integral linear combination of elementary cycles, say $c^1 = \sum_{i=1}^n a_i\gamma_i^1$, so that $\Gamma_i = \Gamma(\gamma_i^1)$ is a curve through P_0, and $h(\Gamma_i) \sim \gamma_i^1$. Hence $h(\prod_{i=1}^n \Gamma_i^{a_i}) = \sum_{i=1}^n a_ih(\Gamma_i) \sim \sum_{i=1}^n a_i\gamma_i^1 = c^1$, and the onto property of h is established.

To complete the proof, we must show that the kernel of $\tilde{h}$ is precisely $[\mathfrak{F}, \mathfrak{F}]$. Since H^1 is commutative, $[\mathfrak{F}, \mathfrak{F}]$ is contained in the kernel of $\tilde{h}$. Therefore we must demonstrate that if $h(C) \sim 0$, then C determines an element of $[\mathfrak{F}, \mathfrak{F}]$. Again since C is homotopic to a 1-cycle, we may assume that $C = \Gamma(c^1)$ and that $h(C) = c^1$. Let us associate with each $s^2 = \langle Q_0, Q_1, Q_2\rangle$ the path

$$\Lambda(\partial s^2) = \Lambda(Q_0) \cdot \overline{Q_0Q_1} \cdot \overline{Q_1Q_2} \cdot \overline{Q_2Q_0} \cdot \Lambda^{-1}(Q_0),$$

where $\Lambda(Q_0)$ is the polygonal path in Δ joining P_0 to Q_0. Furthermore, to any 1-simplex $s' = \langle Q_0, Q_1\rangle$, we associate the path

$$\Lambda(s') = \Lambda(Q_0) \cdot \overline{Q_0Q_1} \cdot \Lambda^{-1}(Q_1).$$

Then let $\lambda(Q_i)$ be the 1-chain whose simplexes compose $\Lambda(Q_i)$. We have

$$h(\Lambda(\partial s^2)) = \lambda(Q_0) + \partial s^2 - \lambda(Q_0) = \partial s^2 \qquad (2)$$

The path $\overline{Q_0Q_1} \cdot \overline{Q_1Q_2} \cdot \overline{Q_2Q_0}$ is homotopic to a point, which means that $\Lambda(\partial s^2)$ is also homotopic to a point and represents the identity element of $\mathfrak{F}$.

Now for any $C = \Gamma(c') = \overline{P_0P_1} \cdot \overline{P_1P_2} \ldots \overline{P_{n-1}P_n}$, $P_n = P_0$, we may write

$$C = \Lambda(P_0) \cdot \overline{P_0P_1} \cdot \Lambda^{-1}(P_1) \cdot \Lambda(P_1) \cdot \overline{P_1P_2} \cdot \Lambda^{-1}(P_2) \cdots$$

$$\cdots \Lambda(P_{n-1}) \cdot \overline{P_{n-1}P_n} \cdot \Lambda^{-1}(P_0),$$

where $\Lambda(P_0) = \overline{P_0P_0}$.

$$C = \Lambda(\overline{P_0P_1}) \cdot \Lambda(\overline{P_1P_2}) \cdots \Lambda(\overline{P_{n-1}, P_n}). \qquad (3)$$

For each $\overline{P_iP_{i+1}}$ we have

$$h(\Lambda(\overline{P_iP_{i+1}})) = \lambda(P_i) + \langle P_i, P_{i+1} \rangle - \lambda(P_{i+1})$$

$$= \langle P_i, P_{i+1} \rangle - \lambda(\partial \langle P_i, P_{i+1} \rangle).$$

Therefore, $h(C) = \sum_{i=0}^{n-1} \langle P_i, P_{i+1} \rangle - \lambda(\partial \sum_{i=0}^{n-1} \langle P_iP_{i+1} \rangle)$, and since $\sum_{i=0}^{n-1} \langle P_i, P_{i+1} \rangle$ is a cycle, its boundary is zero and the last term vanishes. Thus if we write $h(C) = \sum_{n=1}^{N} a_n s_n^1$, a_n tells us the sum of the exponents of $\Lambda(s_n^1)$ in the representation (3) of C.

Now we assume that $h(C) \sim 0$, which implies that

$$h(C) = \partial \sum_{n=1}^{N} b_n s_n^2 = \sum_{n=1}^{N} b_n \partial s_n^2.$$

Let us define the curve $A = \prod_{n=1}^{N} [\Lambda(\partial s_n^2)]^{b_n}$. According to (2),

$$h(A) = h\left(\prod_{n=1}^{N} [\Lambda(\partial s_n^2)]^{b_n} \right) = \sum_{n=1}^{N} b_n h(\Lambda(\partial s_n^2))$$

$$= \sum_{n=1}^{N} b_n \partial s_n^2 = h(C),$$

and $h(CA^{-1}) = h(C) - h(A) = 0$. Thus CA^{-1} is a product of closed curves $\Lambda(s_n^1)$ in which each appears with a sum of exponents equal to zero. But this is just the criterion for CA^{-1} to determine an element of the commutator subgroup of $\mathfrak{F}$. Since each $\Lambda(\partial s_n^2) \approx 1$, we have $A \approx 1$ and $CA^{-1} \approx C$, so that C also determines an element of $[\mathfrak{F}, \mathfrak{F}]$. This completes the proof that $H^1 \cong \mathfrak{F}/[\mathfrak{F}, \mathfrak{F}]$ and proves the invariance of H^1.

The insight given us by the preceding theorem allows us to define a homology group of cycles composed of arbitrary closed curves rather than simplicial 1-cycles on S. Therefore, the homology classes of curves can be defined in an arbitrary 2-dimensional manifold in which there is no triangulation. We shall make use of this fact in subsequent chapters when we use homology on Riemann surfaces which will only be proved triangulable in Chapter 9.

A 1-cycle c is now a finite integral linear combination of closed curves c_i, say $c = \sum_{i=1}^{N} a_i c_i$. Here we shall no longer require that each c_i pass through P_0. On each c_i, we select a point Q_i and consider c_i as starting and ending at Q_i. Let j_i represent an arc joining P_0 to Q_i. Then $j_i c_i j_i^{-1} = C_i$ is a closed curve through P_0 and represents an element of $\mathfrak{F}(P_0)$. We say that $c = \sum_{i=1}^{N} a_i c_i$ is homologous to zero and write $c \sim 0$ if and only if $\prod_{i=1}^{N} C_i^{a_i}$ represents an element in $[\mathfrak{F}, \mathfrak{F}]$, the commutator subgroup of $\mathfrak{F}(P_0)$.

We must now show that this definition depends only upon c and not upon the points Q_i and paths j_i selected. Indeed, if a different path j_i' had been used to join P_0 to Q_i, the curve $J_i = j_i' j_i^{-1}$ is a closed curve through P_0. Then $C_j' = j_i' c_i j_i^{-1} = (j_i' j_i^{-1})(j_i c_i j_i^{-1})(j_i j_i^{-1}) = J_i C_i J_i^{-1}$. If $\prod_{i=1}^{N} C_i^{a_i} \in [\mathfrak{F}, \mathfrak{F}]$, then $\prod_{i=1}^{N} C_i'^{a_i} = \prod_{i=1}^{N} (J_i C_i J_i^{-1})^{a_i} \in [\mathfrak{F}, \mathfrak{F}]$ follows from the observation that each J_i appears with sum of exponents equal to zero. Thus $c \sim 0$ does not depend upon the choice of the j_i's. Next select another point Q_i' on c_i and let c_i' represent the same curve c_i but reparametrized to start and end at Q_i'. Let l_i represent the arc of c_i from Q_i to Q_i' and use as the arc from P_0 to Q_i' the arc $j_i l_i$. Then $C_i = j_i c_i j_i^{-1}$, while $C_i' = j_i l_i c_i' l_i^{-1} j_i^{-1}$. We note that $l_i c_i' l_i^{-1}$ is the same curve as $c_i l_i l_i^{-1}$ and that $l_i l_i^{-1} \approx 1$, so $l_i c_i' l_i^{-1} \approx c_i$ and $C_i' \approx C_i$. Thus $\prod_{i=1}^{N} C_i^{a_i}$ and $\prod_{i=1}^{N} C_i'^{a_i}$ represent the same element of $\mathfrak{F}(P_0)$, and if the first is in $[\mathfrak{F}, \mathfrak{F}]$ so is the second.

If c_1 and c_2 are two 1-cycles, we say that c_1 is homologous to c_2 and write $c_1 \sim c_2$ if $c_1 - c_2 \sim 0$. From the definition, $c_1 + c_2 \sim c_2 + c_1$, or $c_1 + c_2 - c_1 - c_2 \sim 0$, since the associated curve $C_1 C_2 C_1^{-1} C_2^{-1}$ represents an element of $[\mathfrak{F}, \mathfrak{F}]$. We denote the additive group of 1-cycles by $\mathfrak{z}^1$. If $c_1 \sim 0$ and $c_2 \sim 0$, then $c_1 - c_2 \sim 0$ and the 1-cycles homologous to zero form a subgroup $\mathfrak{B}^1$ of $\mathfrak{z}^1$. We define $\mathfrak{K}^1 = \mathfrak{z}^1/\mathfrak{B}^1$ and call $\mathfrak{K}^1$ the *first homology group* of S. Since each element of $\mathfrak{z}^1$ defines an element of $\mathfrak{F}(P_0)$, while each closed curve through P_0 is itself a member of $\mathfrak{z}^1$, and since we have identified with zero those cycles in $\mathfrak{B}^1$ which correspond precisely to the curves in $[\mathfrak{F}, \mathfrak{F}]$, we see that $\mathfrak{IC}^1 \cong \mathfrak{F}/[\mathfrak{F}, \mathfrak{F}]$. On a triangulated surface, we then have $\mathfrak{IC}^1 \cong H^1$. Furthermore, each 1-cycle in $\mathfrak{z}^1$ can be deformed homotopically into a simplicial 1-cycle and is hence homologous to a simplicial 1-cycle. Finally, a simplicial 1-cycle is homologous to zero in this new sense if and only if it is simplicially homologous to zero. Thus we have a valid extension of the simplicial homology group to homology using arbitrary closed curves.

To complete the analogy between the homology groups using simplicial cycles and those using closed curves, we shall denote by $\sigma^1 = (\alpha, I)$ a curve (not necessarily closed) on S, and call it a *singular 1-simplex*. Points P on S will be called singular 0-simplexes and will be denoted by $\langle P \rangle$. An integral linear combination of singular 0-simplexes, $\sum_{n=1}^{N} a_n \langle P_n \rangle$, where the a_n are integers, is called a *singular 0-chain*. If $\sigma^1 = (\alpha, I)$ and $\alpha(0) = P$, $\alpha(1) = Q$, then we define $\partial \sigma^1 = \langle Q \rangle - \langle P \rangle$ as the *boundary* of σ^1. A *singular 1-chain* γ^1 is an integral linear combination of singular 1-simplexes, $\gamma^1 = \sum_{n=1}^{N} a_n \sigma_n^1$, and we define $\partial \gamma^1 = \sum_{n=1}^{N} a_n \partial \sigma_n^1$. Defining addition of 1-chains as before, we get a group of singular 1-chains, in which the singular 1-cycles are those singular chains γ^1 with $\partial \gamma^1 = 0$. As in the case of simplicial 1-cycles, each singular 1-cycle may be written as an integral linear combination of closed curves through a certain point on S, and we say that γ^1 is homologous to zero if γ^1 represents a curve in $[\mathfrak{F}, \mathfrak{F}]$, and γ_1^1 is homologous to $\gamma_2^1 (\gamma_1^1 \sim \gamma_2^1)$ if $\gamma_1^1 - \gamma_2^1 \sim 0$. The group of homology classes of singular 1-cycles is precisely the group $\mathfrak{IC}^1$.

5–9 Homology on compact surfaces. The only homology groups so far computed are H^0 and H^2. We have seen that for compact surfaces $b_0 = 1$ and $b_2 = 1$. Since the homology groups are topological invariants, to compute H^1 we need consider only the normal forms (polygons with edges identified) with a conveniently selected triangulation.

The normal form of a compact surface of genus $g \geq 1$ is a $4g$-sided polygon Π with the symbol $\mathbf{a}_1 \mathbf{b}_1 \mathbf{a}_1^{-1} \mathbf{b}_1^{-1} \mathbf{a}_2 \mathbf{b}_2 \mathbf{a}_2^{-1} \mathbf{b}_2^{-1} \ldots \mathbf{a}_g \mathbf{b}_g \mathbf{a}_g^{-1} \mathbf{b}_g^{-1}$. The triangulation Δ that we shall use is indicated in Fig. 5–27. This triangulation has the property that no two simplexes have the same set of vertices, so that the vertices completely specify each simplex. Each edge $\mathbf{a}_i$ and $\mathbf{b}_i$ is a simplicial 1-cycle (from P_0 to P_0), and we shall prove that the $2g$ 1-cycles $\mathbf{a}_1, \mathbf{b}_1, \ldots, \mathbf{a}_g, \mathbf{b}_g$ form a homology basis for the homology group H^1.

We shall begin by proving that the closed curves $\mathbf{a}_1, \mathbf{b}_1, \mathbf{a}_2, \mathbf{b}_2, \ldots, \mathbf{a}_g, \mathbf{b}_g$ generate the fundamental group. Let C be an arbitrary closed curve on S. By the simplicial-approximation theorem (Lemma 5–2), C is homotopic to a simplicial 1-cycle γ in Δ. Select arbitrarily some interior point Q of a triangle in Δ. Let $\gamma = (\alpha, I)$, where α maps I into the normal polygon Π.

For values of $t \in I$ for which γ meets $\mathbf{a}_i$ or $\mathbf{b}_i$, $\alpha(t)$ is not well defined, since two points on the boundary of Π correspond to each point on $\mathbf{a}_i$ or $\mathbf{b}_i$ on S, the compact surface of genus g obtained when equivalent edges of Π are identified. For convenience, we shall make an arbitrary choice of one of the two points to be $\alpha(t)$. The ray from Q to $\alpha(t)$ intersects the boundary of Π at a point we denote by $\beta(t)$. Let $\Theta(t, s)$ be the point on the segment from $\alpha(t)$ to $\beta(t)$ which divides it in the ratio s to $1 - s$, $0 \leq s \leq 1$; that is,

$$\Theta(t, s) = (1 - s)\alpha(t) + s\beta(t).$$

For points $\alpha(t)$ on the boundary of Π, $\Theta(t, s) = \alpha(t)$ for all s, so that Θ is a homotopic deformation of γ into a closed curve C' on S which lies entirely on the $\mathbf{a}_i$ and $\mathbf{b}_i$, $i = 1, 2, \ldots, g$. We now apply the simplicial-approximation theorem (Lemma 5–2) once again to C' to get that C' is homotopic to a simplicial 1-cycle γ' composed of 1-simplexes in Δ which lie along the 1-cycles $\mathbf{a}_i$ and $\mathbf{b}_i$, $i = 1, 2, \ldots, g$.

The 1-cycle γ' is therefore given by (see Fig. 5–27)

$$\gamma' = \sum_{i=1}^{g} [\mu_1^{(i)}\langle P_0, Q_{i,1}\rangle + \mu_2^{(i)}\langle Q_{i,1}, Q_{i,2}\rangle + \mu_3^{(i)}\langle Q_{i,2}, P_0\rangle + \mu_4^{(i)}\langle P_0, Q_{i,3}\rangle$$
$$+ \mu_5^{(i)}\langle Q_{i,3}, Q_{i,4}\rangle + \mu_6^{(i)}\langle Q_{i,4}, P_0\rangle],$$

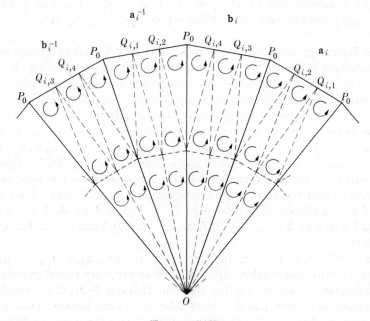

FIGURE 5–27.

where the $\mu_j^{(i)}$'s are integers and

$$\partial\gamma' = \sum_{i=1}^{g} (\mu_1^{(i)} - \mu_2^{(i)})\langle Q_{i,1}\rangle + (\mu_2^{(i)} - \mu_3^{(i)})\langle Q_{i,2}\rangle + (\mu_4^{(i)} - \mu_5^{(i)})\langle Q_{i,3}\rangle$$
$$+ (\mu_5^{(i)} - \mu_6^{(i)})\langle Q_{i,4}\rangle + (\mu_6^{(i)} - \mu_4^{(i)})$$
$$+ \mu_3^{(i)} - \mu_1^{(i)})\langle P_0\rangle.$$

Since $\partial\gamma' = 0$, $\mu_1^{(i)} = \mu_2^{(i)} = \mu_3^{(i)}$ and $\mu_4^{(i)} = \mu_5^{(i)} = \mu_6^{(i)}$, and since

$$\mathbf{a}_i = \langle P_0, Q_{i,1}\rangle + \langle Q_{i,1}, Q_{i,2}\rangle + \langle Q_{i,2}, P_0\rangle$$

and

$$\mathbf{b}_i = \langle P_0, Q_{i,3}\rangle + \langle Q_{i,3}, Q_{i,4}\rangle + \langle Q_{i,4}, P_0\rangle,$$

we have

$$\gamma' = \sum_{i=1}^{g} \mu_1^{(i)}\mathbf{a}_i + \mu_4^{(i)}\mathbf{b}_i.$$

Since $C \approx \gamma'$, we have that C is homotopic to an integral linear combination of the $\mathbf{a}_i$ and $\mathbf{b}_i$, and hence the $\mathbf{a}_i$ and $\mathbf{b}_i$ generate the fundamental group.

Since $\mathbf{a}_1 \mathbf{b}_1 \mathbf{a}_1^{-1} \mathbf{b}_1^{-1} \mathbf{a}_2 \mathbf{b}_2 \mathbf{a}_2^{-1} \mathbf{b}_2^{-1} \ldots \mathbf{a}_g \mathbf{b}_g \mathbf{a}_g^{-1} \mathbf{b}_g^{-1}$ forms the boundary of the simply connected polygon Π, we see that these $2g$ generators satisfy the homotopy relation

$$\mathbf{a}_1 \mathbf{b}_1 \mathbf{a}_1^{-1} \mathbf{b}_1^{-1} \ldots \mathbf{a}_g \mathbf{b}_g \mathbf{a}_g^{-1} \mathbf{b}_g^{-1} \approx 1.$$

It can also be shown that this homotopy relation and the trivial relations $\mathbf{a}_i \mathbf{a}_i^{-1} \approx 1$ and $\mathbf{b}_i \mathbf{b}_i^{-1} \approx 1$ generate all relations of the fundamental group. Since we shall not need this result, we shall not present the proof here.

Since the homology group H^1 is the abelianized fundamental group, the $\mathbf{a}_i$, $\mathbf{b}_i$, $i = 1, 2, \ldots, g$, generate the homology group too. We must show that they are homologously linearly independent. Suppose that $\sum_{i=1}^{g} \lambda_i\mathbf{a}_i + \mu_i\mathbf{b}_i \sim 0$, so that $\sum_{i=1}^{g} \lambda_i\mathbf{a}_i + \mu_i\mathbf{b}_i = \partial\sigma^2$, where $\sigma^2 = \sum_{i=1}^{N} \nu_i s_i^2$ and the s_i^2 are 2-simplexes in Δ. If the triangle s_1^2 appears in σ^2 with coefficient ν_1, then the triangles in Δ having an edge interior to Π in common with s_1^2 must also appear with coefficient ν_1, for their common edge does not appear in $\partial\sigma^2$. Since any triangle in Δ can be joined to s_1^2 with a chain of triangles each adjacent pair of which meet along an edge interior to Π, we see that σ^2 contains each triangle in Δ exactly once with the same coefficient, say ν. Then

$$\sigma^2 = \nu \sum_{i=1}^{N} s_i^2,$$

where s_i^2, $i = 1, 2, \ldots, N$, represents each triangle in Δ once and

$$\partial\sigma^2 = \nu \sum_{i=1}^{g} \mathbf{a}_i + \mathbf{b}_i - \mathbf{a}_i - \mathbf{b}_i = 0.$$

Therefore, $\sum_{i=1}^{g} \lambda_i \mathbf{a}_i + \mu_i \mathbf{b}_i = 0$ and $\lambda_i = \mu_i = 0$, $i = 1, 2, \ldots, g$. This proves that the $\mathbf{a}_i$ and $\mathbf{b}_i$ are linearly independent and form a homology basis when $g \geq 1$, making the first Betti number $b_1 = 2g$.

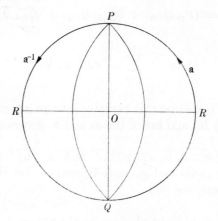

FIGURE 5–28.

In the case $g = 0$, the normal polygon has two edges, $\mathbf{a}$ and $\mathbf{a}^{-1}$. A triangulation is given in Fig. 5–28. As before, any closed curve C can be deformed homotopically into a linear combination of the outer edges of Π, which now are $\mathbf{a}$ and $\mathbf{a}^{-1}$. Thus $C \approx \mu\mathbf{a} + \nu\mathbf{a}^{-1} = (\mu - \nu)\mathbf{a}$. In order for $(\mu - \nu)\mathbf{a}$ to be a cycle, $\partial(\mu - \nu)\mathbf{a} = (\mu - \nu)[\langle P \rangle - \langle Q \rangle] = 0$ and we conclude that $\mu = \nu$ or $C \approx 0$. Thus for the case $g = 0$, $b_1 = 0$; so we may say, in general, that for a compact orientable surface of genus $g \geq 0$, $b_1 = 2g$.

The fact that $b_1 = 2g$ for any compact surface tells us that two compact orientable surfaces are topologically equivalent if and only if they have the same genus; for the Betti numbers are topological invariants and two normal polygons of different genus could not be homeomorphic.

Let Δ be an arbitrary triangulation of an orientable compact surface S. Let a_n represent the number of n-simplexes in Δ. The sum

$$\sum_{n=0}^{2} (-1)^n a_n = \chi$$

is called the *Euler characteristic* of S_Δ. We now prove that χ is a topological invariant and $\chi = 2 - 2g$ on a surface of genus g.

The a_n n-simplexes form a basis for the group of n-chains $C^n(S_\Delta)$. Since Z^n, the group of n-cycles, is a subgroup of C^n, we can select a basis $z_1^{(n)}$, $z_2^{(n)}, \ldots, z_{k_n}^{(n)}$ of n-cycles which may be extended to form a basis $z_1^n, z_2^n, \ldots,$ $z_{a_n}^n$ for C^n. Furthermore, $B^{n-1} \cong C^n/Z^n$, so that B^{n-1} is isomorphic to the subgroup of C^n generated by $z_{k_n+1}^n, \ldots, z_{a_n}^n$. Therefore B^{n-1} is generated by a basis containing $r_{n-1} = a_n - k_n$ elements. Since $C^0 = Z^0$, we have $r_{-1} = 0$. Furthermore, $H^n = Z^n/B^n$, and H^n has a basis of b_n elements, $b_n = k_n - r_n$. Therefore $a_n = b_n + r_{n-1} + r_n$, and

$$\chi = \sum_{n=0}^{2} (-1)^n a_n = \sum_{n=0}^{2} (-1)^n b_n + r_2.$$

The fact that $B^2 = 0$ means that there are no nonzero 2-boundaries, $r_2 = 0$, and

$$\chi = \sum_{n=0}^{2} (-1)^n b_n$$

which is the Euler-Poincaré formula, proving that χ is a topological invariant. On a compact orientable surface of genus g, $b_0 = 1$, $b_1 = 2g$, $b_2 = 1$, and

$$\chi = 2 - 2g.$$

On a compact orientable surface of genus g, let Δ be an arbitrary triangulation. A 1-cycle is called *simple* if it is of the form

$$\langle P_0, P_1 \rangle + \langle P_1, P_2 \rangle + \cdots + \langle P_{n-1}, P_0 \rangle,$$

where $P_i \neq P_j$ if $i \neq j$. A finite number of 1-cycles $\gamma_1, \gamma_2, \ldots, \gamma_m$, no two of which have a 1-simplex in common, forms a chain C and we say that C *divides* S if the set $S - C$ is not connected. In the normal form of S, it is clear that the homology basis $\mathbf{a}_1, \mathbf{b}_1, \mathbf{a}_2, \mathbf{b}_2, \ldots, \mathbf{a}_g, \mathbf{b}_g$ forms a system of simple 1-cycles which do not divide S; for the interior of the polygon is connected. Thus on a surface of genus g, we can find a system of at least $2g$ nondividing simple 1-cycles in a suitable triangulation.

We shall prove that on a surface of genus g, any system of more than $2g$ simple 1-cycles divides S. Let $z_1, z_2, \ldots, z_r, r > 2g$, be such a system.

We must show that $S - C$, where $C = |z_1| \cup |z_2| \cup \cdots \cup |z_r|$, is not connected. Since $b_1 = 2g$, we know that $z_1, z_2, \ldots, z_r$ are homologously dependent. Thus there is a 2-chain c^2 such that

$$k_1 z_1 + k_2 z_2 + \cdots + k_r z_r = \partial c^2, \quad \text{with} \quad \sum_{i=1}^{r} k_i^2 > 0.$$

Since no two z_i and z_j have a 1-simplex in common, $\partial c^2 \neq 0$. Thus $|c^2|$ cannot be empty. If $|c^2|$ is the whole of S, let $\bar{c}^2$ be the 2-chain that has the value 1 on each coherently oriented 2-simplex in Δ. If $c^2 = \sum_{i=1}^{N} \lambda_i s_i^2$, the 2-chain $\gamma^2 = c^2 - \lambda_1 \bar{c}^2 = \sum_{i=2}^{N} \mu_i s_i^2$ does not contain s_1^2. Since $\partial \bar{c}^2 = 0$, we have

$$k_1 z_1 + k_2 z_2 + \cdots + k_r z_r = \partial \gamma^2.$$

so that γ^2 is neither empty nor all of S.

Let $G_1 = |\gamma^2| - |\partial \gamma^2|$ and $G_2 = S - |\gamma^2|$. Then $G_1 \cup G_2 = S - |\partial \gamma^2|$; G_1 and G_2 are open sets and $G_1 \cap G_2 = 0$. Since $|\partial \gamma^2| \subset C$, $S - C$ is not connected and the system of r simple 1-cycles $z_1, z_2, \ldots, z_r$ divides S. We have thus proved that *on a surface of genus g, the maximum number of cycles in a system of nondividing simple 1-cycles is $2g$.*

PROBLEMS

1. Show that in a closed chain of triangles which cannot be coherently oriented, there is a closed curve which is not two-sided.

2. Compute the homology groups of the annulus of Fig. 5–24.

3. Compute the homology groups of the projective plane in Fig. 5–6.

4. We may define a compact surface with boundary (denoted by S) as a compact surface of genus g from which a finite number of disjoint disks $D_1, D_2, \ldots, D_r, r > 0$, have been removed. ($D_i$ is the interior of the topological image of $|z| \leq 1$.) If the boundary of D_i is r_i, each point P_0 of r_i has a neighborhood (relative to S) which is homeomorphic to a semicircle $x^2 + y^2 < 1$, $y \geq 0$, with P_0 corresponding to $(0, 0)$ and a segment of r_i corresponding to $y = 0$, $-1 < x < 1$. Prove that S has as normal form a polygon with the symbol

$$q_1 r_1 q_1^{-1} \cdots q_r r_r q_r^{-1} a_1 b_1 a_1^{-1} b_1^{-1} \cdots a_g b_g a_g^{-1} b_g^{-1},$$

where the q_i are cuts made from the point P (common to all a_i and b_i) to each r_i. We say that S has genus g and r boundary curves.

5. If S is a compact surface with boundary, we construct a new surface $\tilde{S}$ called the *double* of S by taking a homeomorphic replica S' of S and identifying the points on the boundaries that correspond under the homeomorphism. Show that when S has genus g and r boundary curves, then $\tilde{S}$ is a compact surface of genus $2g + r - 1$.

CHAPTER 6

DIFFERENTIALS AND INTEGRALS

6–1 Second-order differentials and surface integrals. We have already seen how the locally euclidean structure of a Riemann surface enables us to carry over to the surface several of the notions of analysis in the plane. We shall now consider how this is to be done for integration.

Let $f = f_1 + if_2$ be a complex-valued continuous function on the Riemann surface S. Assume that G is a region lying within one parametric disk D in which $\Phi(P) = (x, y)$ is a local parameter. We may be tempted to say that the integral of f over G is

$$\iint_G f = \iint_{\Phi(G)} g(x, y) \, dx \, dy, \tag{1}$$

where $g(x, y) = f[\Phi^{-1}(x, y)]$ and the integral on the right side is the double integral of the continuous function g over a region in the plane.† But since the coordinate system $\Phi(P)$ was arbitrarily selected from many, we may by chance have taken $\Psi(P) = (u, v)$ as our local parameter in a disk containing G. Then we would have said

$$\iint_G f = \iint_{\Psi(G)} h(u, v) \, du \, dv, \tag{2}$$

where $h(u, v) = f[\Psi^{-1}(u, v)]$. But the integrals (1) and (2) are not necessarily equal. The change of local parameter on the Riemann surface is given by $(u, v) = \Psi[\Phi^{-1}(x, y)]$, where $w = u + iv$ is an analytic function of $z = x + iy$. We then have

$$\iint_{\Phi(G)} g(x, y) \, dx \, dy = \iint_{\Psi(G)} h(u, v) \frac{\partial(x, y)}{\partial(u, v)} \, du \, dv, \tag{3}$$

---

†For convenience, we shall represent the area element in the (x, y)-plane as $dx \, dy$. This does not mean that we have selected an order of iteration in the double integral. Integrals are taken in the sense of Lebesgue.

where $\partial(x, y)/\partial(u, v) = |dz/dw|^2$ is the functional determinant of the coordinate change. The integral (3) is equal to (2) only when $|dz/dw| \equiv 1$, which is indeed a very special case.

Now we begin to see what stands before us in our attempt to define integration on S. First, we must worry about the way the integral depends upon the selection of local coordinates in G and, second, we must consider regions G which do not lie entirely within one coordinate disk and ask how to patch the pieces together. These problems did not arise in the definition of integrals in the plane because we had a single (macroscopic) coordinate system over the whole plane, usually held fixed throughout any discussion.

One possible mode of approach would be to divide the Riemann surface into small pieces (triangles if the surface is known to be triangulable) each of which is in a single coordinate disk, and fix the local parameter in each throughout the whole discussion. Then for an arbitrary region G, the fixed subdivision of S divides G into pieces in each of which a parameter has been fixed in terms of which the function f can be integrated as in (1). Then $\iint_G f$ is the sum of the integrals over the pieces of G. If we take another fixed subdivision of S, the integral $\iint_G f$ would, in general, have a different value. This approach suffers several disadvantages, among which is the fact that we should like to introduce an intrinsic definition of integration which does not depend upon a fixed selection of local coordinates. This is in keeping with the spirit of making things invariant under changes of local coordinates, which will motivate many of the subsequent considerations. Furthermore, we have not assumed that the Riemann surface can be triangulated or subdivided into a countable number of sets each lying in a single parametric disk. Even though we shall later prove this, we should not make use of this property here. Thus we begin to look in another direction for a definition of the integral.

Our difficulty arises when we try to integrate a function over a region G on S; for under change of coordinates, the integral does not remain invariant. Therefore let us look for something else to integrate. Here (3) gives us the clue to what to do next. We must require that

$$g(x, y) \, dx \, dy = g(x(u, v), y(u, v)) \, \frac{\partial(x, y)}{\partial(u, v)} \, du \, dv. \qquad (4)$$

Thus the expression we integrate must be of the form $g(x, y) \, dx \, dy$ and must satisfy (4) when variables are changed. This leads us to define a second-order differential Ω in a region G of S as follows:

A (*second-order*) *differential* Ω in a region G of S is an expression, defined in G, which in any local parameter (x, y) has the form

$$\Omega(x, y) = g(x, y) \, dx \, dy,$$

where g is a complex-valued function of (x, y) which transforms according to (4) when local coordinates are changed; that is, if $u = u(x, y), v = v(x, y)$, then

$$\Omega(u, v) = h(u, v) \, du \, dv,$$

where

$$h(u, v) = g(x(u, v), y(u, v)) \frac{\partial(x, y)}{\partial(u, v)}. \tag{5}$$

If locally $\Omega = g(x, y) \, dx \, dy$, we may require that $g(x, y)$ satisfy certain regularity conditions, but to be sure that these conditions have meaning for Ω, we must see to it that these properties are preserved when local coordinates are changed. In new local coordinates, $\Omega = h(u, v) \, du \, dv$, where (5) defines h and $\partial(x, y)/\partial(u, v) = |dz/dw|^2$, in which dz/dw is an analytic function when $z = x + iy$, $w = u + iv$. Thus some of the conditions we may impose upon $g(x, y)$ are integrability, continuity, differentiability, etc., since $h(u, v)$ then also shares the corresponding property. We speak of Ω as having this property. Thus $\Omega \in C$ in G if $g(x, y) \in C^n$ in the local representations of Ω; or Ω is integrable if locally $g(x, y)$ is integrable. Furthermore, Ω is *real* if $g(x, y)$ is a real-valued function in any local representation, and Ω is *positive* if $g(x, y)$ is positive in any local representation; this definition is meaningful because $\partial(x, y)/\partial(u, v) = |dz/dw|^2 > 0$ for conformal mappings.

If f is a complex-valued function defined in the region G, the expression $f\Omega$ expressed in terms of the local parameter $\Phi(P) = (x, y)$ as

$$f(\Phi^{-1}(x, y))g(x, y) \, dx \, dy$$

is also a second-order differential in G; for if we change variables to $\Psi(P) = (u, v)$, we get

$$f(\Psi^{-1}(u, v))g(x(u, v), y(u, v)) \frac{\partial(x, y)}{\partial(u, v)} = f(\Psi^{-1}(u, v))h(u, v),$$

which is the proper transformation law. Furthermore, if Ω_1 and Ω_2 are differentials represented locally as $g_1(x, y) \, dx \, dy$ and $g_2(x, y) \, dx \, dy$, then $\Omega_1 + \Omega_2$ is the differential represented locally as $[g_1(x, y) + g_2(x, y)] \, dx \, dy$.

If the region G lies in a single parametric disk and if Ω is integrable in G, then the integral $\iint_G \Omega$ is well defined independently of the local coordinates selected to represent Ω, since

$$\iint_G \Omega(x, y) = \iint_{\Phi(G)} g(x, y) \, dx \, dy = \iint_{\Psi(G)} g(x(u, v), y(u, v)) \frac{\partial(x, y)}{\partial(u, v)} \, du \, dv$$

$$= \iint_{\Psi(G)} h(u, v) \, du \, dv = \iint_G \Omega(u, v).$$

We now consider the problem of extending this to regions G reaching beyond a single parametric disk. For this, we introduce the notion of a partition of unity.

Let us assume that a region G has a compact closure $\overline{G}$ on S. Each point of $\overline{G}$ has about it a parametric disk $D(P)$ with local parameter $\Phi(P) = (x, y)$, $z = x + iy$, in terms of which D is given as $|z| < 1$. Let $U(P)$ denote the subset of $D(P)$ determined by the conditions $-a < x < a$, $-b < y < b$, $a < \frac{1}{2}$, $b < \frac{1}{2}$. Since $\overline{G}$ is compact, a finite number of the sets $U(P)$ cover $\overline{G}$; call these $U_1, U_2, \ldots, U_n$, with each U_k contained in the parametric disk D_k with local parameter $\Phi_k(P) = (x, y)$. Define the function f_k on S as follows:

$$f_k(P) = \begin{cases} (x^2 - a^2)^4(y^2 - b^2)^4, & P \in U_k, \\ 0, & P \in S - U_k. \end{cases}$$

Thus $f_k(P) > 0$ for $P \in U_k$, $f_k(P) = 0$ for $P \notin U_k$, and $f_k \in C^2$ on S. At any point $P_0 \in \overline{G}$, the sum $\sum_{k=1}^n f_k(P_0) > 0$, since P_0 is in some U_j and $f_j(P_0) > 0$ while all other $f_k(P_0) \geq 0$. Therefore, we may define the functions e_k, $k = 1, 2, \ldots, n$, on $\overline{G}$:

$$e_k(P) = \frac{f_k(P)}{\sum_{j=1}^n f_j(P)}.$$

The functions e_k, $k = 1, 2, \ldots, n$, have the properties

(a) $$e_k(P) > 0 \qquad \text{for } P \in U_k,$$

(b) $$e_k(P) = 0 \qquad \text{for } P \notin U_k,$$

(c) $$\sum_{k=1}^n e_k(P) \equiv 1 \qquad \text{for } P \in \overline{G},$$

(d) $$e_k \in C^2 \qquad \text{in } \overline{G}.$$

Any collection of functions $\{e_k\}$, which satisfies (a) through (d), defines a *partition of unity* for $\overline{G}$ relative to the covering $\{U_k\}$.

Let Ω be an integrable second-order differential in G which has the representation $g_k(x, y) \, dx \, dy$ in each parametric disk D_k. We note that $\Omega = \Omega \sum_{k=1}^n e_k = \sum_{k=1}^n (e_k\Omega)$ in G. This leads us to define

$$\iint_G \Omega = \sum_{k=1}^n \iint_{G \cap U_k} (\Omega e_k) = \sum_{k=1}^n \iint_{\Phi(G \cap U_k)} e_k(\Phi^{-1}(x, y))g_k(x, y) \, dx \, dy, \qquad (6)$$

since in each $G \cap U_k$, the integral of Ωe_k has been invariantly defined. It remains to prove that the value of (6) depends only upon G and Ω and not upon the particular partition of unity used.

Let $\tilde{e}_k$, $k = 1, 2, \ldots, m$, form another partition of unity for $\overline{G}$ relative to the covering $\{\tilde{U}_k\}$. The local parameter in $\tilde{U}_k$ will be denoted by $\Phi_k(P) = (\tilde{x}, \tilde{y})$. According to (6),

$$\iint\limits_G \Omega = \sum_{k=1}^{n} \iint\limits_{G \cap U_k} \Omega e_k = \sum_{k=1}^{n} \iint\limits_{G \cap U_k} \Omega e_k \sum_{j=1}^{m} \tilde{e}_j,$$

since $\sum_{j=1}^{m} \tilde{e}_j \equiv 1$ in G. Since the integral in each $G \cap U_k$ is additive, we may write

$$\iint\limits_G \Omega = \sum_{k=1}^{n} \sum_{j=1}^{m} \iint\limits_{G \cap U_k} \Omega e_k \tilde{e}_j.$$

The function $e_k \tilde{e}_j$ is different from zero only in the set $U_k \cap \tilde{U}_j$; here we change variables from (x, y) to $(\tilde{x}, \tilde{y})$ to get

$$\iint\limits_{G \cap U_k \cap \tilde{U}_j} \Omega(x, y) e_k \tilde{e}_j = \iint\limits_{G \cap U_k \cap \tilde{U}_j} \Omega(\tilde{x}, \tilde{y}) e_k \tilde{e}_j.$$

We sum over j and k to get

$$\iint\limits_G \Omega = \sum_{k=1}^{n} \sum_{j=1}^{m} \iint\limits_{G \cap U_k \cap \tilde{U}_j} \Omega(x, y) e_k \tilde{e}_j = \sum_{j=1}^{n} \iint\limits_{G \cap \tilde{U}_j} \Omega(\tilde{x}, \tilde{y}) \tilde{e}_j,$$

since $e_k = 0$ outside U_k, $\cup_{k=1}^{n} U_k \supset G$, and $\sum_{k=1}^{n} e_k \equiv 1$ in G. But the last expression is just the definition of $\iint_G \Omega$ in terms of the $\tilde{e}_j$'s, so the definition is independent of the partition employed, and the integral of a second-order differential is now defined for any region G with compact closure.

If the region G does not have compact closure, we extend our previous definition as follows. Let V represent any region with compact closure contained in G. Assume first that the differential Ω is real and non-negative in G. Then $\iint_V \Omega$ has already been defined, and we define

$$\iint\limits_G \Omega = \underset{V \subset G}{\text{l.u.b.}} \iint\limits_V \Omega.$$

For any differential Ω in G, the absolute value $|\Omega|$ can be defined to be the differential whose local representation is $|g(x, y)|\, dx\, dy$. This is a valid definition for differentials; for if (u, v) is used as local parameter instead of (x, y) and if $z = x + iy$, $w = u + iv$, we have

$$|h(u, v)| = \left| g(x(u, v), y(u, v)) \left| \frac{dz}{dw} \right|^2 \right| = |g(x(u, v), y(u, v))| \left| \frac{dz}{dw} \right|^2 ,$$

which is the correct transformation law. For Ω real, $\Omega = \Omega^+ - \Omega^-$, where $\Omega^+ = \frac{1}{2}(|\Omega| + \Omega)$ and $\Omega^- = \frac{1}{2}(|\Omega| - \Omega)$, and Ω^+ and Ω^- are both non-negative and real. The integral of an arbitrary real integrable differential Ω over an arbitrary region G is now defined as

$$\iint\limits_{G} \Omega = \iint\limits_{G} \Omega^+ - \iint\limits_{G} \Omega^-,$$

when both integrals on the right are finite. For any complex-valued integrable differential Ω, the integrals of the real and imaginary parts are defined, and the integral of Ω over G is defined as

$$\iint\limits_{G} \Omega = \iint\limits_{G} \operatorname{Re} \Omega + i \iint\limits_{G} \operatorname{Im} \Omega.$$

We should verify that the integral so defined is additive. For regions G with compact closures, the additivity follows from the additivity of the Lebesgue integral in the plane, since each term in (6) is additive. For arbitrary regions G, it will suffice to prove additivity for non-negative differentials Ω_1 and Ω_2, for which

$$\iint\limits_{G} \Omega_1 = \operatorname*{l.u.b.}_{V \subset G} \iint\limits_{V} \Omega_1 \quad \text{and} \quad \iint\limits_{G} \Omega_2 = \operatorname*{l.u.b.}_{U \subset G} \iint\limits_{U} \Omega_2,$$

where U and V are arbitrary regions with compact closures in G. Then

$$\iint\limits_{G} (\Omega_1 + \Omega_2) = \operatorname*{l.u.b.}_{V \subset G} \iint\limits_{V} (\Omega_1 + \Omega_2) \leq \operatorname*{l.u.b.}_{V \subset G} \iint\limits_{V} \Omega_1 + \operatorname*{l.u.b.}_{U \subset G} \iint\limits_{U} \Omega_2.$$

On the other hand, given $\epsilon > 0$, there exist sets U_0 and V_0 such that

$$\iint_{V_0} \Omega_1 > \iint_G \Omega_1 - \frac{\epsilon}{2} \quad \text{and} \quad \iint_{U_0} \Omega_2 > \iint_G \Omega_2 - \frac{\epsilon}{2}.$$

The union $U_0 \cup V_0$ is an open set but not necessarily connected. Join a point $P_0 \in U_0$ to $Q_0 \in V_0$ with an arc C in G, and cover C with a finite number of parametric disks in G, the union of which we denote by W_0. Then $U_0 \cup V_0 \cup W_0 = W$ is a region with compact closure in G and

$$\iint_W \Omega_1 \geq \iint_{V_0} \Omega_1, \qquad \iint_W \Omega_2 \geq \iint_{U_0} \Omega_2,$$

so that

$$\iint_G (\Omega_1 + \Omega_2) \geq \iint_W (\Omega_1 + \Omega_2) = \iint_W \Omega_1 + \iint_W \Omega_2 \geq \iint_{V_0} \Omega_1 + \iint_{U_0} \Omega_2$$

$$\geq \iint_G \Omega_1 + \iint_G \Omega_2 - \epsilon,$$

proving the additivity, since ϵ is arbitrarily small.

6–2 First-order differentials and line integrals.   If $C = (\alpha, I)$ is a differentiable curve in the (x, y)-plane, and $p(x, y)$ and $q(x, y)$ are continuous complex-valued functions in a region containing C, we customarily define the line integral to be

$$\int_C p\, dx + q\, dy = \int_{t=0}^{1} \left\{ p(\alpha_1(t), \alpha_2(t)) \frac{d\alpha_1}{dt} + q(\alpha_1(t), \alpha_2(t)) \frac{d\alpha_2}{dt} \right\} dt$$

$$= \int_{t=0}^{1} \left\{ p(x, y) \frac{dx}{dt} + q(x, y) \frac{dy}{dt} \right\} dt, \tag{1}$$

where $\alpha(t) = (\alpha_1(t), \alpha_2(t)) = (x, y)$, α_1 and α_2 being differentiable functions of t in $0 \leq t \leq 1$. We now seek an extension of this definition to a line integral on a Riemann surface S. With this in mind, let us introduce new variables by a conformal change of variables $z = g(w)$, $w = u + iv$, $z = x + iy$. Then C is given by $w = g^{-1}(\alpha_1(t) + i\alpha_2(t))$ and

$$\frac{dx}{dt} = \frac{\partial x}{\partial u} \frac{du}{dt} + \frac{\partial x}{\partial v} \frac{dv}{dt}, \qquad \frac{dy}{dt} = \frac{\partial y}{\partial u} \frac{du}{dt} + \frac{\partial y}{\partial v} \frac{dv}{dt}.$$

Therefore

$$\int_C p(x, y)\, dx + q(x, y)\, dy$$

$$= \int_{t=0}^{1} \left\{ \left[p(\alpha_1(t), \alpha_2(t)) \frac{\partial x}{\partial u} + q(\alpha_1(t), \alpha_2(t)) \frac{\partial y}{\partial u} \right] \frac{du}{dt} \right\}$$

$$+ \left\{ \left[p(\alpha_1(t), \alpha_2(t)) \frac{\partial x}{\partial v} + q(\alpha_1(t), \alpha_2(t)) \frac{\partial y}{\partial v} \right] \frac{dv}{dt} \right\} dt$$

$$= \int_C \tilde{p}(u, v)\, du + \tilde{q}(u, v)\, dv, \tag{2}$$

where

$$\tilde{p}(u, v) = p(x(u, v), y(u, v)) \frac{\partial x}{\partial u} + q(x(u, v), y(u, v)) \frac{\partial y}{\partial u},$$

$$\tilde{q}(u, v) = p(x(u, v), y(u, v)) \frac{\partial x}{\partial v} + q(x(u, v), y(u, v)) \frac{\partial y}{\partial v}. \tag{3}$$

Thus we see that the expression we integrate is the (first-order) differential $p(x, y)\, dx + q(x, y)\, dy$, which transforms into $\tilde{p}(u, v)\, du + \tilde{q}(u, v)\, dv$ in which $\tilde{p}, \tilde{q}$ are related to p, q by (3) when we change variables. This is the clue to what expressions we integrate on the surface S.

If G is a region on S, we say that a (*first-order*) *differential* ω on G is an expression defined in G which in any local parameter (x, y) has the form

$$\omega(x, y) = p(x, y)\, dx + q(x, y)\, dy,$$

where p and q are complex-valued functions of (x, y) and which transform into

$$\omega(u, v) = \tilde{p}(u, v)\, du + \tilde{q}(u, v)\, dv,$$

where $p, q, \tilde{p}, \tilde{q}$ satisfy (3) when local parameters are changed. If f is a complex-valued function on G, then $f\omega$ is the first-order differential which is expressed in terms of the local parameter $\Phi(P) = (x, y)$ as

$$f\omega = f(\Phi^{-1}(x, y))p(x, y)\, dx + f(\Phi^{-1}(x, y))q(x, y)\, dy;$$

for the under the change of variable $x + iy = g(u + iv)$, this transforms as

$$f[\Phi^{-1}(x(u, v), y(u, v))]\tilde{p}(u, v)$$

$$= f[\Phi^{-1}(x(u, v), y(u, v))] \left\{ p(x(u, v), y(u, v)) \frac{\partial x}{\partial u} + q(x(u, v), y(u, v)) \frac{\partial y}{\partial u} \right\},$$

$$f[\Phi^{-1}(x(u, v), y(u, v))]\tilde{q}(u, v)$$

$$= f[\Phi^{-1}(x(u, v), y(u, v))]\left\{p(x(u, v), y(u, v))\frac{\partial x}{\partial v} + q(x(u, v), y(u, v))\frac{\partial y}{\partial v}\right\},$$

which is the correct transformation rule for differentials. If $\omega_1 = p_1\,dx + q_1\,dy$ and $\omega_2 = p_2\,dx + q_2\,dy$ locally, then $\omega_1 + \omega_2$ is the differential whose local representation is $(p_1 + p_2)\,dx + (q_1 + q_2)\,dy$.

If the differentiable curve $C = (\alpha, I)$ lies entirely within one local parametric disk with parameter $\Phi(P) = (x, y)$, if $\Phi(C) = (\Phi \circ \alpha, I)$, and if the differential ω is defined and continuous in a region containing the curve C, then the line integral of ω over C,

$$\int_C \omega = \int_{\Phi(C)} p\,dx + q\,dy,$$

is well defined according to (2). There still remains the problem of extending this definition to curves $C = (\alpha, I)$ that extend beyond one parametric disk. Since the carrier of C is compact, we can divide the interval $0 \le t \le 1$ into a finite number of pieces $0 = t_0 < t_1 < \cdots < t_n = 1$ so that the image of each segment $I_i : t_{i-1} \le t \le t_i$ lies interior to a single parametric disk. Then we let $C_i = (\alpha, I_i)$ and define

$$\int_C \omega = \sum_{i=1}^n \int_{C_i} \omega.$$

This definition is independent of the subdivision employed. To verify this, first consider a refinement of the given subdivision which merely adds a single new point t' between t_{i-1} and t_i dividing C_i into C_i' and C_i''. From the additivity of the line integral and the fact that in a single coordinate disk the line integral is invariant under change of variables, we have

$$\int_{C_i} \omega = \int_{C_i'} \omega + \int_{C_i''} \omega,$$

and $\int_C \omega$ has the same value when computed with this refinement. Since any refinement can be obtained by successively adding single points, $\int_C \omega$ keeps the same value under any refinement of a given subdivision. Then if $0 = t_0' < t_1' < \cdots < t_m' = 1$ is a second subdivision of the unit interval I, the two subdivisions may be superimposed to get a common refinement of each. The integral as defined by the refinement is equal to both of the original integrals, which in turn are equal to each other.

If $C = C_1 C_2 \ldots C_n$ is a piecewise differentiable curve with each C_i differentiable, we define

$$\int_C \omega = \sum_{i=1}^{n} \int_{C_i} \omega.$$

Thus we have defined the line integral of a continuous differential ω over a piecewise differentiable curve.

As in the case of second-order differentials, we say that a differential ω has a certain property if the local coefficients p and q in $\omega = p\,dx + q\,dy$ have this property and the property is preserved under changes in local coordinates.

Let f be a complex-valued function on S with continuous first partial derivatives; that is, if $\Phi(P) = (x, y)$ are local coordinates in a parametric disk D, then $f[\Phi^{-1}(x, y)]$ can be differentiated and $\partial f/\partial x$ and $\partial f/\partial y$ are continuous functions locally. Then we may define the *total differential df* of f as

$$df = \frac{\partial f}{\partial x}\,dx + \frac{\partial f}{\partial y}\,dy.$$

This total differential of f is indeed a first-order differential on S with $p = \partial f/\partial x$ and $q = \partial f/\partial y$; for if $x = x(u, v)$, $y = y(u, v)$ gives us a change of variables, we have

$$\frac{\partial f}{\partial u} = \frac{\partial f}{\partial x}\frac{\partial x}{\partial u} + \frac{\partial f}{\partial y}\frac{\partial y}{\partial u}, \qquad \frac{\partial f}{\partial v} = \frac{\partial f}{\partial x}\frac{\partial x}{\partial v} + \frac{\partial f}{\partial y}\frac{\partial y}{\partial v},$$

which is the transformation rule (3). A differential which is the total differential of a function $f \in C^2$ on S is called an *exact differential*.

If ω is an exact differential, we have locally $\omega = p\,dx + q\,dy$, where

$$\frac{\partial p}{\partial y} = \frac{\partial q}{\partial x}. \tag{4}$$

Conversely, when the condition (4) is satisfied in a simply connected plane region, ω is the total differential of some function f. Thus when the differential ω satisfies (4) in each parametric disk, ω is locally an exact differential. However, when we continue throughout S the locally defined function $f[\Phi^{-1}(x, y)]$ for which locally $\omega = df$, we may find that it is not single-valued on S, so that in the large, ω is not the total differential of a single-valued function on S. A differential ω which has continuous first derivatives in a region G on S which satisfy (4) in each parametric disk and hence is locally exact is called a *closed differential* in G.

If ω is a closed differential and $C = (\alpha, I)$ is a differentiable curve lying in one parametric disk D, so that $x = \alpha_1(t)$, $y = \alpha_2(t)$, $t \in I$, expresses C in D, we have $\omega = df(x, y)$ in D and

$$\int_C \omega = \int_C df = \int_{t=0}^1 df(\alpha_1(t), \alpha_2(t)) = f(\alpha(1)) - f(\alpha(0)).$$

Thus if $\alpha(0) = P_0$ and $\alpha(1) = P_1$, we can write

$$\int_C \omega = f(P_1) - f(P_0),$$

so that the integral depends only upon the values of f at the end points of C. If C extends beyond a single parametric disk, we may divide it into arcs $C_k = (\alpha, I_k)$, where I_k is the interval $t_{k-1} \leq t \leq t_k$ for

$$0 = t_0 < t_1 < t_2 < \cdots < t_n = 1,$$

so that each arc C_k lies in a single parametric disk D_k. Let $\alpha(t_k) = P_k$ be the end points of the arcs C_k. Then locally $\omega = df_k$, where $f_k(P)$ is defined for $P \in D_k$. In D_k, f_k is determined up to an additive constant, but the difference $f_k(P) - f_k(Q)$ with $P, Q \in D_k$ is well determined, independently of the coordinates used in D_k. Now

$$\int_C \omega = \sum_{k=1}^n \int_{C_k} df_k = \sum_{k=1}^n \{f_k(P_k) - f_k(P_{k-1})\}. \tag{5}$$

In defining the line integral of a differential ω, we had to restrict ourselves to piecewise differentiable curves on S. When ω is closed on S, however, we can use (5) to extend the definition of the line integral of ω to arbitrary curves. In particular, let $C = (\alpha, I)$ be a curve on S and let $C_1, C_2, \ldots, C_n$ be a subdivision of C such that each arc C_k lies in a single parametric disk D_k as above. Since ω is closed, $\omega = df_k$ for some function $f_k(P)$ defined in D_k, and we merely define in the notation of (5):

$$\int_C \omega = \sum_{k=1}^n \{f_k(P_k) - f_k(P_{k-1})\} = \sum_{k=1}^n \{f_k(\alpha(t_k)) - f_k(\alpha(t_{k-1}))\}.$$

We must show that this definition is independent of the subdivision of C. Under refinement in which a new point t' is added, say $t_{k-1} < t' < t_k$, we have that the arcs $C_k' = (\alpha, I_k')$ and $C_k'' = (\alpha, I_k'')$, where $I_k': t_{k-1} \leq t \leq t'$ and $I_k'': t' \leq t \leq t_k$ are both in D_k, and if $\alpha(t') = P'$,

$$\{f_k(P') - f_k(P_{k-1})\} + \{f_k(P_k) - f_k(P')\} = f_k(P_k) - f_k(P_{k-1}).$$

Since an arbitrary refinement can be obtained by adding one point at a time, there is no change in the value of the integral under refinement. Now if $0 = t_0' < t_1' < \cdots < t_m' = 1$ is another subdivision of C, we consider the third subdivision consisting of all the points t_k, t_j', $k = 0, 1, \ldots, n$, $j = 0, 1, \ldots, m$. This is a common refinement of the first two subdivisions, and the integral calculated by this refinement is equal to both of the original integrals, which in turn must be equal. Thus $\int_C \omega$ is well defined for ω closed and C arbitrary.

If $C = (\alpha, I)$, then $C^{-1} = (\beta, I)$, where $\beta(t) = \alpha(1 - t)$. Then the subdivision of C used in the definition of $\int_C \omega$ defines a subdivision of C^{-1} using the same points $\beta(1 - t_k) = P_k$, and

$$\int_{C^{-1}} \omega = \sum_{k=1}^{n} \{f_{n-k}(P_{n-k}) - f_{n-k}(P_{n-k+1})\}$$

$$= \sum_{k=1}^{n} \{f_k(P_{k-1}) - f_k(P_k)\}$$

$$= -\sum_{k=1}^{n} \{f_k(P_k) - f_k(P_{k-1})\}$$

$$= -\int_C \omega.$$

Furthermore, if $C = C_1 C_2$, then $\int_{C_1 C_2} \omega = \int_{C_1} \omega + \int_{C_2} \omega$. If $C = (\alpha, I)$ is a constant curve for which $\alpha(t) \equiv P_0$ then $P_k = P_{k-1} = P_0$ in the above definition of integral, and $\int_C \omega = 0$.

If ω is an exact differential, $\omega = df$ where f is defined on all of S. Then for any curve $C = (\alpha, I)$ we have

$$\int_C \omega = \int_C df = f(\alpha(1)) - f(\alpha(0)).$$

If ω is exact and C is a closed curve, $\alpha(1) = \alpha(0)$ and

$$\int_C \omega = 0.$$

THEOREM 6-1. *If the curves $C_0 = (\alpha_0, I)$ and $C_1 = (\alpha_1, I)$ are homotopic and if ω is a closed differential, then*

$$\int_{C_0} \omega = \int_{C_1} \omega.$$

Indeed, let Φ be the continuous mapping of $I \times I$ into S deforming C_0 into C_1: $\Phi(t, 0) = \alpha_0(t)$, $\Phi(t, 1) = \alpha_1(t)$, $t \in I$, and $\Phi(0, s) = \alpha_0(0) = \alpha_1(0)$, $\Phi(1, s) = \alpha_0(1) = \alpha_1(1)$, $s \in I$. The square $I \times I$ can be subdivided into n^2 equal squares with the diameter $\sqrt{2}/n$ of each square less than the Lebesgue number of the covering of $I \times I$ obtained by taking inverse images under Φ of parametric disks on S. The image of each small square is entirely within a single parametric disk. For each small square with vertices at

$$\left(\frac{j}{n}, \frac{k}{n}\right), \ \left(\frac{j+1}{n}, \frac{k}{n}\right), \ \left(\frac{j+1}{n}, \frac{k+1}{n}\right), \ \left(\frac{j}{n}, \frac{k+1}{n}\right),$$

$$j, k = 0, 1, \ldots, n-1$$

the mapping by Φ of the circumference with the indicated orientation is a closed curve $\Gamma_{j,k}$ lying in a single parametric disk. Thus the local exactness of ω implies that $\int_{\Gamma_{j,k}} \omega = 0$. Each edge of the square lying interior to $I \times I$ is the edge of two adjacent squares and has opposite orientations in each. Therefore

$$0 = \sum_{j,k=0}^{n-1} \int_{\Gamma_{j,k}} \omega = \int_{C_0} \omega + \int_C \omega + \int_{C_1^{-1}} \omega + \int_{\widetilde{C}^{-1}} \omega,$$

where C represents the curve $\Phi(1, s)$, $s \in I$, and $\widetilde{C}$ represents the curve $\Phi(0, s)$, $s \in I$. Since $\Phi(0, s) \equiv \alpha_0(0)$ and $\Phi(1, s) \equiv \alpha_0(1)$, we have

$$\int_C \omega = 0 \quad \text{and} \quad \int_{\widetilde{C}^{-1}} \omega = 0.$$

Thus $\int_{C_0} \omega + \int_{C_1^{-1}} \omega = 0$, and the assertion is proved. In particular, if C_1 is a constant curve (point), then $\int_{C_1} \omega = 0$. This means that *if the closed curve C is homotopic to a point and ω is a closed differential, then $\int_C \omega = 0$.*

This tells us that the line integral of a closed differential really depends only upon the homotopy class of a closed curve. Moreover, the integral over $C_1 C_2$ is the same as the integral over $C_2 C_1$, so that $\int_C \omega = 0$ whenever C represents a closed curve in the commutator subgroup of the fundamental group. Consequently, $\int_C \omega$ depends only upon the homology class of the curve C, and we can state:

THEOREM 6–2. *If C_1 is homologous to C_2 and ω is a closed differential, then $\int_{C_1} \omega = \int_{C_2} \omega$. If $C \sim 0$, then $\int_C \omega = 0$.*

From now on, we shall combine additively the curves over which we integrate and identify each with an element in the homology group of closed curves.

6–3 Stokes' theorem. In this section we shall prove Stokes' theorem on S, which gives us a relation between a line integral over the boundary of a region and a surface integral over the region. Let ω be a first-order differential which is locally represented as $\omega(x, y) = p(x, y)\,dx + q(x, y)\,dy$, where the p and q have continuous first partial derivatives with respect to x and y; that is, $\omega \in C^1$. We define a second-order differential $d\omega$ (called the *exterior derivative* of ω) which is locally given by

$$d\omega = \left(\frac{\partial q}{\partial x} - \frac{\partial p}{\partial y}\right) dx\,dy.$$

To prove that this is a second-order differential, we must show that under the change of variables $x = x(u, v)$, $y = y(u, v)$, the function $\partial q/\partial x - \partial p/\partial y$ transforms properly. According to (3) of Section 6–2,

$$\frac{\partial \tilde{q}}{\partial u} = \frac{\partial p}{\partial x}\frac{\partial x}{\partial u}\frac{\partial x}{\partial v} + \frac{\partial p}{\partial y}\frac{\partial y}{\partial u}\frac{\partial x}{\partial v} + p\frac{\partial^2 x}{\partial u\,\partial v} + \frac{\partial q}{\partial x}\frac{\partial x}{\partial u}\frac{\partial y}{\partial v} + \frac{\partial q}{\partial y}\frac{\partial y}{\partial u}\frac{\partial y}{\partial v} + q\frac{\partial^2 y}{\partial u\,\partial v},$$

$$\frac{\partial \tilde{p}}{\partial v} = \frac{\partial p}{\partial x}\frac{\partial x}{\partial v}\frac{\partial x}{\partial u} + \frac{\partial p}{\partial y}\frac{\partial y}{\partial v}\frac{\partial x}{\partial u} + p\frac{\partial^2 x}{\partial u\,\partial v} + \frac{\partial q}{\partial x}\frac{\partial x}{\partial v}\frac{\partial y}{\partial u} + \frac{\partial q}{\partial y}\frac{\partial y}{\partial v}\frac{\partial y}{\partial u} + q\frac{\partial^2 y}{\partial u\,\partial v}.$$

Therefore,

$$\frac{\partial \tilde{q}}{\partial u} - \frac{\partial \tilde{p}}{\partial v} = \left(\frac{\partial q}{\partial x} - \frac{\partial p}{\partial y}\right)\left(\frac{\partial x}{\partial u}\frac{\partial y}{\partial v} - \frac{\partial x}{\partial v}\frac{\partial y}{\partial u}\right),$$

which is the correct transformation rule (5) of Section 6–1.

A differential ω is said to be equal to zero at a point P_0 on S if $\omega = p(x, y)\,dx + q(x, y)\,dy$ in terms of local coordinates $\Phi(P) = (x, y)$ with $\Phi(P_0) = (0, 0)$, we have $p(0, 0) = q(0, 0) = 0$. Similarly, a second-order differential Ω which is represented locally by $\Omega = g(x, y)\,dx\,dy$ is said to vanish at P_0 if $g(0, 0) = 0$. These definitions are invariant under the transformation rule. The *carrier* of a differential ω or Ω is the closure of the set of points at which the differential is not zero.

We shall not prove Stokes' theorem for an arbitrary region on S but only for special ones which we shall designate regular regions. A region G is called a *regular region* if (a) its closure is compact on S, (b) its boundary is composed of a finite number of piecewise analytic curves, and (c) G lies on only one side of the boundary. Since each piecewise analytic curve in the boundary of G has two sides, we have required that each piecewise analytic curve C in the boundary of G be contained in a region N which C divides into two parts, only one of which meets G. We shall denote the boundary of G by ∂G and assign an orientation to each curve C in ∂G in such a way that G lies to the left of C (on the left side of a tangent vector pointed in the direction we assign as the positive direction on C).

In the euclidean plane, consider the rectangle R: $-a < x < a$, $-b < y < b$ and a differential $\omega = p(x, y)\, dx + q(x, y)\, dy$ which is in C^1 on $\overline{R}$. Then Stokes' theorem (also called Green's theorem) says

$$\int_{\partial R} p(x, y)\, dx + q(x, y)\, dy = \iint_R \left(\frac{\partial q}{\partial x} - \frac{\partial p}{\partial y}\right) dx\, dy,$$

or simply

$$\int_{\partial R} \omega = \iint_R d\omega.$$

The proof is an immediate consequence of iterating the integral on the right:

$$\int_{-b}^{b} dy \int_{-a}^{a} \frac{\partial q}{\partial x}\, dx = \int_{-b}^{b} [q(a, y) - q(-a, y)]\, dy$$

$$= \int_{-b}^{b} q(a, y)\, dy - \int_{-b}^{b} q(-a, y)\, dy = \int_{\partial R} q(x, y)\, dy$$

and

$$\int_{-a}^{a} dx \int_{-b}^{b} \frac{\partial p}{\partial y}\, dy = \int_{-a}^{a} [p(x, b) - p(x, -b)]\, dx$$

$$= \int_{-a}^{a} p(x, b)\, dx - \int_{-a}^{a} p(x, -b)\, dx = -\int_{\partial R} p(x, y)\, dx.$$

Another useful form of Stokes' theorem is obtained if ω is replaced by $f\omega$, where $f \in C^1$ in $\overline{R}$. Then p is replaced by fp and q by fq and we get

$$\int_{\partial R} f(p\, dx + q\, dy) = \iint_R f\left(\frac{\partial q}{\partial x} - \frac{\partial p}{\partial y}\right) dx\, dy + \iint_R \left(q\frac{\partial f}{\partial x} - p\frac{\partial f}{\partial y}\right) dx\, dy, \quad (1)$$

which is an analogue of the formula for integration by parts.

We are now in a position to state and prove *Stokes' theorem* on a surface S:

THEOREM 6–3. *Let G be a regular region on S and ω be a first-order differential in C^1 on $\overline{G}$. Then*

$$\int_{\partial G} \omega = \iint_G d\omega. \tag{2}$$

There are only a finite number of points $P_1, P_2, \ldots, P_m$ on ∂G at which ∂G is not analytic. We fix a parametric disk D_k about P_k such that $D_k \cap D_j = \phi$, $j \neq k$, with local parameter $z = \varphi_k(P)$, $|z| < 1$ in D_k. For each $\rho < \frac{1}{3}$, we define the function $f_{k,\rho}$ in D_k by†

$$f_{k,\rho}(P) = \begin{cases} 0, & \text{for } |z| < \rho, \quad z = \varphi_k(P), \\ \dfrac{1}{\rho^4}(|z| - \rho)^2(|z| - 3\rho)^2, & \text{for } \rho \leq |z| \leq 2\rho, \quad z = \varphi_k(P), \\ 1, & \text{for } 2\rho < |z| < 1, \quad z = \varphi_k(P). \end{cases}$$

The function $f_{k,\rho}$ is in C^1 on D_k and is non-negative. We now define a function f_ρ on S as

$$f_\rho(P) = \begin{cases} f_{k,\rho}(P), & \text{for } P \in D_k, \quad k = 1, 2, \ldots, m, \\ 1, & \text{for } P \in S - \cup_{k=1}^m D_k. \end{cases}$$

Thus $f_\rho \in C^1$ on S and has the property that it vanishes in the disk $|z| < \rho$ about each of the points $P_1, P_2, \ldots, P_m$ and is 1 outside of the union of the D_k's. We shall first prove Stokes' theorem for the differential $\omega_\rho = f_\rho \omega$ which vanishes in a neighborhood of each point $P_1, P_2, \ldots, P_m$, and then obtain the general theorem by noting that $\lim_{\rho \to 0} f_\rho \equiv 1$ in G.

We shall cover $\overline{G}$ by open sets as follows: To each point interior to G we associate a parametric disk in which we take a rectangle $U: -a < x < a$, $-b < y < b$ lying entirely within G. To each point of ∂G other than $P_1, P_2, \ldots, P_m$ we associate a parametric disk in which the segment C of ∂G appears as the real axis and then take a rectangle $V: -a < x < a$, $-b < y < b$, with $y = 0$, $-a < x < a$, along C. To each point P_k we associate a rectangle $W_k: -a < x < a$, $-b < y < b$ lying entirely within $|z| < \rho$ in D_k. From this open covering, we can extract a finite covering U_i, $i = 1, 2, \ldots, m + n + k$, where $U_i = W_i$, $i = 1, \ldots, m$; the U_i, $i = m + 1, \ldots, m + n$, are selected from the V sets; and the

---

†This device was presented by C. Chevalley in Bourbaki Seminar Notes.

U_i, $i = m + n + 1, \ldots, m + n + k$, are selected from the U sets of the covering. Let $\{e_i\}$, $i = 1, \ldots, m + n + k$, be a partition of unity for $\overline{G}$ relative to the covering $\{U_i\}$. We then have

$$\iint_G d\omega_\rho = \sum_{i=1}^{m+n+k} \iint_{U_i \cap G} e_i \, d\omega_\rho. \tag{3}$$

In each integral in the sum on the right side of (3) for which $m + n + 1 \leq i \leq m + n + k$, $U_i \subset G$ and is simply a euclidean rectangle to which we can apply the formula (1) for integration by parts to get

$$\iint_{U_i} e_i \, d\omega_\rho = \int_{\partial U_i} e_i \omega_\rho - \iint_{U_i} \left(f_\rho q \frac{\partial e_i}{\partial x} - f_\rho p \frac{\partial e_i}{\partial y} \right) dx \, dy$$

$$= -\iint_{U_i} \left(f_\rho q \frac{\partial e_i}{\partial x} - f_\rho p \frac{\partial e_i}{\partial y} \right) dx \, dy,$$

since $e_i = 0$ on ∂U_i. Similarly, in each integral in the sum on the right side of (3) for which $m + 1 \leq i \leq m + n$, $U_i \cap G$ is a rectangle $-a < x < a$, $0 < y < b$, and

$$\iint_{U_i \cap G} e_i \, d\omega_\rho = \int_{\partial(U_i \cap G)} e_i \omega_\rho - \iint_{U_i \cap G} \left(f_\rho q \frac{\partial e_i}{\partial x} - f_\rho p \frac{\partial e_i}{\partial y} \right) dx \, dy$$

$$= \int_{C_i} e_i \omega_\rho - \iint_{U_i \cap G} \left(f_\rho q \frac{\partial e_i}{\partial x} - f_\rho p \frac{\partial e_i}{\partial y} \right) dx \, dy,$$

where C_i represents the arc of ∂G in U_i. Finally, the first m terms in the sum on the right side of (3) vanish, since $\omega_\rho = 0$ in each W_i. Summarizing, we get

$$\iint_G d\omega = \sum_{i=m+1}^{m+n} \int_{C_i} e_i \omega_\rho - \sum_{i=m+1}^{m+n+k} \iint_{U_i \cap G} \left(f_\rho q \frac{\partial e_i}{\partial x} - f_\rho p \frac{\partial e_i}{\partial y} \right) dx \, dy. \tag{4}$$

We shall prove that the first sum on the right side of (4) is the integral of ω_ρ over ∂G. Since $e_i = 0$ on ∂G except on C_i, then $\int_{C_i} e_i \omega_\rho = \int_{\partial G} e_i \omega_\rho$. Hence

$$\sum_{i=m+1}^{m+n} \int_{C_i} e_i \omega_\rho = \sum_{i=m+1}^{m+n} \int_{\partial G} e_i \omega_\rho = \int_{\partial G} \sum_{i=m+1}^{m+n} e_i \omega_\rho.$$

Furthermore, $\omega_\rho = 0$ in $U_i \cap \partial G$, $i = 1, \ldots, m$, so that $\int_{\partial G} e_i \omega_\rho = 0$ for $i = 1, \ldots, m$. This enables us to write

$$\int_{\partial G} \sum_{i=m+1}^{m+n} e_i \omega_\rho = \int_{\partial G} \sum_{i=1}^{m+n} e_i \omega_\rho.$$

For any point P_0 on ∂G, the sets U_i, $i = m + n + 1, \ldots, m + n + k$, do not contain P_0, so $\sum_{i=1}^{m+n} e_i(P_0) = 1$ and we have, finally, in (4)

$$\sum_{i=m+1}^{m+n} \int_{C_i} e_i \omega_\rho = \int_{\partial G} \omega_\rho.$$

For the last sum in (4), we observe that $f_\rho p = 0$ and $f_\rho q = 0$ in U_i, $i = 1, \ldots, m$, so we may add the terms from $i = 1$ to $i = m$ in the sum without changing anything. Then select in G any parametric disk $D\colon \tilde{z} = \tilde{\varphi}(P)$; in each U_i such that $U_i \cap D \neq \phi$, we can write e_i, $f_\rho p$, and $f_\rho q$ in terms of $\tilde{z}$ and take note of the contribution of the integrals over D to the sum. We have

$$\sum_{i=1}^{m+n+k} \iint_D \left(f_\rho q \frac{\partial e_i}{\partial \tilde{x}} - f_\rho p \frac{\partial e_i}{\partial \tilde{y}} \right) d\tilde{x}\, d\tilde{y}$$

$$= \iint_D \left[f_\rho q \sum_{i=1}^{m+n+k} \frac{\partial e_i}{\partial \tilde{x}} - f_\rho p \sum_{i=1}^{m+n+k} \frac{\partial e_i}{\partial \tilde{y}} \right] d\tilde{x}\, d\tilde{y}$$

$$= \iint_D \left[f_\rho q \frac{\partial}{\partial \tilde{x}} \sum_{i=1}^{m+n+k} e_i - f_\rho q \frac{\partial}{\partial \tilde{y}} \sum_{i=1}^{m+n+k} e_i \right] d\tilde{x}\, d\tilde{y} = 0,$$

since $\sum_{i=1}^{m+n+k} e_i \equiv 1$. This proves Stokes' theorem for $\omega_\rho = f_\rho \omega$.

As ρ decreases, the only changes in $\iint_G d\omega_\rho$ and in $\int_{\partial G} \omega_\rho$ are due to the contributions in the disks D_k, $k = 1, \ldots, m$, since outside the D_k's, $\omega_\rho = \omega$. Then in D_k,

$$\iint_{D_k \cap G} d\omega_\rho = \iint_{D_k \cap G} \frac{\partial (f_\rho q)}{\partial x} - \frac{\partial (f_\rho p)}{\partial y}\, dx\, dy$$

$$= \iint_{D_k \cap G} f_\rho \left(\frac{\partial q}{\partial x} - \frac{\partial p}{\partial y} \right) dx\, dy + \iint_{D_k \cap G} \left(q \frac{\partial f_\rho}{\partial x} - p \frac{\partial f_\rho}{\partial y} \right) dx\, dy$$

$$= I_\rho + J_\rho.$$

The function f_ρ converges boundedly to 1 in $D_k \cap G$, so that

$$\lim_{\rho \to 0} I_\rho = \iint_{D_k \cap G} d\omega.$$

In D_k, $\partial f_\rho / \partial x = 0$ and $\partial f_\rho / \partial y = 0$ except in A_ρ: $\rho \le |z| \le 2\rho$, where direct calculation shows that grad $f_\rho \le 12/\rho$. In $D_k \cap G$, we have $|p(x, y)| < M$ and $|q(x, y)| < M$ for some M, so that

$$|J_\rho| = \left| \iint_{A_\rho \cap G} \left(q \frac{\partial f_\rho}{\partial x} - p \frac{\partial f_\rho}{\partial y} \right) dx\, dy \right| \le 2M \iint_{A_\rho \cap G} \text{grad } f_\rho\, dx\, dy$$

$$\le \pi \rho^2 \frac{24M}{\rho} \le 24M\pi\rho.$$

Thus $\lim_{\rho \to 0} J_\rho = 0$, and we conclude that

$$\lim_{\rho \to 0} \iint_G d\omega_\rho = \iint_G d\omega.$$

Similarly, since f_ρ converges boundedly to 1 on ∂G with the exception of a finite number of points $P_1, P_2, \ldots, P_m$, we conclude that

$$\lim_{\rho \to 0} \int_{\partial G} \omega_\rho = \int_{\partial G} \omega,$$

and we have completed the proof of (2).

6–4 The exterior differential calculus. The introduction of differentials on a Riemann surface S enabled us to define an invariant theory of integration on S. The manipulation of these differentials is greatly simplified by the introduction of a set of formal rules called the *exterior differential calculus*, originated by E. Cartan (Ref. 13).

We shall find it convenient to refer to complex-valued functions on S as *differentials of order zero*, and denote them by lower-case Latin letters $f, g, \ldots$. Differentials of first order, which locally look like $p\, dx + q\, dy$, will be denoted by lower-case Greek letters, $\omega, \pi, \gamma, \ldots$, while differentials of the second order, which are represented locally as $A(x, y)\, dx\, dy$, will be denoted by capital Greek letters, $\Omega, \Gamma, \ldots$. Sums of differentials of like order have already been defined. We shall now define the exterior product of two differentials in such a way that the (exterior) product of a differential of order k and a differential of order n is a differential of order $k + n$, if $k + n \leq 2$, and is identically zero if $k + n > 2$. The product of two zero-order differentials f and g is denoted by fg, and $(fg)(P) = f(P) \cdot g(P)$ where $f(P) \cdot g(P)$ is the ordinary product of the complex numbers $f(P)$ and $g(P)$. The product of a zero-order differential f and a first-order differential $\omega = p\,dx + q\,dy$ is the differential $f\omega = (fp)\,dx + (fq)\,dy$. To define the product of two first-order differentials, we first establish the convention that

$$dx\,dx = 0, \qquad dy\,dy = 0, \qquad dx\,dy = -dy\,dx.$$

Then, assuming the distributive law for multiplication and addition, we get the product of two first-order differentials $\omega_1 = p_1\,dx + q_1\,dy$, $\omega_2 = p_2\,dx + q_2\,dy$:

$$\begin{aligned}
\omega_1\omega_2 &= (p_1\,dx + q_1\,dy)(p_2\,dx + q_2\,dy) \\
&= p_1p_2\,dx\,dx + p_1q_2\,dx\,dy + q_1p_2\,dy\,dx + q_1q_2\,dy\,dy \\
&= (p_1q_2 - q_1p_2)\,dx\,dy.
\end{aligned}$$

We must verify that this differential is actually a second-order differential by showing that $p_1q_2 - q_1p_2$ satisfies the correct transformation law, but this is a simple calculation. The multiplication so defined is not commutative; rather, we have $\omega_1\omega_2 = -\omega_2\omega_1$. The product of a zero-order differential f and a second-order differential Ω: $A\,dx\,dy$ is the second-order differential $f\Omega = (fA)\,dx\,dy$. It is easy to verify that the multiplication here defined is associative and distributive with respect to addition.

We shall now introduce a linear differential operator d which will act on kth order differentials and yield a differential of order $k + 1$, $k \leq 1$. In general, d locally represents the linear operator $(\partial/\partial x)\,dx + (\partial/\partial y)\,dy$, which is applied as follows: If $f \in C^1$, $df = (\partial f/\partial x)\,dx + (\partial f/\partial y)\,dy$. If $\omega \in C^1$, then

$$\begin{aligned}
d\omega &= (dp)\,dx + (dq)\,dy = \left(\frac{\partial p}{\partial x}\,dx + \frac{\partial p}{\partial y}\,dy\right)dx + \left(\frac{\partial q}{\partial x}\,dx + \frac{\partial q}{\partial y}\,dy\right)dy \\
&= \left(\frac{\partial q}{\partial x} - \frac{\partial p}{\partial y}\right)dx\,dy,
\end{aligned}$$

which is the second-order differential encountered in Stokes' theorem. Applying d to a second-order differential Ω yields $d\Omega = (dA)\,dx\,dy = ((\partial A/\partial x)\,dx + (\partial A/\partial y)\,dy)\,dx\,dy = 0$. It is interesting to note that the operator d has the property that $dd = 0$; that is, for $f \in C^2$, $ddf = ((\partial^2 f/\partial x\,\partial y) - (\partial^2 f/\partial y\,\partial x))\,dx\,dy = 0$, and for $\omega \in C^2$, $dd\omega = 0$ since $d\omega$ is a second-order differential.

For sums of differentials, the operator d is linear. For products, we get

$$d(fg) = f\,dg + g\,df,$$

$$d(f\omega) = (df)\omega + f\,d\omega = -\omega\,(df) + f\,(d\omega).$$

Another useful linear operator is the conjugation operator $*$ which is defined only for first-order differentials. If $\omega = p\,dx + q\,dy$, we define

$$*\omega = -q\,dx + p\,dy.$$

We must verify that $*\omega$ is a differential by selecting another local parameter (u, v) and checking the transformation law. We have

$$-\tilde{q}\,du + \tilde{p}\,dv = -\left(p\frac{\partial x}{\partial v} + q\frac{\partial y}{\partial v}\right)du + \left(p\frac{\partial x}{\partial u} + q\frac{\partial y}{\partial u}\right)dv.$$

Since coordinate changes are conformal, $\partial x/\partial u = \partial y/\partial v$ and $\partial x/\partial v = -\partial y/\partial u$. Thus

$$-\tilde{q}\,du + \tilde{p}\,dv = -\left(-p\frac{\partial y}{\partial u} + q\frac{\partial x}{\partial u}\right)du + \left(p\frac{\partial y}{\partial v} - q\frac{\partial x}{\partial v}\right)dv$$

$$= -q\left(\frac{\partial x}{\partial u}\,du + \frac{\partial x}{\partial v}\,dv\right) + p\left(\frac{\partial y}{\partial u}\,du + \frac{\partial y}{\partial v}\,dv\right)$$

$$= -q\,dx + p\,dy,$$

which is the correct transformation rule. The differential $*\omega$ is called the (star) conjugate of ω.

We shall list several noteworthy properties of the conjugation operator $*$. If $\omega_1 = p_1\,dx + q_1\,dy$ and $\omega_2 = p_2\,dx + q_2\,dy$ locally, we have

$$*\text{ is linear: } *(\omega_1 + \omega_2) = *\omega_1 + *\omega_2, \qquad *(f\omega) = f(*\omega), \tag{1}$$

$$**\omega = *(*\omega) = -\omega, \tag{2}$$

$$\omega_1*\omega_2 = \omega_2*\omega_1 = (p_1p_2 + q_1q_2)\,dx\,dy, \tag{3}$$

$$\omega*\omega = (p^2 + q^2)\,dx\,dy. \tag{4}$$

If we write $d = (\partial/\partial x)\,dx + (\partial/\partial y)\,dy$, we can define the operator $*d = -(\partial/\partial y)\,dx + (\partial/\partial x)\,dy$. Then for $f \in C^1$,

$$*(df) = *\left(\frac{\partial f}{\partial x}\,dx + \frac{\partial f}{\partial y}\,dy\right) = -\frac{\partial f}{\partial y}\,dx + \frac{\partial f}{\partial x}\,dy = (*d)f, \qquad (5)$$

enabling us to write $*df$ unambiguously. If, for $f \in C^2$, $\omega = *df$, we say ω is *coexact*.

Since $*$ operates only on first-order differentials, $*d\omega$ can only have the meaning $(*d)\omega$. Then

$$*d\omega = \left(-\frac{\partial}{\partial y}\,dx + \frac{\partial}{\partial x}\,dy\right)(p\,dx + q\,dy) = \left(-\frac{\partial q}{\partial y} - \frac{\partial p}{\partial x}\right)dx\,dy,$$

while

$$d*\omega = \left(\frac{\partial}{\partial x}\,dx + \frac{\partial}{\partial y}\,dy\right)(-q\,dx + p\,dy) = \left(\frac{\partial p}{\partial x} + \frac{\partial q}{\partial y}\right)dx\,dy.$$

Hence

$$*d\omega = -d*\omega. \qquad (6)$$

If, for $\omega \in C^1$, $d*\omega = 0$, we say that ω is *co-closed*. If $d*\omega = 0$, $*\omega$ is locally exact, and locally $*\omega = df$ or $\omega = *d(-f)$, so that a co-closed differential is locally coexact.

A particularly useful operator on functions $f \in C^2$ is $\Delta = d*d$; for

$$\Delta f = d*df = \left(\frac{\partial^2 f}{\partial x^2} + \frac{\partial^2 f}{\partial y^2}\right)dx\,dy. \qquad (7)$$

We shall call Δ the *Laplace operator*. Various forms of Stokes' theorem can now be neatly expressed in terms of these operators. For $f \in C^1$ and $\omega \in C^1$ in $\overline{G}$ for a regular region G, $d(f\omega) = -\omega\,df + f\,d\omega$, and we can say that $\iint_G d(f\omega) = -\iint_G \omega\,df + \iint_G f\,d\omega$. By Stokes' theorem, $\iint_G d(f\omega) = \int_{\partial G} f\omega$, so we get

$$\iint_G f\,d\omega = \int_{\partial G} f\omega + \iint_G \omega\,df, \qquad (8)$$

which is a restatement of formula (1) of Section 6–3 for integration by parts on S. If $g \in C^2$ in $\overline{G}$, we can replace ω in (8) by $*dg$; then

$$\iint_G f(d*dg) = \int_{\partial G} f*dg + \iint_G (*dg)\,df,$$

or

$$\iint\limits_{G} f \, \Delta g = \int\limits_{\partial G} f {*} dg - \iint\limits_{G} df {*} dg. \qquad (9)$$

If we interchange the roles of f and g in (9), assuming here that $f \in C^2$, $g \in C^2$ in $\overline{G}$, and then subtract the two formulas, we obtain

$$\iint\limits_{G} (f \, \Delta g - g \, \Delta f) = \int\limits_{\partial G} (f {*} dg - g {*} df). \qquad (10)$$

Let D represent a parametric disk about a point P_0 on ∂G and let $C = (\alpha, I)$ represent an analytic arc in ∂G which lies in D. In terms of the local coordinates $\Phi(P) = (x, y)$ in D, the parameter of arc length s along C is given by

$$s = \int_{t=0}^{t} \sqrt{\left(\frac{dx}{dt}\right)^2 + \left(\frac{dy}{dt}\right)^2} \, dt,$$

where $\Phi[\alpha(t)] = (x(t), y(t))$. Then $\int_C df = \int_C (\partial f/\partial s) \, ds$ and $\int_C {*} df = \int_C [-(\partial f/\partial y) \, dx + (\partial f/\partial x) \, dy] = -\int_C (\partial f/\partial n) \, ds$, where $\partial f/\partial n$ represents the directional derivative of f in the direction of the normal to C pointing *into* G; that is, to the left of the oriented tangent vector to C. In this sense, we can say

$$\int\limits_{\partial G} df = \int\limits_{\partial G} \frac{\partial f}{\partial s} \, ds, \qquad \int\limits_{\partial G} {*} df = -\int\limits_{\partial G} \frac{\partial f}{\partial n} \, ds. \qquad (11)$$

We end this section with another special consequence of Stokes' theorem which will be especially useful later.

THEOREM 6–4. *If $f \in C^1$ and $\omega \in C^1$ on a Riemann surface S and either f or ω has a compact carrier K on S, then*

$$\iint\limits_{S} d(f\omega) = \iint\limits_{S} f \, d\omega - \iint\limits_{S} \omega \, df = 0. \qquad (12)$$

The proof is divided into the consideration of two cases: (a) S compact, and (b) S not compact.

(a) When S is compact, we may cover S by a finite number of local rectangles U_i, $i = 1, 2, \ldots, n$, and form a partition of unity $\{e_i\}$ for S relative to the $\{U_i\}$. Thus, applying (8) in each U_i, we get

$$\iint_S d(f\omega) = \sum_{i=1}^n \iint_{U_i} e_i \, d(f\omega) = \sum_{i=1}^n \left\{ \int_{\partial U_i} e_i f\omega + \iint_{U_i} f\omega \, de_i \right\}$$

$$= \iint_S f\omega \, d\left(\sum_{i=1}^n e_i \right) = 0,$$

since $e_i = 0$ on ∂U_i and $\sum_{i=1}^n e_i \equiv 1$. But $\iint_S d(f\omega) = \iint_S f \, d\omega - \iint_S \omega \, df$, proving (12).

(b) When S is not compact, we can cover K with a finite number of parametric disks D_i, $i = 1, 2, \ldots, n$, the boundary of each being an analytic curve $|z| = 1$. Then $G = \cup_{i=1}^n D_i$ is a region on S with compact closure whose boundary is composed of a finite number of piecewise analytic curves. On ∂G, either f or ω vanishes, so application of (8) gives (12).

6–5 Harmonic and analytic differentials. A differential ω is called exact when there is a function $f \in C^2$ on S such that $\omega = df$. A differential ω is called closed if it is locally exact, i.e., if in each parametric disk D, there is a function f defined and in C^2 in D such that $\omega = df$. A necessary and sufficient condition for $\omega \in C^1$ on S to be closed is $\partial p/\partial y = \partial q/\partial x$, and since $d\omega = ((\partial q/\partial x) - (\partial p/\partial y)) \, dx \, dy$, we can state this as follows:

THEOREM 6–5. *A differential ω is closed if and only if $\omega \in C^1$ and $d\omega = 0$ on S.*

Every exact differential is closed ($ddf = 0$), but the converse is not true.

If ω is a closed differential and C is any curve on S, we have defined $\int_C \omega$. If C is a closed curve, we call $\int_C \omega$ the *period* of ω on C. If C and C' are homologous closed curves, $\int_C \omega = \int_{C'} \omega$, so that the period depends only upon the homology class of C. In particular, when $C \sim 0$ and $d\omega = 0$, then $\int_C \omega = 0$. If ω is exact and C is a closed curve, we have shown that $\int_C \omega = 0$, or all periods of an exact differential are zero. We shall now prove the converse.

THEOREM 6–6. *A closed differential ω is exact if and only if all its periods are zero.*

Fix a point Q on S and observe that the integral $\int_Q^P \omega$ is well defined for any point P on S if we understand it to mean the integral over any path from Q to P; for if C_1 and C_2 are any two curves from Q to P, $C_1 C_2^{-1}$ is a closed curve and $\int_{C_1 C_2^{-1}} \omega = 0$. We may therefore define the function $F(P) = \int_Q^P \omega$. We shall now prove that $F \in C^1$ and $dF = \omega$. At any point P_0 on S, we take a parametric disk D with local parameter $\Phi(P) = (x, y)$, $\Phi(P_0) = (0, 0)$. Then for any point P in D, we have $F(P) = \int_Q^{P_0} \omega + \int_{P_0}^P \omega$, where the last integral is taken over a line segment in D from P_0 to P.

Now we compute $\partial F/\partial x$ and $\partial F/\partial y$ at $(0, 0)$, where $\omega = p\,dx + q\,dy$:

$$\frac{\partial F}{\partial x} = \lim_{x \to 0} \frac{1}{x} [F(\Phi^{-1}(x, 0)) - F(\Phi^{-1}(0, 0))]$$

$$= \lim_{x \to 0} \frac{1}{x} \int_0^x p(x, 0)\,dx = p(0, 0),$$

$$\frac{\partial F}{\partial y} = \lim_{y \to 0} [F(\Phi^{-1}(0, y)) - F(\Phi^{-1}(0, 0))]$$

$$= \lim_{y \to 0} \frac{1}{y} \int_0^y q(0, y)\,dy = q(0, 0).$$

Since $\partial F/\partial x = p$, $\partial F/\partial y = q$, and $p, q \in C^1$, we have $F \in C^2$ and $\omega = dF$.

A function $f \in C^2$ is called *harmonic* on S if $\Delta f = 0$. This means that locally $\partial^2 f/\partial x^2 + \partial^2 f/\partial y^2 = 0$. A differential $\omega \in C^1$ on S is called a *harmonic differential* if in each parametric disk D, ω is the total differential of a harmonic function in D. If ω is harmonic, the fact that it is locally a total differential means that ω is closed and hence $d\omega = 0$; then $\omega = df$ and $d*df = 0$ in D, or simply $d*\omega = 0$. Conversely, when $d\omega = 0$ and $d*\omega = 0$, the first implies $\omega = df$ locally and the second implies $d(*df) = 0$, and f is harmonic so that ω is harmonic. We have therefore proved the following theorem.

THEOREM 6–7. $\omega \in C^1$ *is harmonic if and only if* $d\omega = 0$ *and* $d*\omega = 0$, *that is, if ω is both closed and co-closed.*

If $\omega = p\,dx + q\,dy$ is a harmonic differential,

$$d\omega = \left(\frac{\partial q}{\partial x} - \frac{\partial p}{\partial y}\right) dx\,dy = 0,$$

$$d*\omega = \left(\frac{\partial p}{\partial x} + \frac{\partial q}{\partial y}\right) dx\,dy = 0.$$

Thus we have locally $\partial p/\partial y = \partial q/\partial x$ and $\partial p/\partial x = -\partial q/\partial y$. But these are just the Cauchy-Riemann equations for p and $-q$, so the differential ω is harmonic if and only if $p - iq$ is locally a regular analytic (holomorphic) function of $z = x + iy$. In what follows, the terms "regular analytic" and "holomorphic" are synonymous.

A function $f \in C^1$ is regular analytic on S when locally $f(x, y) = u(x, y) + iv(x, y)$ and u and v satisfy the Cauchy-Riemann equations. We shall now express this condition in a manner involving the differential of f; we have $df = du + i\,dv$, where

$$dv = \frac{\partial v}{\partial x}\,dx + \frac{\partial v}{\partial y}\,dy = -\frac{\partial u}{\partial y}\,dx + \frac{\partial u}{\partial x}\,dy = *du,$$

so that du and dv are conjugate differentials. Thus we can write

$$df = du + i*du, \qquad *df = *du - i\,du = -i\,df.$$

On the other hand, if $f \in C^1$ and $*df = -i\,df$, f is holomorphic, for this condition implies that $dv = *du$, which implies the Cauchy-Riemann equations. Thus we have obtained a criterion for f to be holomorphic on S that is expressed in terms of operators on S: namely, $f \in C^1$ *is holomorphic on S if and only if* $*df = -i\,df$. We have also shown that if the real functions u and v satisfy $dv = *du$, then u and v are conjugate harmonic functions, for they satisfy the Cauchy-Riemann equations.

A differential ω on S is called a *regular analytic* or *holomorphic differential* if in each parametric disk it is the total differential of a holomorphic function defined in that disk. A differential $\omega \in C^1$ is locally exact if and only if $d\omega = 0$. We then have locally $\omega = df$, and for f to be holomorphic, $*df = -i\,df$ or $*\omega = -i\omega$. Thus we may state as a criterion for the analyticity of a differential:

THEOREM 6–8. $\omega \in C^1$ *is holomorphic on S if and only if $d\omega = 0$ and $*\omega = -i\omega$.*

If ω is holomorphic, we note that $d\omega = 0$ and $d*\omega = -i\,d\omega = 0$, so that ω is also harmonic.

Let us examine the conditions imposed on the coefficients p and q by the requirement that $*\omega = -i\omega$. We have $*\omega = -q\,dx + p\,dy$ and $-i\omega = -ip\,dx - iq\,dy$. Thus $*\omega = -i\omega$ is equivalent to $q = ip$, or $\omega = p\,dx + ip\,dy = p(dx + i\,dy)$. It seems natural to define $dz = dx + i\,dy$; with this convention, we see that $*\omega = -i\omega$ *if and only if locally $\omega = p\,dz$.* We call a differential which satisfies $*\omega = -i\omega$ a *pure* differential. A differential ω is holomorphic if and only if it is closed and pure. If ω is pure, the condition $d\omega = 0$ means that $d(p\,dx + ip\,dy) = 0$ or $\partial p/\partial y = i\,\partial p/\partial x$. If $p = u + iv$, where u and v are real, then $\partial u/\partial y = -\partial v/\partial x$ and $\partial u/\partial x = \partial v/\partial y$, which are the Cauchy-Riemann equations for p. Therefore ω is analytic if and only if locally $\omega = p\,dz$, where p is a holomorphic function of $z = x + iy$. For a holomorphic differential $\omega = p\,dz$, the transformation rule (3) of Section 6–2 becomes

$$\tilde{p}(u, v) = p(x, y)\left(\frac{\partial x}{\partial u} + i\frac{\partial y}{\partial u}\right) = p(x, y)\,\frac{dz}{dw},$$

so that $\tilde{p}\,dw = p(dz/dw)\,dw = p\,dz$, where we have set $w = u + iv$.

We shall define the *modulus* of a holomorphic differential ω to be $|\omega| = |p(x, y)| \, |dz| = |p(x, y)| \sqrt{dx^2 + dy^2}$ locally. If variables are changed to (u, v), we have $p \, dz = \tilde{p} \, dw$, $w = u + iv$, and $|\omega| = |\tilde{p}(u, v)| \, |dw| = |\tilde{p}(u, v)| \sqrt{du^2 + dv^2}$. We may use this to define the integral of $|\omega|$ over a differentiable curve $C = (\alpha, I)$. First assume that C lies in one parametric disk with local coordinates $\Phi(P) = (x, y)$. Then we set $\Phi[\alpha(t)] = (x(t), y(t))$, $0 \le t \le 1$, and define

$$\int_C |\omega| = \int_{t=0}^1 |p(x(t), y(t))| \sqrt{\left(\frac{dx}{dt}\right)^2 + \left(\frac{dy}{dt}\right)^2} \, dt.$$

This definition is clearly invariant under changes of coordinates. If C extends beyond a single parametric disk, we subdivide C into arcs $C_1, C_2, \ldots, C_n$, each lying in one parametric disk, and set

$$\int_C |\omega| = \sum_{i=1}^n \int_{C_i} |\omega|.$$

Again it is a simple matter to verify that the integral on the left is independent of the subdivision. We observe that $\int_C |\omega|$ is always a non-negative number. In particular, if $C^{-1} = (\beta, I)$, $\beta(t) = \alpha(1 - t)$, lies in one parametric disk with $\Phi[\beta(t)] = (\beta_1(t), \beta_2(t))$ and $\Phi[\alpha(t)] = (\alpha_1(t), \alpha_2(t))$, we have

$$\int_{C^{-1}} |\omega| = \int_{t=0}^1 |p(\beta_1(t), \beta_2(t))| \sqrt{\left(\frac{d\beta_1(t)}{dt}\right)^2 + \left(\frac{d\beta_2(t)}{dt}\right)^2} \, dt$$

$$= \int_{t=0}^1 |p(\alpha_1(1 - t), \alpha_2(1 - t))| \sqrt{\left(\frac{d\alpha_1(1 - t)}{dt}\right)^2 + \left(\frac{d\alpha_2(1 - t)}{dt}\right)^2} \, dt$$

$$= \int_{u=1}^0 |p(\alpha_1(u), \alpha_2(u))| \sqrt{\left(-\frac{d\alpha_1(u)}{du}\right)^2 + \left(-\frac{d\alpha_2(u)}{du}\right)^2} \, (-du)$$

$$= \int_{u=0}^1 |p(\alpha_1(u), \alpha_2(u))| \sqrt{\left(\frac{d\alpha_1(u)}{du}\right)^2 + \left(\frac{d\alpha_2(u)}{du}\right)^2} \, du$$

$$= \int_C |\omega|.$$

Thus $\int_{C^{-1}} |\omega| = \int_C |\omega|$ for any differentiable (or, in fact, piecewise differentiable) curve C.

If f is a holomorphic function on S, then locally

$$df = \frac{\partial f}{\partial x}\, dx + \frac{\partial f}{\partial y}\, dy = \left(\frac{\partial u}{\partial x} + i\,\frac{\partial v}{\partial x}\right) dx + \left(\frac{\partial u}{\partial y} + i\,\frac{\partial v}{\partial y}\right) dy$$

$$= \left(\frac{\partial u}{\partial x} + i\,\frac{\partial v}{\partial x}\right)(dx + i\, dy) = f'(z)\, dz,$$

and we have simply $df = f'(z)\, dz$, where $f'(z)$ denotes the derivative of f with respect to the complex variable $z = x + iy$.

For any closed differential ω in a regular region G, Stokes' theorem says that $\int_{\partial G} \omega = \iint_G d\omega = 0$. Since any holomorphic differential is closed, we have the *Cauchy theorem*:

THEOREM 6–9. *If ω is a holomorphic differential and G is a regular region, then*

$$\int_{\partial G} \omega = 0. \tag{1}$$

If ω is a harmonic differential, $d\omega = 0$ and $d*\omega = 0$. Thus $*\omega$ also satisfies $d(*\omega) = 0$ and $d*(*\omega) = -d\omega = 0$, which implies that $*\omega$ is also harmonic. The differential $*\omega$ is called the *conjugate harmonic differential* to ω. Then the differential $\gamma = \omega + i*\omega$ is holomorphic, for clearly $d\gamma = d\omega + id*\omega = 0$ and $*\gamma = *\omega - i\omega = -i\gamma$. Therefore, to every harmonic differential corresponds the holomorphic differential $\omega + i*\omega$.

We shall now define a complex conjugate of a differential which is to be distinguished from the star conjugate already introduced. For the complex-valued function $f = g + ih$, we set $\bar{f} = g - ih$. Then the complex conjugate $\bar{\omega}$ of the differential $\omega = p\, dx + q\, dy$ is the differential $\bar{\omega} = \bar{p}\, dx + \bar{q}\, dy$, where $\bar{p}$ and $\bar{q}$ are the complex conjugates of the complex-valued functions p and q. For $\Omega = A\, dx\, dy$, we simply set $\bar{\Omega} = \bar{A}\, dx\, dy$. The complex conjugation operator is linear and commutes with d and $*$; that is, $d\bar{\omega} = \overline{d\omega}$ and $*\bar{\omega} = \overline{*\omega}$. When ω is a complex differential,

$$\gamma = \frac{\omega + \bar{\omega}}{2} = \frac{p + \bar{p}}{2}\, dx + \frac{q + \bar{q}}{2}\, dy$$

is a real differential called the real part of ω. If ω is harmonic, its real part is also harmonic and, in particular, the real part of every holomorphic differential is harmonic. Conversely, if a real harmonic differential γ is given, then $\omega = \gamma + i*\gamma$ is a holomorphic differential with real part γ, so that every real harmonic differential is the real part of a holomorphic differential. This nice duality between real harmonic differentials and holomorphic differentials does not hold for functions. The real harmonic function f on S may not have a single-valued conjugate harmonic function g satisfying $\partial f/\partial x = \partial g/\partial y$, $\partial f/\partial y = -\partial g/\partial x$, so that there may be no single-valued holomorphic function on S having f for its real part. To show the existence of holomorphic differentials on S, it is enough to show the existence of real harmonic differentials. Then to see whether there are any single-valued holomorphic functions on S, we merely determine whether any of the holomorphic differentials are exact.

The harmonic and holomorphic functions and differentials so far considered have been in class C^1 in a region G or on all of the Riemann surface S; these are called *regular* functions and differentials. We shall also be interested in functions and differentials which fail to be in C^1 at isolated points, at which the function or differential is said to be *singular*. Let h be a function which is defined in a neighborhood U of a point P_0 and is harmonic (or analytic) and regular in $U - P_0$. We say that the harmonic (or analytic) function f has the singularity h at P_0 if $f - h$ is regular and harmonic (analytic) in U. Similarly, if θ is a differential which is defined in the neighborhood U of P_0 and which is harmonic (analytic) and regular in $U - P_0$, we say that a harmonic (analytic) differential ω has the singularity θ at P_0 if $\omega - \theta$ is regular and harmonic (analytic) in U.

If an analytic function f expressed in the local parameter $\varphi(P) = z = x + iy$, $\varphi(P_0) = 0$, has the series expansion

$$g(z) = f(\varphi^{-1}(z)) = a_n z^n + a_{n+1} z^{n+1} + \cdots, \qquad a_n \neq 0,$$

then f is said to have a *zero* of order n if $n > 0$ and a *pole* of order $-n$ if $n < 0$. The order of a pole or a zero is invariant under coordinate changes. Locally n is characterized by being the only integer k for which

$$\lim_{z \to 0} z^{-k} g(z)$$

has a finite nonzero value. If we change coordinates by a conformal mapping $z = \zeta(w)$, $\zeta(0) = 0$, $\zeta'(0) \neq 0$, we get $\tilde{g}(w) = g(\zeta(w))$, and $\lim_{w \to 0} w^{-n} \tilde{g}(w) = \lim_{w \to 0} w^{-n} g(\zeta(w)) = \lim_{w \to 0} (w^{-n}/z^{-n}) z^{-n} g(z) = \zeta'(0)^n \lim_{z \to 0} z^{-n} g(z) \neq 0$ and is finite. Thus the order of a zero or a pole is invariantly defined.

If f has a pole of order n at P_0, its singularity or principal part is given by

$$h(\varphi^{-1}(z)) = \frac{a_{-n}}{z^n} + \frac{a_{-n+1}}{z^{n-1}} + \cdots + \frac{a_{-1}}{z}.$$

An analytic function whose only singularities on the surface S are poles is called a *meromorphic function*.

We shall also be interested in analytic differentials which have the local representation

$$\omega = p(z)\, dz = (a_n z^n + a_{n+1} z^{n+1} + \cdots)\, dz, \qquad a_n \neq 0.$$

Here again we say that ω has a *zero* of order n at P_0 if $n > 0$ and a *pole* of order $-n$ if $n < 0$. The order n is invariantly defined, for under the conformal mapping $z = \zeta(w)$, $\zeta(0) = 0$, $\zeta'(0) \neq 0$, we have $\tilde{p}(w) = p(\zeta(w))\,(d\zeta/dw)$, so that

$$\lim_{w \to 0} w^{-n}\tilde{p}(w) = \lim_{w \to 0} \frac{w^{-n}}{\zeta(w)^{-n}}\, \zeta(w)^{-n} p(\zeta(w)) \frac{d\zeta}{dw} = \zeta'(0) \lim_{z \to 0} z^{-n} p(z),$$

which is finite and nonzero when and only when $\lim_{z \to 0} z^{-n} p(z)$ is both finite and nonzero, and this property characterizes n. If ω has a pole of order n its singularity differential is

$$\theta = (a_{-n} z^{-n} + a_{-n+1} z^{-n+1} + \cdots + a_{-1} z^{-1})\, dz.$$

A pole of order 1 is called a *simple pole*. An analytic differential whose only singularities on S are poles is called a *meromorphic differential*.

Let D be a parametric disk $|z| < r$ about P_0 in which ω has no singularity other than a pole at P_0 with principal part θ. Then in D, $\omega - \theta$ is holomorphic and

$$\int_{\partial D} \omega = \int_{\partial D} \theta - \int_{\partial D} (\omega - \theta).$$

By the Cauchy theorem (1), $\int_{\partial D} (\omega - \theta) = 0$ and

$$\int_{\partial D} \omega = \int_{\partial D} \theta = \sum_{k=1}^{N} \int_{\varphi=0}^{2\pi} i a_{-k} r^{1-k} e^{i(1-k)\varphi}\, d\varphi = 2\pi i a_{-1}.$$

Since the integral $\int_{\partial D} \omega$ is invariant under changes of local parameter, the coefficient a_{-1} in the local series expansion of ω is invariant. The coefficient a_{-1} in ω is called the *residue* of ω.

THEOREM 6–10. *The sum of the residues of a meromorphic differential ω on a compact surface S is zero.*

Since S is compact, there can be only a finite number of isolated points $P_1, P_2, \ldots, P_m$ at which ω has poles. Assume that the residue of ω at P_k

is $a_{-1}^{(k)}$. Place a parametric disk D_k about each P_k, small enough so that $D_k \cap D_j = \phi, j \neq k$. Then $G = S - \cup_{k=1}^{m} D_k$ is a regular region on S, and we have $\int_{\partial G} \omega = 0$ by (1). However, ∂G consists of the curves ∂D_k traversed in the negative sense relative to D_k; hence

$$\int_{\partial G} \omega = - \sum_{k=1}^{m} \int_{\partial D_k} \omega = -2\pi i \sum_{k=1}^{m} a_{-1}^{(k)} = 0,$$

proving our assertion.

THEOREM 6–11. *If $\omega_1 = p_1\,dz$ and $\omega_2 = p_2\,dz$ are two meromorphic differentials on S, then $\omega_1/\omega_2 = p_1(z)/p_2(z) = f(z)$ defines a meromorphic function on S.*

For locally $f(z)$ has as its only singularities the poles of ω_1 and the zeros of ω_2. That it assigns only one value to a given point on S (independent of the local coordinates used) is clear from the fact that ω_1 and ω_2 transform as differentials: if $z = \zeta(w)$ is a conformal change of coordinates, then

$$\tilde{p}_1(w) = p_1(z)\,(dz/dw), \qquad \tilde{p}_2(w) = p_2(z)\,(dz/dw),$$

and

$$\tilde{p}_1(w)/\tilde{p}_2(w) = p_1(z)/p_2(z),$$

so that the same numerical value is assigned to a given point regardless of which coordinate system is used.

If f is a meromorphic function on S, then df and df/f are meromorphic differentials. If f locally has the series expansion

$$g(z) = f(\varphi^{-1}(z)) = a_n z^n + a_{n+1} z^{n+1} + \cdots$$

$$= z^n(a_n + a_{n+1} z + \cdots), \qquad a_n \neq 0,$$

then locally

$$\frac{df}{f} = \frac{g'(z)}{g(z)}\,dz = d(\log g(z)) = \left(\frac{n}{z} + b_0 + b_1 z + \cdots\right) dz.$$

Thus the residue of df/f at a zero or pole of f is precisely the order of the zero or the negative of the order of the pole. The fact that the sum of the residues is zero on a compact surface tells us that *for a meromorphic function on a compact Riemann surface, the sum N of the orders of the zeros is equal to the sum P of the orders of the poles.* If this same argument is applied to the meromorphic function $f - A$ for some complex number A, we see that the sum of the number of times f assumes any value A on a compact surface (counting multiplicity) is the same as the sum of the orders of the poles of f. We have now proved:

THEOREM 6–12. *A meromorphic function assumes every value the same number of times on a compact Riemann surface.*

On the sphere, the meromorphic functions are precisely the rational functions and we have here extended this well-known property of rational functions to an arbitrary compact Riemann surface.

If G is a regular region on S and ω is an analytic differential in $\overline{G}$ with poles at $P_1, P_2, \ldots, P_m$ interior to G, the residue at P_k being $a_{-1}^{(k)}$, $k = 1, 2, \ldots, m$, then

$$\int_{\partial G} \omega = 2\pi i \sum_{k=1}^{m} a_{-1}^{(k)}.$$

Again let D_k be a parametric disk about P_k with $\overline{D}_k \subset G$ and $D_k \cap D_j = \phi$ when $j \neq k$. Then $G' = G - \cup_{k=1}^{m} D_k$ is a regular region and $\int_{\partial G'} \omega = \int_{\partial G} \omega - \sum_{k=1}^{m} \int_{\partial D_k} \omega = 0$, while $\int_{\partial D_k} \omega = 2\pi i a_{-1}^{(k)}$.

If f is an analytic function in $\overline{G}$ which has a finite number of zeros and poles interior to G, and is regular on ∂G, then $(1/2\pi i) \int_{\partial G} (df/f)$ is the sum of the residues of df/f in G and hence is equal to $N - P$, the zero sum minus the pole sum for f. We then have

$$\int_{\partial G} \frac{df}{f} = 2\pi i (N - P),$$

where N represents the sum of the orders of the zeros of f in G, and P represents the sum of the orders of the poles of f in G.

PROBLEMS

The problems in this set and at the end of Chapter 7 lead to the deRham and Hodge theorems for compact Riemann surfaces.

1. Let S be a compact Riemann surface of genus g with a given triangulation Δ. That we may assume that each triangle is bounded by analytic arcs will be demonstrated in Chapter 9. Prove that the set of all differentials of order $n(= 0, 1, 2)$ with coefficients of class C^{2-n} on S form a group $D_n^*(S)$ under addition.

2. Two groups G and H are said to be *paired* to a third group K [we write $(G, H) \rightarrow K$] if there is a function (g, h), $g \in G$, $h \in H$, distributive in both variables, with values in K (see Lefschetz, Ref. 30, pp. 59–61). Let $C^n(S_\Delta)$

represent the group of simplicial n-chains on S_Δ. Show that $C^n(S_\Delta)$ and $D_n^*(S)$ are paired to the complex numbers K when we set for

$$n = 0: \quad \left(\sum_{i=1}^m \alpha_i \langle P_i \rangle, f \right) = \sum_{i=1}^m \alpha_i f(P_i),$$

$$n = 1: \quad \left(\sum \alpha_i s_i^1, \omega \right) = \sum_{i=1}^m \alpha_i \int_{s_i^1} \omega,$$

$$n = 2: \quad \left(\sum_{i=1}^m \alpha_i s_i^2, \Omega \right) = \sum_{i=1}^m \alpha_i \iint_{s_i^2} \Omega.$$

3. Prove that for $c^{n+1} \in C^{n+1}(S_\Delta)$ and $\omega^n \in D_n^*(S)$, we have $(\partial c^{n+1}, \omega^n) = (c^{n+1}, d\omega^n)$ for $n = 0, 1, 2$ (for $n = 2$, both sides are zero).

4. A differential $\omega^n \in D_n^*(S)$, $n = 0, 1, 2$, is called closed if $d\omega^n = 0$ and is called exact if there exists a differential $\pi^{n-1} \in D_{n-1}^*(S)$ such that $\omega^n = d\pi^{n-1}$. Show that the exact differentials form a subgroup $B_n^*(S)$ of the closed differentials, which themselves form a subgroup $Z_n^*(S)$ of $D_n^*(S)$. Then define $H_n^*(S) = Z_n^*(S)/B_n^*(S)$, which is called the nth deRham cohomology group of S.

5. Let $Z^n(S_\Delta)$ be the group of simplicial n-cycles. Case $n = 1$ of Problem 2 defines a pairing $(Z^1(S_\Delta), Z_1^*(S)) \to K$. Prove that $B_1^*(S)$ is the annihilator of $Z^1(S_\Delta)$; that is,

   (a) $(c, \omega) = 0$ when $c \in Z^1(S_\Delta)$ and $\omega \in B_1^*(S)$;
   (b) $(c, \omega) = 0$ for all $c \in Z^1(S_\Delta)$ implies $\omega \in B_1^*(S)$.

6. Let $B^n(S_\Delta)$ be the group of simplicial n-boundaries. In the pairing $(Z^1(S_\Delta), Z_1^*(S)) \to K$, prove that $B^1(S_\Delta)$ is the annihilator of $Z_1^*(S)$, that is,

   (a) $(c, \omega) = 0$ when $c \in B^1(S_\Delta)$ and $\omega \in Z_1^*(S)$;
   (b) $(c, \omega) = 0$ for all $\omega \in Z_1^*(S)$ implies $c \in B^1(S_\Delta)$ (the construction of π_1 in Section 10–1 will be useful to display a differential with given period on a given cycle).

7. If c_1 and c_2 are in $Z^1(S_\Delta)$ and ω_1 and ω_2 are in $Z_1^*(S)$, show that $(c_1, \omega_1) = (c_2, \omega_2)$ when $c_1 - c_2 \in B^1(S_\Delta)$ and $\omega_1 - \omega_2 \in B_1^*(S)$. Prove that this enables us to define a pairing $(H^1(S_\Delta), H_1^*(S)) \to K$, where K represents the complex numbers. Show that in this pairing

   (a)   for any $[c] \in H^1(S_\Delta)$, the relation $([c], [\omega]) = 0$ for all $[\omega] \in H_1^*(S)$ implies that $[c] = 0$;
   (b)   for any $[\omega] \in H_1^*(S)$, the relation $([c], [\omega]) = 0$ for all $[c] \in H^1(S_\Delta)$ implies that $[\omega] = 0$. Such a pairing is called an orthogonal pairing.

8. Carry out a similar analysis for $n = 0$ and $n = 2$.

CHAPTER 7

THE HILBERT SPACE OF DIFFERENTIALS

7-1 Definition and properties of Hilbert space. In the chapter following this, a proof will be given for the existence of harmonic differentials with prescribed properties on our arbitrary abstract Riemann surface. The language used in the proof will be made considerably briefer and more easily understood if the notions of Hilbert space are introduced. A Hilbert space is a generalization of an n-dimensional vector space which actually enjoys most of the important properties of the n-dimensional vector spaces. It is defined precisely as follows.

A set H of elements (points) $x, y, z, \ldots$ is called a (*complex*) *Hilbert space* if it satisfies the following axioms.

A. H is a complex vector space; that is, for any points $x, y, z, \ldots$ in H:

    1. Addition $(+)$ of elements is defined [so that to $x \in H$, $y \in H$ corresponds $(x + y) \in H$] which is associative and commutative.

    2. There exists an element 0 in H such that $0 + x = x$ for any $x \in H$.

    3. Every element $x \in H$ has an additive inverse; that is, an element $-x$ with the property $x + (-x) = 0$.

    4. For any complex number α (called a scalar) and any $x \in H$, there is associated an element αx in H. This scalar multiplication is distributive and associative: if α, β are complex numbers and $x, y \in H$, then $(\alpha + \beta)x = \alpha x + \beta x$, $\alpha(x + y) = \alpha x + \alpha y$, $(\alpha\beta)x = \alpha(\beta x)$.

    5. $1 \cdot x = x$ for all $x \in H$.

B. A complex-valued bilinear functional (x, y), called the *inner product*, which enjoys the following properties, is defined in H:

    1. $(x, y) = \overline{(y, x)}$; that is, the inner product is Hermitian.

    2. $(\alpha x, y) = \alpha(x, y)$ for all complex α. From B1, we get $(x, \alpha y) = \bar{\alpha}(x, y)$.

    3. $(x + y, z) = (x, z) + (y, z)$.

    4. $(x, x) \geq 0$ and $(x, x) = 0$ if and only if $x = 0$.

C. If we define the norm of an element $x \in H$ to be $\|x\| = \sqrt{(x, x)}$ and the distance between x and $y \in H$ to be $\rho(x, y) = \|x - y\|$, then H is complete in this norm. This means that if $\{x_n\}$ is a sequence of points in H and if, for any positive number ϵ, there exists an integer N such that $\rho(x_m, x_n) < \epsilon$ for $m > N$, $n > N$, then there is an element $x \in H$ such that $\lim_{n \to \infty} \rho(x_n, x) = 0$.

If the scalars are restricted to be real numbers and the inner product is real-valued, we say that H is a *real Hilbert space*.

THEOREM 7–1. *For any* $x \in H$, $0x = 0$ *and* $(-1)x = -x$.

The first follows from B2 and B4, since $(0x, 0x) = 0(x, x) = 0$ implies $0x = 0$.   Then $x + (-1)x = (1 - 1)x = 0$,   from which follows $(-1)x = -x$.

THEOREM 7–2. *With the distance function* $\rho(x, y) = ||x - y||$, H *is a complete metric space.*†

That $\rho(x, y) = 0$ implies that $x = y$ and $\rho(x, y) = \rho(y, x)$ are true follows from B1 and B4. The triangle inequality will follow from the *Schwarz inequality*, which states that for $x \in H$, $y \in H$,

$$|(x, y)| \leq ||x|| \cdot ||y||. \tag{1}$$

To prove (1), observe that from B4, for any complex number λ,

$$||x - \lambda y||^2 \geq 0.$$

But from C,

$$||x - \lambda y||^2 = (x - \lambda y \cdot x - \lambda y) = (x, x) - \lambda(y, x) - \bar{\lambda}(x, y) + \lambda\bar{\lambda}(y, y)$$
$$= ||x||^2 - 2 \operatorname{Re} \bar{\lambda}(x, y) + |\lambda|^2 ||y||^2.$$

If $(x, y) = re^{i\theta}$, and $\lambda = \mu e^{i\theta}$, for r and μ real, it follows that $\bar{\lambda} \cdot (x, y) = \mu \cdot |(x, y)|$ is real. Then

$$||x - \lambda y||^2 = ||x||^2 - 2\mu|(x, y)| + \mu^2 ||y||^2 \geq 0$$

for all real μ, and we conclude that the discriminant of this quadratic equation in μ is nonpositive, that is, $|(x, y)|^2 - ||x||^2 ||y||^2 \leq 0$, which is (1). Equality can occur when and only when $x = \lambda y$ for some complex number λ.

---

†Some authors add to the definition of a Hilbert space the requirement that H be a separable metric space. The trend now is to omit separability from the definition of an abstract Hilbert space, and we shall follow this trend.

To get the triangle inequality $\rho(x, y) \leq \rho(x, z) + \rho(z, y)$ from the Schwarz inequality (1), we note that

$$||x + y||^2 = (x + y, x + y) = ||x||^2 + 2 \operatorname{Re} (x, y) + ||y||^2.$$

Since $2 \operatorname{Re} (x, y) \leq 2|(x, y)| \leq 2||x|| \cdot ||y||$, we have

$$||x + y||^2 \leq ||x||^2 + 2||x|| \cdot ||y|| + ||y||^2 = (||x|| + ||y||)^2.$$

Taking the square root on both sides yields

$$||x + y|| \leq ||x|| + ||y||. \tag{2}$$

Since $(x - z) + (z - y) = x - y$, (2) becomes

$$||x - y|| = ||(x - z) + (z - y)|| \leq ||x - z|| + ||z - y||,$$

which is the triangle inequality for ρ, proving that H is a metric space. Condition C requires that the metric space H be complete.

As was remarked earlier, the simplest example of a Hilbert space is the n-dimensional complex vector space in which elements are n-tuples of complex numbers $x = (x_1, x_2, \ldots, x_n)$. Addition is defined as $(x_1, x_2, \ldots, x_n) + (y_1, y_2, \ldots, y_n) = (x_1 + y_1, x_2 + y_2, \ldots, x_n + y_n)$, and scalar multiplication is defined as $\alpha(x_1, x_2, \ldots, x_n) = (\alpha x_1, \alpha x_2, \ldots, \alpha x_n)$. For the inner product of $x = (x_1, x_2, \ldots, x_n)$ and $y = (y_1, y_2, \ldots, y_n)$, we set $(x, y) = x_1 \bar{y}_1 + x_2 \bar{y}_2 + \cdots + x_n \bar{y}_n$. It is easily verified that all the conditions A, B, C are fulfilled by this space.

A good model to keep in mind is the real n-dimensional vector space. Here the elements are n-tuples of real numbers $x = (x_1, x_2, \ldots, x_n)$, and the real numbers are used for scalar multiplication. The inner product $(x, y) = x_1 y_1 + x_2 y_2 + \cdots + x_n y_n$ is real and conditions A, B, C are satisfied. In particular, the 3-dimensional vector space affords us a very useful model, since we can use our intuition about geometrical properties.

The Hilbert space in which we shall be interested is that composed of measurable differentials ω on a Riemann surface S which satisfy the conditions that $\omega * \bar{\omega}$ be Lebesgue integrable and $||\omega||^2 = \iint_S \omega * \bar{\omega}$ be finite. If locally $\omega = p\, dx + q\, dy$, then $\omega * \bar{\omega} = (p\bar{p} + q\bar{q})\, dx\, dy$. Thus the requirement that ω be measurable means that locally p and q are measurable and the requirement that $\omega * \bar{\omega}$ be Lebesgue integrable means that locally $|p|^2$ and $|q|^2$ are integrable.

The addition and multiplication of differentials as defined in Chapter 6 satisfy conditions A, except possibly for the closure with respect to addition and scalar multiplication, which we verify by noting that if locally $\omega_1 = p_1 \, dx + q_1 \, dy$ and $\omega_2 = p_2 \, dx + q_2 \, dy$, then $\omega_1 + \omega_2 = (p_1 + p_2) \, dx + (q_1 + q_2) \, dy$ and the coefficients $(p_1 + p_2)$ and $(q_1 + q_2)$ are locally square integrable. Indeed, we have

$$|p_1 + p_2|^2 = |p_1|^2 + |p_2|^2 + p_1 \bar{p}_2 + \bar{p}_1 p_2,$$

while

$$0 \leq |p_1 - p_2|^2 = |p_1|^2 + |p_2|^2 - p_1 \bar{p}_2 - \bar{p}_1 p_2,$$

so that

$$p_1 \bar{p}_2 + \bar{p}_1 p_2 \leq |p_1|^2 + |p_2|^2 \quad \text{and} \quad |p_1 + p_2|^2 \leq 2(|p_1|^2 + |p_2|^2).$$

Thus $||\omega_1 + \omega_2||^2 \leq 2(||\omega_1||^2 + ||\omega_2||^2)$. For scalar multiplication by the complex number α, $||\alpha \omega_1|| = |\alpha| \cdot ||\omega_1||$, so that $\omega_1 + \omega_2$ and $\alpha \omega_1$ have finite norm if ω_1 and ω_2 both have finite norm.

By the inner product of two differentials ω_1 and ω_2, we mean

$$(\omega_1, \omega_2) = \iint_S \omega_1 * \bar{\omega}_2. \tag{3}$$

Locally we have $\omega_1 = p_1 \, dx + q_1 \, dy$, $\omega_2 = p_2 \, dx + q_2 \, dy$, so that $\omega_1 * \bar{\omega}_2 = (p_1 \bar{p}_2 + q_1 \bar{q}_2) \, dx \, dy$, and this is the differential we integrate over S to form (ω_1, ω_2). [It will be necessary later to talk about the space of differentials defined on a subset S' of S, in which case we shall denote the inner product $(\omega_1, \omega_2)_{S'} = \iint_{S'} \omega_1 * \bar{\omega}_2$ with the letter S' on the lower right of the parentheses and the norm as $||\omega||_{S'}^2 = (\omega, \omega)_{S'}$.] From the linearity of the integral and the operators $*$ and $^-$, we conclude properties B1 to B4. Furthermore, since $\omega * \bar{\omega} = (|p|^2 + |q|^2) \, dx \, dy$, $(\omega, \omega) \geq 0$ for all ω. The second part of B4 causes us some concern, for the coefficients p and q may be different from zero on a set of Lebesgue measure zero in any parametric disk and still have $(\omega, \omega) = 0$. Thus in order to have condition B4 fulfilled, we must establish the convention that any differential ω that is zero except for a set of measure zero in every parametric disk is the zero element of the space. Thus we identify any two differentials whose difference is zero except on a set of Lebesgue measure zero locally, and the symbol ω now represents the equivalence class of differentials that agree up to sets of measure zero locally. Now $(\omega, \omega) = 0$ if and only if $\omega = 0$. Since the union of two sets of measure zero is still a set of measure zero, the operations of addition and scalar multiplication are defined for these equivalence classes of differentials. In what follows, one should verify each time that any definition given in terms of a class representative is independent of the representative chosen. We shall omit these simple verifications.

THEOREM 7–3. *Let $L^2(S)$ denote the set of equivalence classes of measurable differentials ω on S with $\omega * \bar{\omega}$ integrable and $\iint_S \omega * \bar{\omega}$ finite (two differentials ω_1 and ω_2 represent the same element of $L^2(S)$ if locally $\omega_1 - \omega_2 = 0$, except possibly on a set of measure zero). With the usual addition, multiplication by complex constants, and the inner product* (3), $L^2(S)$ *is a Hilbert space.*

It remains yet to prove the completeness of $L^2(S)$, for which we must show that every Cauchy sequence ω_n, $n = 1, 2, \ldots$, in $L^2(S)$ has a limit in $L^2(S)$. The proof of this theorem will depend upon some theorems in Lebesgue integration and is analogous to the proof of the completeness of L^p spaces ($p \geq 1$) found in most texts on integration (e.g., Munroe, Ref. 32, p. 243). One result we shall use is Fatou's lemma, which states that if $\{f_n\}$ is a sequence of non-negative real-valued integrable functions in a bounded open set G of the (x, y)-plane, and if $f_0 = \underline{\lim}_{n \to \infty} f_n$, then f_0 is integrable if and only if $\underline{\lim} \iint_G f_n \, dx \, dy$ is finite; if this is the case, then

$$\iint\limits_G f_0 \, dx \, dy \leq \varliminf_{n \to \infty} \iint\limits_G f_n \, dx \, dy.$$

Since the $\{\omega_n\}$ form a Cauchy sequence in norm, there exists a sequence of integers N_k, $k = 1, 2, \ldots$, with $N_{k+1} > N_k$ such that

$$\|\omega_m - \omega_n\| < \frac{1}{8^k}, \qquad m \geq N_k, \quad n \geq N_k. \tag{4}$$

This means that for an arbitrary region V with compact closure on S

$$\iint\limits_V (\omega_{N_{k+1}} - \omega_{N_k}) * (\bar{\omega}_{N_{k+1}} - \bar{\omega}_{N_k}) < \frac{1}{8^k}.$$

We now cover $\overline{V}$ by a finite number of open parametric rectangles U_i, $i = 1, 2, \ldots, M$, and form a partition of unity for $\overline{V}$ relative to $\{U_i\}$. Then if $\omega_{N_k} = p_{N_k}^{(i)} \, dx + q_{N_k}^{(i)} \, dy$ in U_i,

$$\sum_{i=1}^{M} \iint\limits_{U_i \cap V} \left\{ \left| p_{N_{k+1}}^{(i)} - p_{N_k}^{(i)} \right|^2 + \left| q_{N_{k+1}}^{(i)} - q_{N_k}^{(i)} \right| \right\} e_i \, dx \, dy < \frac{1}{8^k}.$$

In particular,

$$\iint\limits_{U_i \cap V} \left| p^{(i)}_{N_{k+1}} - p^{(i)}_{N_k} \right|^2 e_i \, dx \, dy < \frac{1}{8^k},$$

where $e_i > 0$ in U_i.

It follows that $|p^{(i)}_{N_{k+1}} - p^{(i)}_{N_k}|\sqrt{e_i} < 1/2^k$ in $U_i \cap V$ except at most on a set A_k of measure $\leq 1/2^k$. For if not, then

$$\iint\limits_{U_i \cap V} \left| p^{(i)}_{N_{k+1}} - p^{(i)}_{N_k} \right|^2 e_i \, dx \, dy \geq \iint\limits_{A_k} \left| p^{(i)}_{N_{k+1}} - p^{(i)}_{N_k} \right|^2 e_i \, dx \, dy$$

$$\geq \frac{1}{4^k} \iint\limits_{A_k} dx \, dy,$$

and in order for the integral on the left to be $\leq 1/8^k$, the integral on the right must be $\geq 1/2^k$. From this we prove that $\lim_{k \to \infty} p^{(i)}_{N_k}(x, y) = p^{(i)}(x, y)$ exists in $U_i \cap V$, except possibly for a set of measure zero. Indeed, for any $m > n$,

$$\left| p^{(i)}_{N_m} - p^{(i)}_{N_n} \right| \leq \sum_{k=n}^{m-1} \left| p^{(i)}_{N_{k+1}} - p^{(i)}_{N_k} \right|$$

$$\leq \sum_{k=n}^{m-1} \frac{1}{\sqrt{e_i}} \frac{1}{2^k} < \frac{1}{\sqrt{e_i}} \sum_{k=n}^{\infty} \frac{1}{2^k} = \frac{1}{\sqrt{e_i}} \frac{1}{2^{n-1}},$$

except at most for a set $\bigcup_{k=n}^{m-1} A_k \subset \bigcup_{k=n}^{\infty} A_k = B_n$, which is of measure $\leq \sum_{k=n}^{\infty} 1/2^k < 1/2^{n-1}$. The B_n form a decreasing sequence of sets whose measures tend to zero, and $|p^{(i)}_{N_m} - p^{(i)}_{N_n}| < (1/\sqrt{e_i})(1/2^{n-1})$, except possibly in B_n, proving that except for a set of measure zero, $\lim_{n \to \infty} p^{(i)}_{N_n}(x, y) = p^{(i)}(x, y)$ exists in $V \cap U_i$. Similarly,

$$\lim_{n \to \infty} q^{(i)}_{N_n}(x, y) = q^{(i)}(x, y),$$

except possibly for a set of measure zero in $V \cap U_i$, and since the U_i cover V, we can define a differential in V which is locally given by $\omega = p^{(i)}(x, y) \, dx + q^{(i)}(x, y) \, dy$. Since V is an arbitrary open set with compact closure in S, ω is defined on all of S. We still have to show that ω is the limit (in norm) of the sequence ω_n and that ω is in $L^2(S)$ (or $\|\omega\| < \infty$).

From (4) we see that $||\omega_m - \omega_n|| < 1/8^k$ when $m \geq N_k$, $n \geq N_k$. Thus if locally $\omega_m = p_m^{(i)} \, dx + q_m^{(i)} \, dy$ in U_i, we have

$$\sum_{i=1}^{m} \iint_{U_i \cap V} \left\{ \left| p_m^{(i)} - p_{N_n}^{(i)} \right|^2 + \left| q_m^{(i)} - q_{N_n}^{(i)} \right|^2 \right\} e_i \, dx \, dy < \frac{1}{8^k}$$

when $m \geq N_k$ and $n \geq k$. By Fatou's lemma, we have

$$\iint_{U_i \cap V} \left| p_m^{(i)} - p^{(i)} \right|^2 e_i \, dx \, dy \leq \lim_{n \to \infty} \iint_{U_i \cap V} \left| p_m^{(i)} - p_{N_n}^{(i)} \right|^2 e_i \, dx \, dy,$$

and the same for the integral with p's replaced by q's. Thus

$$\iint_V (\omega_m - \omega) * (\bar{\omega}_n - \bar{\omega})$$

$$= \sum_{i=1}^{m} \iint_{U_i \cap V} \left\{ \left| p_m^{(i)} - p^{(i)} \right|^2 + \left| q_m^{(i)} - q^{(i)} \right|^2 \right\} e_i \, dx \, dy < \frac{1}{8^k}$$

for $m \geq N_k$, and since V is an arbitrary region with compact closure on S,

$$||\omega_m - \omega|| = \operatorname*{l.u.b.}_{V \subset S} \iint_V (\omega_m - \omega) * (\bar{\omega}_m - \bar{\omega}) \leq \frac{1}{8^k},$$

and ω is the limit in norm of $\{\omega_n\}$. Finally, to prove that ω is in $L^2(S)$, we set $\omega = \omega - \omega_m + \omega_m$ and use the triangle inequality $||\omega|| \leq ||\omega - \omega_m|| + ||\omega_m||$, observing that both expressions on the right are finite. This completes the proof that $L^2(S)$ is a complete space.

A nice property of the inner product in any Hilbert space is that it is a continuous function of both its arguments; i.e.,

THEOREM 7–4. *If* $\lim_{n \to \infty} ||x - x_n|| = 0$, *and* $\lim_{n \to \infty} ||y - y_n|| = 0$, *then* $(x, y) = \lim_{n \to \infty} (x_n, y_n)$.

This follows immediately from the inequality

$$|(x, y) - (x_n, y_n)| = |(x - x_n, y) - (x - x_n, y - y_n) + (x, y - y_n)|$$

$$\leq |(x - x_n, y)| + |(x - x_n, y - y_n)| + |(x, y - y_n)|$$

$$\leq ||x - x_n|| \cdot ||y|| + ||x - x_n|| \cdot ||y - y_n||$$

$$+ ||x|| \cdot ||y - y_n||.$$

A subset H_1 of a Hilbert space H is called a *subspace* of H if H_1 is it-self a Hilbert space with the operations and inner product defined for H. A simple example of a subspace of the 3-dimensional real vector space consists of those vectors lying in a plane through the origin, such as all triplets $(x_1, x_2, 0)$. A simple example of a subspace of $L^2(S)$ is the set of all differentials ω in $L^2(S)$ which vanish outside of a fixed sub-set V of S. We observe that a subset H_1 of H is a subspace if it is a complex vector space which is closed in the norm of the space; that is, if $x_n \in H_1$ and $\lim_{n\to\infty} ||x_n - x_0|| = 0$, then $x_0 \in H_1$. Directly from the definitions, we also conclude that if H_1 and H_2 are subspaces of a Hilbert space H, then $H_1 \cap H_2$, the set of all elements common to H_1 and H_2, is again a subspace of H.

In the 3-dimensional real vector space, the inner product of two nonzero vectors $x = (x_1, x_2, x_3)$ and $y = (y_1, y_2, y_3)$ can be written as

$$(x, y) = x_1 y_1 + x_2 y_2 + x_3 y_3 = ||x|| \cdot ||y|| \cos \theta,$$

where θ is the angle between the two vectors. Then x is orthogonal to y if and only if $(x, y) = 0$. We shall carry this definition over to an abstract Hilbert space and say: two elements x and y in H are *orthogonal* if and only if $(x, y) = 0$. From B4 we conclude that 0 is the only element in H which is orthogonal to itself. Furthermore,

$$(0, y) = (x - x, y) = (x, y) - (x, y) = 0,$$

so 0 is orthogonal to every element in H and is indeed the only element in H which is orthogonal to every element in H.

Two subspaces H_1 and H_2 of H are said to be *orthogonal* if $(x, y) = 0$ for all $x \in H_1$ and $y \in H_2$. We write $H_1 \perp H_2$ to indicate that H_1 and H_2 are orthogonal. Let H_1 be a subspace of H and let $H_1^\perp$ represent the set of those elements $y \in H$ for which $(x, y) = 0$ holds for all $x \in H_1$. Thus $H_1^\perp$ consists of those elements which are orthogonal to all elements of H_1. We call $H_1^\perp$ the *orthogonal complement* of H_1.

THEOREM 7–5. *If H_1 is a subspace of H, then $H_1^\perp$ is also a subspace of H.*

By the preceding remarks, it is enough to show that $H_1^\perp$ is a complex vector space closed in H. If x and y are in $H_1^\perp$ and $z \in H_1$, then for arbitrary complex numbers α and β, we have

$$(\alpha x + \beta y, z) = \alpha(x, z) + \beta(y, z) = 0 + 0 = 0,$$

so that $\alpha x + \beta y \in H_1^\perp$, which means that $H_1^\perp$ is a complex vector space.

Let $\{x_n\}$ be a sequence of elements of $H_1^\perp$ which converges in norm to an element $x_0 \in H$. If z is any element of H_1, we have

$$(x_0, z) = \lim_{n\to\infty} (x_n, z) = 0,$$

proving that $x_0 \in H_1^\perp$ and consequently that $H_1^\perp$ is closed in H.

If H_1 and H_2 are given subspaces of H, by their *direct sum* $H_3 = H_1 \oplus H_2$, we understand the set of all elements $x \in H$ of the form $x = x_1 + x_2$, $x_1 \in H_1$ and $x_2 \in H_2$. H_3 will not in general be a subspace of H, since it may not be closed in H. However, we form the closure $\overline{H_1 \oplus H_2}$ of $H_1 \oplus H_2$ by adjoining to $H_1 \oplus H_2$ all elements $x \in H$ which are limits in norm of sequences of elements in $H_1 \oplus H_2$. Then $\overline{H_1 \oplus H_2}$ is a subspace of H and is indeed the smallest subspace of H containing both H_1 and H_2.

It is a noteworthy fact and one we shall make use of later that if we take for H_1 any subspace of H and for H_2 its orthogonal complement, then $H_1 \oplus H_1^\perp$ is closed and is moreover the whole space H. We state this in the following theorem:

THEOREM 7–6. *Let H_1 be a subspace of H and let $H_1^\perp$ be its orthogonal complement. Then*

$$H = H_1 \oplus H_1^\perp; \tag{5}$$

that is, every element $x \in H$ may be written in the form $x = x_1 + x_2$, $x_1 \in H_1$ and $x_2 \in H_1^\perp$, and this representation is unique.

Once we have proved the existence of one such decomposition, the uniqueness is trivial; for if $x = x_1 + x_2 = y_1 + y_2$, then $x_1 - y_1 \in H_1$ and $y_2 - x_2 \in H_1^\perp$; hence $(x_1 - y_1, y_2 - x_2) = 0$. But $x_1 - y_1 = y_2 - x_2$, so that $x_1 - y_1$ is orthogonal to itself and $x_1 - y_1 = 0$, which implies that $y_2 - x_2 = 0$, proving the uniqueness.

Before carrying out the proof of the decomposition, let us examine an example in the 2-dimensional real vector space. If we wished to decompose a vector $x \in \mathcal{E}^2$ into its components along two mutually perpendicular axes, how would we proceed? We would naturally drop a perpendicular y_1 from the end of x to the H_1-axis and set $x_1 = x + y_1$. Then $x_2 = x - x_1 \in H_1^\perp$, while $x_1 \in H_1$ gives us the desired decomposition (Fig. 7–1). To carry this process over to more general Hilbert spaces than $\mathcal{E}^2$, it is necessary to characterize the dropping of a perpendicular from the "end point" of a given element to a subspace in a manner which can be applied in the more general spaces. This characterization is provided by the fundamental property of the perpendicular; namely, that of all vectors going from the end point of x to the H_1-axis, x_2 has the minimum length.

Thus our problem has become one of finding an element of minimum length, a technique frequently employed in existence proofs. In a Hilbert space H, the length of the element x is $||x||$. Thus, by analogy, we should expect that the decomposition of $x \in H$ which we seek will be given by the vectors $x_1 \in H_1$ and $x - x_1 \in H_1^\perp$ (if they exist) which minimize $||x - x_1||$ for all $x \in H_1$. For this method to work, we must show that (a) there exists an $\bar{x}_1 \in H_1$ such that $||x - \bar{x}_1||$ is a minimum and (b) $x - \bar{x}_1 \in H_1^\perp$.

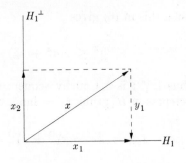

FIGURE 7–1.

To prove (a), let $x \in H$ and $d^2 = $ g.l.b.$_{x_1 \in H_1} ||x - x_1||^2$. Then there will surely exist a sequence of elements of H_1, say $\{x_1^{(n)}\}$, such that

$$||x - x_1^{(n)}||^2 = d^2 + \epsilon_n, \qquad \lim_{n \to \infty} \epsilon_n = 0, \quad \epsilon_n \geq 0.$$

Now

$$||x_1^{(m)} - x_1^{(n)}||^2 = ||(x_1^{(m)} - x) - (x_1^{(n)} - x)||^2$$
$$= ||x_1^{(m)} - x||^2 - 2 \operatorname{Re} (x_1^{(m)} - x, x_1^{(n)} - x)$$
$$+ ||x_1^{(n)} - x||^2$$

and

$$||x_1^{(m)} + x_1^{(n)} - 2x||^2 = ||x_1^{(m)} - x||^2 + 2 \operatorname{Re} (x_1^{(m)} - x, x_1^{(n)} - x)$$
$$+ ||x_1^{(n)} - x||^2.$$

Adding these two equations gives

$$||x_1^{(m)} - x_1^{(n)}||^2 = 2||x_1^{(m)} - x||^2 + 2||x_1^{(n)} - x||^2$$
$$- ||x_1^{(m)} + x_1^{(n)} - 2x||^2. \qquad (6)$$

Since $\frac{1}{2}(x_1^{(m)} + x_1^{(n)}) \in H_1$ when $x_1^{(m)} \in H_1$ and $x_1^{(n)} \in H_1$, it follows from the definition of d that

$$\left|\left| x - \frac{x_1^{(m)} + x_1^{(n)}}{2} \right|\right|^2 \geq d^2$$

or

$$||x_1^{(m)} + x_1^{(n)} - 2x||^2 \geq 4d^2.$$

Using this in (6) gives

$$||x_1^{(m)} - x_1^{(n)}||^2 \leq 2(d^2 + \epsilon_m) + 2(d^2 + \epsilon_n) - 4d^2 \leq 2(\epsilon_m + \epsilon_n).$$

Thus $\{x_1^{(n)}\}$ is a Cauchy sequence which converges because of the completeness of H_1; thus $\bar{x}_1 = \lim_{n\to\infty} x_1^{(n)}$ exists and

$$||x - \bar{x}_1|| = ||x - x_1^{(n)} + x_1^{(n)} - \bar{x}_1|| \leq ||x - x_1^{(n)}|| + ||x_1^{(n)} - \bar{x}_1||$$

for all n. Since $\lim_{n\to\infty} ||x - x_1^{(n)}|| = d$ and $\lim_{n\to\infty} ||x_1^{(n)} - \bar{x}_1|| = 0$, we have $||x - \bar{x}_1|| = d$, and $\bar{x}_1$ is the element of H_1 minimizing $||x - x_1||$ for all $x_1 \in H_1$.

It remains to prove (b), that is, that $x - \bar{x}_1 \in H_1^{\perp}$. In fact, let x_1 be any nonzero element of H_1. Then $\bar{x}_1 + \lambda x_1 \in H$ for all complex numbers λ and

$$||x - \lambda x_1 - \bar{x}_1||^2 \geq d^2$$

or

$$||x - \bar{x}_1||^2 - \lambda(x_1, x - \bar{x}_1) - \bar{\lambda}\overline{(x_1, x - \bar{x}_1)} + |\lambda|^2 ||x_1||^2 \geq d^2.$$

Using $||x - \bar{x}_1||^2 = d^2$, we get

$$2 \operatorname{Re} \{\lambda(x_1, x - \bar{x}_1)\} \leq |\lambda|^2 ||x_1||^2.$$

If $(x_1, x - \bar{x}_1) = re^{i\theta}$, set $\lambda = |\lambda|e^{-i\theta}$ to get

$$2|\lambda| \cdot |(x_1, x - \bar{x}_1)| \leq |\lambda|^2 \cdot ||x_1||^2,$$

or, simply, $2|(x_1, x - \bar{x}_1)| \leq |\lambda| \cdot ||x_1||^2$. Since $|\lambda|$ can be made arbitrarily small for fixed x_1, it follows that $(x_1, x - \bar{x}_1) = 0$. Thus (a) and (b) have been proved and our theorem is established.

From (a) and (b), we can draw a bit more information.

THEOREM 7–7. *If H_1 and H_2 are orthogonal subspaces of H, then $H_1 \oplus H_2$ is also a subspace of H.*

We must show that $\overline{H_1 \oplus H_2} = H_1 \oplus H_2$. Let $x \in \overline{H_1 \oplus H_2}$ and apply (a) and (b) to get an element $\bar{x}_1 \in H_1$ such that $||x - \bar{x}_1|| \leq ||x - x_1||$ for all $x_1 \in H_1$; then $\bar{y} = x - \bar{x}_1 \in H_1^{\perp}$ and $\bar{y} \in \overline{H_1 \oplus H_2}$. We have $\bar{y} = \lim_{n\to\infty} (y_1^{(n)} + y_2^{(n)})$, $y_1^{(n)} \in H_1$ and $y_2^{(n)} \in H_2$. But $\lim_{n\to\infty} (y_1^{(n)}, y_1^{(n)} + y_2^{(n)}) = \lim_{n\to\infty} (y_1^{(n)}, \bar{y}) = 0$, while $(y_1^{(n)}, y_1^{(n)} + y_2^{(n)}) = (y_1^{(n)}, y_1^{(n)}) = ||y_1^{(n)}||^2$. Therefore

$$\lim_{n\to\infty} ||y_1^{(n)}|| = 0 \quad \text{and} \quad \bar{y} = \lim_{n\to\infty} y_2^{(n)} \in H_2,$$

proving our assertion.

7–2 Smoothing operators. In this section we shall define an operator which acts on differentials in L^2 and takes them into differentials in C^1, preserving certain valuable properties of the differential. We shall restrict our attention to a disk D given by $|z| < 1$, in the euclidean plane. In order to define the smoothing operator for differentials in $L^2(D)$, we shall first define it for functions f on D such that f is integrable on D and $\iint_D |f|^2 \, dx \, dy < \infty$. For convenience, we shall also denote this class of functions by $L^2(D)$. It will always be clear from context whether $L^2(D)$ denotes a class of differentials or functions on D. By D_ρ we shall mean the disk $|z| < 1 - \rho$.

We first introduce the function

$$s_\rho(x, y) = \begin{cases} k(\rho^2 - x^2 - y^2)^2, & x^2 + y^2 < \rho^2, \\ 0, & x^2 + y^2 \geq \rho^2, \end{cases} \tag{1}$$

where k is chosen so that $\iint_{D_{1-\rho}} s_\rho(x, y) \, dx \, dy = 2\pi \int_0^\rho k(\rho^2 - r^2)^2 r \, dr = 1$; that is, $k = 3/(\pi\rho^6)$.

We note that $s_\rho(x, y)$ has continuous first partial derivatives with respect to x and y in the whole (x, y)-plane. The smoothing operator M_ρ applied to a complex-valued function $f \in L^2(D)$ gives us a new function $M_\rho f$ where

$$M_\rho f(x, y) = \int_0^{2\pi} \int_0^\rho f(x + r \cos\theta, y + r \sin\theta) s_\rho(r \cos\theta, r \sin\theta) r \, dr \, d\theta. \tag{2}$$

So long as $\rho < 1$ and $(x, y,) \in D_\rho$, the point $(x + r \cos\theta, y + r \sin\theta)$, $0 \leq r < \rho$, is in D where f is integrable; thus $M_\rho f$ is defined for all $(x, y) \in D_\rho$. Some other forms of (2) that are useful are

$$M_\rho f(x, y) = \iint_{D_{1-\rho}} f(x + \xi, y + \eta) s_\rho(\xi, \eta) \, d\xi \, d\eta \tag{3}$$

and

$$M_\rho f(x, y) = \iint_D f(\xi, \eta) s_\rho(\xi - x, \eta - y) \, d\xi \, d\eta. \tag{4}$$

For the differential $\omega = p(x, y) \, dx + q(x, y) \, dy \in L^2(D)$, we define

$$M_\rho \omega = [M_\rho p(x, y)] \, dx + [M_\rho q(x, y)] \, dy.$$

We see immediately that M_ρ is a linear operator on $L^2(D)$ which takes each $\omega \in L^2(D)$ into $M_\rho\omega$ defined on D_ρ. We now set out to prove that M_ρ has the following four properties:

M1. *If $\omega \in L^2(D)$, $M_\rho\omega \in C^1(D_\rho)$.*

M2. *If ω is harmonic in D, $M_\rho\omega = \omega$ in D_ρ.*

M3. *For $\omega \in L^2(D)$, $\lim_{\rho \to 0} \|\omega - M_\rho\omega\|_{D_\rho} = 0$.*

M4. *If the carrier of $\gamma \subset D_\rho$, then the carrier of $M_\rho\gamma \subset D$ and*

$$(M_\rho\omega, \gamma)_{D_\rho} = (\omega, M_\rho\gamma)_D.$$

To establish property M1, we shall compute $\partial(M_\rho p)/\partial x$ and prove its continuity. The same argument can also be used to establish the existence and continuity of the other derivatives involved. Since $\partial s_\rho/\partial x$ is continuous in $\overline{D}$, it is bounded there, say $|\partial s_\rho/\partial x| < M$, and we have

$$\left| \frac{s_\rho(x + h, y) - s_\rho(x, y)}{h} \right| = \left| \frac{1}{h} \int_x^{x+h} \frac{\partial s_\rho(x, y)}{\partial x} \, dx \right|$$

$$\leq \frac{1}{h} \int_x^{x+h} \left| \frac{\partial s_\rho(x, y)}{\partial x} \right| dx \leq M.$$

Furthermore, the difference quotient converges to the derivative $\partial s_\rho/\partial x$ at each point, so we may apply the Lebesgue dominated-convergence theorem to

$$\frac{M_\rho p(x + h, y) - M_\rho p(x, y)}{h}$$

$$= \iint_D p(\xi, \eta) \, \frac{s_\rho(\xi - x - h, \eta - y) - s_\rho(\xi - x, \eta - y)}{h} \, d\xi \, d\eta$$

to obtain

$$\frac{\partial M_\rho p(x, y)}{\partial x} = \iint_D p(\xi, \eta) \, \frac{\partial s_\rho(\xi - x, \eta - y)}{\partial x} \, d\xi \, d\eta.$$

To prove the continuity, we observe that $\partial s_\rho/\partial x$ is uniformly continuous, so that given $\epsilon > 0$, there is a $\delta > 0$ such that if $(x - x')^2 + (y - y')^2 < \delta^2$,

$$\left| \frac{\partial s_\rho(x', y')}{\partial x} - \frac{\partial s_\rho(x, y)}{\partial x} \right| < \epsilon.$$

Then

$$\left| \frac{\partial M_\rho p(x', y')}{\partial x} - \frac{\partial M_\rho p(x, y)}{\partial x} \right|$$

$$\leq \iint\limits_D |p(\xi, \eta)| \left| \frac{\partial s_\rho(\xi - x', \eta - y')}{\partial x} - \frac{\partial s_\rho(\xi - x, \eta - y)}{\partial x} \right| d\xi \, d\eta$$

$$\leq \epsilon \iint\limits_D |p(\xi, \eta)| \, d\xi \, d\eta,$$

and for $p \in L^2(D)$, the last expression goes to zero with ϵ.

Property M2 will be proved in two stages. If ω is harmonic in D, then $\omega = df$, where f is a harmonic function in D Then we prove that (a) for $f \in C^1(D)$,

$$M_\rho \, df = dM_\rho f, \tag{5}$$

and that (b) for a harmonic function $f \in D$,

$$M_\rho f(x, y) = f(x, y) \tag{6}$$

in D_ρ. Putting these together gives $M_\rho \omega = M_\rho \, df = dM_\rho f = df = \omega$.

To prove (a), we must show that

$$\left(M_\rho \frac{\partial f}{\partial x} \right) dx + \left(M_\rho \frac{\partial f}{\partial y} \right) dy = \frac{\partial}{\partial x} (M_\rho f) \, dx + \frac{\partial}{\partial y} (M_\rho f) \, dy.$$

We shall demonstrate that $M_\rho(\partial f/\partial x) = (\partial/\partial x) M_\rho f$; the proof for the corresponding expression in y is analogous. Since $f \in C^1(D)$, we can apply Leibniz' rule for differentiating under the integral sign to get

$$\frac{\partial}{\partial x} M_\rho f(x, y) = \frac{\partial}{\partial x} \iint\limits_{D_{1-\rho}} f(x + \xi, y + \eta) s_\rho(\xi, \eta) \, d\xi \, d\eta$$

$$= \iint\limits_{D_{1-\rho}} \frac{\partial}{\partial x} f(x + \xi, y + \eta) s_\rho(\xi, \eta) \, d\xi \, d\eta = M_\rho \frac{\partial}{\partial x} f(x, y).$$

Next, to prove (b), we observe that for $r < \rho$, $s_\rho(r \cos \theta, r \sin \theta) = k(\rho^2 - r^2)^2$ is a function of r alone, so that

$$M_\rho f(x, y) = \int_0^\rho rk(\rho^2 - r^2)^2 \int_0^{2\pi} f(x + r \cos \theta, y + r \sin \theta) \, d\theta \, dr.$$

If we show that

$$\int_0^{2\pi} f(x + r\cos\theta, y + r\sin\theta)\, d\theta = 2\pi f(x, y), \qquad (7)$$

then $M_\rho f(x, y) = 2\pi \int_0^\rho k(\rho^2 - r^2)^2 r\, dr\, f(x, y) = f(x, y)$ by our choice of k. But (7) is precisely the Mean Value Theorem for harmonic functions which, for completeness, will be proved here. Application of Stokes' theorem and (11) of Section 6–4 to $*df$ tells us that for any circle D: $(x - a)^2 + (y - b)^2 < r^2$,

$$\int_{\partial D} \frac{\partial f}{\partial n}\, ds = \int_{\partial D} *df = \iint_D d*df = 0.$$

But in polar coordinates, $x - a = r\cos\theta$, $y - b = r\sin\theta$, this says that $\int_0^{2\pi} (\partial f/\partial r)\, r\, d\theta = 0$, or $r(\partial/\partial r)\int_0^{2\pi} f(a + r\cos\theta, b + r\sin\theta)\, d\theta = 0$. Thus $\int_0^{2\pi} f(a + r\cos\theta, b + r\sin\theta)\, d\theta$ is independent of r, and as $r \to 0$, we get

$$\int_0^{2\pi} f(a + r\cos\theta, b + r\sin\theta)\, d\theta$$

$$= \lim_{r\to 0} \int_0^{2\pi} f(a + r\cos\theta, b + r\sin\theta)\, d\theta$$

$$= \int_0^{2\pi} f(a, b)\, d\theta = 2\pi f(a, b),$$

proving our assertion.

To prove M3, we must show that as $\rho \to 0$,

$$\|\omega - M_\rho\omega\|_{D_\rho}^2 = \iint_{D_\rho} [|p - M_\rho p|^2 + |q - M_\rho q|^2]\, dx\, dy \to 0.$$

We shall show that $\lim_{\rho\to 0} \iint_{D_\rho} |p - M_\rho p|^2\, dx\, dy = 0$, the proof for q being the same. Furthermore, $p = p_1 + ip_2$, so that

$$\iint_{D_\rho} |p - M_\rho p|^2\, dx\, dy = \iint_{D_\rho} [|p_1 - M_\rho p_1|^2 + |p_2 - M_\rho p_2|^2]\, dx\, dy,$$

and it is enough to prove that $\iint_{D_\rho} |p_1 - M_\rho p_1|^2\, dx\, dy \to 0$ or, in other words, we may assume p real.

Since $p \in L^2(D)$, given $\epsilon > 0$, we can approximate p by a continuous function g in $\overline{D}$ such that $\iint_D |g - p|^2 \, dx \, dy < \epsilon^2$. Then we can write

$$\left[\iint_{D_\rho} |p - M_\rho p|^2 \, dx \, dy \right]^{1/2} \leq \left[\iint_{D_\rho} |p - g|^2 \, dx \, dy \right]^{1/2}$$

$$+ \left[\iint_{D_\rho} |g - M_\rho g|^2 \, dx \, dy \right]^{1/2}$$

$$+ \left[\iint_{D_\rho} |M_\rho g - M_\rho p|^2 \, dx \, dy \right]^{1/2} \qquad (8)$$

Since g is uniformly continuous in D, there is a $\delta > 0$ such that

$$|g(x', y') - g(x, y)| < \epsilon \qquad \text{if} \qquad (x - x')^2 + (y - y')^2 < \delta^2.$$

We can now say that if $\rho < \delta$,

$$|M_\rho g(x, y) - g(x, y)| = \left| \iint_{D_{1-\rho}} \{g(x + \xi, y + \eta) - g(x, y)\} s_\rho(\xi, \eta) \, d\xi \, d\eta \right|$$

$$\leq \iint_{D_{1-\rho}} |g(x + \xi, y + \eta) - g(x, y)| s_\rho(\xi, \eta) \, d\xi \, d\eta$$

$$\leq \epsilon \iint_{D_{1-\rho}} s_\rho(\xi, \eta) \, d\xi \, d\eta = \epsilon.$$

Hence

$$\left[\iint_{D_\rho} |g - M_\rho g|^2 \, dx \, dy \right]^{1/2} \leq \sqrt{\pi} \, \epsilon$$

when $\rho < \delta$. To complete the proof, we must show that

$$\iint_{D_\rho} |M_\rho[g - p]|^2 \, dx \, dy \leq \epsilon^2.$$

We have from the Schwarz integral inequality that

$$|M_\rho[g(x, y) - p(x, y)]|^2$$

$$= \left| \iint\limits_{D_{1-\rho}} \{g(x + \xi, y + \eta) - p(x + \xi, y + \eta)\} s_\rho(\xi, \eta) \, d\xi \, d\eta \right|^2$$

$$\leq \iint\limits_{D_{1-\rho}} |g(x + \xi, y + \eta) - p(x + \xi, y + \eta)|^2 s_\rho(\xi, \eta) \, d\xi \, d\eta$$

$$\times \iint\limits_{D_{1-\rho}} s_\rho(\xi, \eta) \, d\xi \, d\eta$$

$$= \iint\limits_{D_{1-\rho}} |g(x + \xi, y + \eta) - p(x + \xi, y + \eta)|^2 s_\rho(\xi, \eta) \, d\xi \, d\eta.$$

Therefore,

$$\iint\limits_{D_\rho} |M_\rho[g - p]|^2 \, dx \, dy$$

$$\leq \iint\limits_{D_\rho} dx \, dy \iint\limits_{D_{1-\rho}} |g(x + \xi, y + \eta) - p(x + \xi, y + \eta)|^2 s_\rho(\xi, \eta) \, d\xi \, d\eta,$$

and application of Fubini's theorem on the right side yields

$$\iint\limits_{D_\rho} |M_\rho[g - p]^2 \, dx \, dy$$

$$\leq \iint\limits_{D_{1-\rho}} s_\rho(\xi, \eta) \, d\xi \, d\eta \iint\limits_{D_\rho} |g(x + \xi, y + \eta) - p(x + \xi, y + \eta)|^2 \, dx \, dy.$$

From our choice of g, the last integral on the right side is $< \epsilon^2$ for all $(\xi, \eta) \in D_\rho$, so that our theorem is proved.

Finally, for M4, if the carrier of a function f is contained in D_ρ, there is a positive number δ such that the carrier of $f \subset D_{\rho+\delta}$. Now from (2), we see that if f vanishes in a disk of radius ρ about (x, y), then $M_\rho f(x, y) = 0$. We may extend the definition of f to the whole (x, y)-plane by setting

$f \equiv 0$ outside of D. Then $M_\rho f$ is defined in D, and since $f \equiv 0$ in $|z| > 1 - \delta - \rho$, $M_\rho f \equiv 0$ in $|z| > 1 - \delta$, so that the carrier of $M_\rho f \subset D$. The same holds when M_ρ is applied to differentials γ with the carrier of $\gamma \subset D_\rho$. We now compute $(M_\rho \omega, \gamma)_{D_\rho}$ and show that it is equal to $(\omega, M_\rho \gamma)_D$ by an application of Fubini's theorem. The inner product $(\omega, M_\rho \gamma)_D$ makes sense, since $M_\rho \gamma$ is now defined in all of D by setting $\gamma = 0$ outside of D_ρ. Let $\omega = p\, dx + q\, dy$ and $\gamma = a\, dx + b\, dy$; then

$$(M_\rho \omega, \gamma)_{D_\rho} = \iint\limits_{D_\rho} M_\rho p(x, y)\overline{a(x, y)} + M_\rho q(x, y)\overline{b(x, y)}\, dx\, dy.$$

We have

$$\iint\limits_{D_\rho} M_\rho p(x, y)\overline{a(x, y)}\, dx\, dy$$

$$= \iint\limits_{D_\rho} \overline{a(x, y)} \left[\iint\limits_D p(\xi, \eta) s_\rho(\xi - x, \eta - y)\, d\xi\, d\eta \right] dx\, dy$$

$$= \iint\limits_D p(\xi, \eta) \left[\iint\limits_{D_\rho} \overline{a(x, y)} s_\rho(\xi - x, \eta - y)\, dx\, dy \right] d\xi\, d\eta$$

$$= \iint\limits_D p(\xi, \eta) \left[\iint\limits_D \overline{a(x, y)} s_\rho(x - \xi, y - \eta)\, dx\, dy \right] d\xi\, d\eta$$

$$= \iint\limits_D p(\xi, \eta)\, \overline{M_\rho a(\xi, \eta)}\, d\xi\, d\eta.$$

Similarly,

$$\iint\limits_{D_\rho} M_\rho q(x, y)\overline{b(x, y)}\, dx\, dy = \iint\limits_D q(\xi, \eta)\, \overline{M_\rho b(\xi, \eta)}\, d\xi\, d\eta,$$

which together prove M4.

7–3 Weyl's lemma and orthogonal projections. Certain subspaces of the Hilbert space $L^2(S)$ of differentials on S will play a fundamental role in our subsequent proof of the existence of harmonic and analytic differentials on the Riemann surface S. These will now be defined.

A complex-valued function f on S is said to be of class $C^k = C^k(S)$ if locally f has continuous kth partial derivatives. We say that $f \in C_0^k =$

$C_0^k(S)$ if f has in addition a compact carrier contained in S. Similarly, we shall say that the differential $\omega \in C^k = C^k(S)$ if its coefficients have continuous kth partial derivatives locally and $\omega \in C_0^k = C_0^k(S)$ if, in addition, ω has a compact carrier in S. It will always be clear from the context whether C^k or C_0^k denote functions or differentials on S.

The subspaces of $L^2(S)$ which we shall use are the following.

$E = E(S)$ *is the closure in* $L^2(S)$ *of the vector space of exact differentials* df, *where* $f \in C_0^2(S)$.

$E^* = E^*(S)$ *is the closure in* $L^2(S)$ *of the vector space of coexact differentials* $*df$, *where* $f \in C_0^2(S)$. (Note that $\omega \in E$ if and only if $*\omega \in E^*$.)

$H = E^\perp \cap (E^*)^\perp$; *that is,* H *consists of all differentials which are orthogonal to both* E *and* E^* *in* $L^2(S)$.

Our first important theorem states that we can decompose $L^2(S)$ into a direct sum of these three subspaces.

THEOREM 7–8. E, E^*, *and* H *are pairwise orthogonal and* $L^2(S) = H \oplus E \oplus E^*$.

This means that every $\omega \in L^2(S)$ has a unique decomposition $\omega = \omega_h + \gamma + \pi$, where $\omega_h \in H$, $\gamma \in E$, $\pi \in E^*$. To prove first that E and E^* are orthogonal subspaces, let $\omega \in E$ and $\gamma \in E^*$. Then in the norm of $L^2(S)$, $\omega = \lim_{n \to \infty} df_n$ and $\gamma = \lim_{n \to \infty} *dg_n$ where $f_n, g_n \in C_0^2$ and $(\omega, \gamma) = \lim_{n \to \infty} (df_n, *dg_n)$. Since the carriers of f_n and g_n are compact, we can apply Theorem 6–4 to obtain

$$(df_n, *dg_n) = -\iint_S (df_n)(d\bar{g}_n) = -\iint_S f_n \, dd\bar{g}_n = 0$$

for all n, and hence $(\omega, \gamma) = 0$, proving that $E \perp E^*$. At the end of Section 7–1 we proved that $E \oplus E^*$ is then a subspace of $L^2(S)$ and

$$L^2(S) = (E \oplus E^*) \oplus (E \oplus E^*)^\perp.$$

We now prove that $H = (E \oplus E^*)^\perp$. If $\omega \in H$ and $\gamma_1 \in E$, $\gamma_2 \in E^*$, then $(\omega, \gamma_1 + \gamma_2) = (\omega, \gamma_1) + (\omega, \gamma_2) = 0$, so that $H \subseteq (E \oplus E^*)^\perp$. On the other hand, if $\omega \in (E \oplus E^*)^\perp$, then $(\omega, \gamma_1 + \gamma_2) = 0$ for all $\gamma_1 \in E$ and $\gamma_2 \in E^*$ and, in particular, $(\omega, \gamma_1) = 0$ and $(\omega, \gamma_2) = 0$. Thus $\omega \in E^\perp \cap (E^*)^\perp = H$, proving that $H \supseteq (E \oplus (E^*)^\perp)$. Combining these gives us our result.

The differentials in E and E^* may be rather badly behaved so far as the regularity properties of their coefficients are concerned. For they are mean limits of differentiable functions and, as the simplest examples show, need not be continuous even at a single point. It is thus a remarkable fact that all the elements of H are harmonic differentials. It is this fact that is the core of the method of orthogonal projections which we use in our existence proofs. We shall now prove the important fact that H consists precisely of the harmonic differentials on S. To do so, we shall use the following lemmas concerning E, E^*, and H.

LEMMA 7–1. *If* $\omega \in C^1$, *then*
(a) $d\omega = 0$ *if and only if* $\omega \in E^{*\perp}$;
(b) $d*\omega = 0$ *if and only if* $\omega \in E^{\perp}$.

We shall prove (a), the proof of (b) being exactly the same. Let us first suppose that $\omega \in C^1$ and $d\omega = 0$. Then for all $f \in C_0^2$, we have

$$(\omega, *df) = - \iint_S \omega(\overline{df}) = - \iint_S \bar{f}\, d\omega = 0$$

by (12) of Section 6–4 and the fact that $d\omega = 0$. If

$$\gamma \in E^*, \qquad \gamma = \lim_{n \to \infty} *df_n, \qquad f_n \in C_0^2,$$

so that $(\omega, \gamma) = \lim_{n \to \infty} (\omega, *df_n) = 0$. Thus $\omega \in E^{*\perp}$. Conversely, if $\omega \in C^1 \cap E^{*\perp}$, we have for all $f \in C_0^2$,

$$0 = (\omega, *df) = \iint_S \omega\, d\bar{f} = \iint_S \bar{f}\, d\omega.$$

If $d\omega \neq 0$ at some point P_0, we can represent $d\omega = A(x, y)\, dx\, dy$ in a parametric disk about P_0 where $A \neq 0$ at P_0. But this means that either $\text{Re } A \neq 0$ or $\text{Im } A \neq 0$ at P_0; say $\text{Re } A > 0$ at P_0 and hence in a neighborhood N of P_0. We can construct a real-valued non-negative function $f \in C_0^2(N)$ which is strictly positive at P_0. Then we extend f to S by saying that $f \equiv 0$ in $S - N$, and we get

$$\text{Re}\,(\omega, *df) = \text{Re} \iint_S \omega\, df = \text{Re} \iint_S f\, d\omega = \text{Re} \iint_N fA\, dx\, dy$$

$$= \iint_N f\, \text{Re } A\, dx\, dy > 0,$$

which is a contradiction, and $d\omega = 0$.

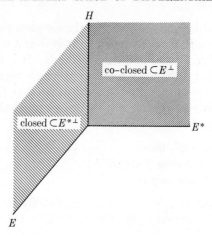

FIGURE 7–2.

A helpful model to keep in mind is afforded by the 3-dimensional real vector space in which three mutually orthogonal axes are selected, one marked E, another E^*, and the third H. Then the (E, H)-plane contains the closed differentials and the (E^*, H)-plane contains the co-closed differentials (see Fig. 7–2).

An immediate consequence of lemma 7–1 is

LEMMA 7–2. $\omega \in C^1 \cap H$ if and only if ω is harmonic.

For if ω is harmonic, $\omega \in C^1$ and $d\omega = d*\omega = 0$, which by lemma 7–1 implies that $\omega \in E^{*\perp} \cap E^\perp = H$. Furthermore, if $\omega \in H \cap C^1$, then by lemma 7–1, $d\omega = 0$ and $d*\omega = 0$ and ω is harmonic.

In view of lemma 7–2, we have to show only that $H \subset C^1$ in order to prove that H consists precisely of all harmonic differentials. The property of being in C^1 is a local one, and if we show that ω is differentiable in an arbitrary parametric disk D we shall have proved the desired result.

For any function $f \in C^2(S)$ with compact carrier contained in D and $\omega \in H$,

$$(\omega, df) = \iint_D \omega *d\bar{f} = 0, \qquad (\omega, *df) = \iint_D \omega \, d\bar{f} = 0.$$

We may look upon D as a Riemann surface itself or let $L^2(D)$ represent the Hilbert space of differentials ω on D for which $\|\omega\|_D^2 = \iint_D \omega *\bar{\omega} < \infty$ with the inner product $(\omega_1, \omega_2)_D = \iint_D \omega_1 *\bar{\omega}_2$. Then $\omega \in L^2(S)$ implies that $\omega \in L^2(D)$, and if $\omega \in H(S)$, for all $f \in C_0^2(D)$ we have $(\omega, df)_D = 0$ and $(\omega, *df)_D = 0$, so that $\omega \in H(D)$. We must now prove a lemma telling us that such an $\omega \in C^1(D)$. This lemma is due to H. Weyl, who first applied it to the case of harmonic vectors in 3-space. Since then this method has also proved very fruitful in proving the existence of harmonic differential forms on more general n-dimensional complex Riemannian manifolds as well as the special case of Riemann surfaces (see, for example, Weyl, Ref. 51, and Kodaira, Ref. 28).

LEMMA 7-3 (Weyl's lemma). *If* $\omega \in L^2(D)$ *and for all* $f \in C_0^2(D)$, $(\omega, df)_D = 0$ *and* $(\omega, *df)_D = 0$, *then* $\omega \in C^1(D)$ *and is hence harmonic in* D.

Observe that if the coefficients of ω are changed on a set of measure zero on D, then the hypotheses of the lemma are still fulfilled. Thus, in the conclusion, the most we can ask is that ω be equal almost everywhere to a differential in $C^1(D)$, but this is precisely the sense in which we understand equality in $L^2(D)$.

Let $\omega \in L^2(D)$ satisfy $(\omega, df)_D = 0$ and $(\omega, *df)_D = 0$ for all $f \in C_0^2(D)$. Then for any $f \in C_0^2(D_\rho)$, $M_\rho\omega$ satisfies

$$(M_\rho\omega, df)_{D_\rho} = (\omega, M_\rho df)_D = (\omega, dM_\rho f)_D = 0$$

and

$$(M_\rho\omega, *df)_{D_\rho} = (\omega, M_\rho *df)_D = (\omega, *dM_\rho f)_D = 0,$$

since $*M_\rho = M_\rho*$ and $M_\rho f \in C_0^2(D)$. The fact that $M_\rho\omega \in C^1(D_\rho)$ enables us to use lemma 7-2, which tells us that $M_\rho\omega$ is harmonic in D_ρ.

We now prove that $M_\rho\omega$ is independent of ρ; that is, if $\rho < \frac{1}{2}$, $\sigma < \frac{1}{2}$, $M_\rho\omega = M_\sigma\omega$ in $D_{\rho+\sigma}$. If we apply M_σ to the differential $M_\rho\omega$ defined in D_ρ, we obtain a differential $M_\sigma M_\rho\omega$ which is defined in $D_{\rho+\sigma}$. Since $M_\rho\omega$ is harmonic in D_ρ, property M2 tells us that $M_\sigma M_\rho\omega = M_\rho\omega$ in $D_{\rho+\sigma}$. Similarly, $M_\rho M_\sigma\omega = M_\sigma\omega$ in $D_{\rho+\sigma}$, so we need only show that $M_\rho M_\sigma\omega = M_\sigma M_\rho\omega$, which is done by an application of Fubini's theorem. If $\omega = p\,dx + q\,dy$,

$$M_\sigma M_\rho p(x, y) = \iint\limits_{D_{1-\sigma}} M_\rho p(x + \xi, y + \eta)s_\sigma(\xi, \eta)\,d\xi\,d\eta$$

$$= \iint\limits_{D_{1-\sigma}} s_\sigma(\xi, \eta)\left[\iint\limits_{D_{1-\rho}} p(x + \xi + u, y + \eta + v)s_\rho(u, v)\,du\,dv\right]d\xi\,d\eta$$

$$= \iint\limits_{D_{1-\rho}} s_\rho(u, v)\left[\iint\limits_{D_{1-\sigma}} p(x + \xi + u, y + \eta + v)s_\sigma(\xi, \eta)\,d\xi\,d\eta\right]du\,dv$$

$$= M_\rho M_\sigma p(x, y).$$

The same holds for q, and so the proof is complete.

Since $M_\rho\omega$ is independent of ρ, we take the limit as $\rho \to 0$ and show that $M_\rho\omega = \omega$. Indeed, property M3 says that $\lim_{\sigma\to 0} ||M_\sigma\omega - \omega||_{D_\sigma} = 0$. However, $D_{\rho+\sigma} \subset D_\sigma$ and $||M_\sigma\omega - \omega||_{D_{\rho+\sigma}} \leq ||M_\sigma\omega - \omega||_{D_\sigma}$, so that $\lim_{\sigma\to 0} ||M_\sigma\omega - \omega||_{D_{\rho+\sigma}} = 0$. In $D_{\rho+\sigma}$, $M_\sigma\omega = M_\rho\omega$ for all $\sigma > 0$, so that $\lim_{\sigma\to 0} ||M_\rho\omega - \omega||_{D_{\rho+\sigma}} = 0$. Furthermore, for any $\delta > 0$, $D_{\rho+\delta} \subset D_{\rho+\sigma}$ so long as $\sigma < \delta$. Therefore

$$||M_\rho\omega - \omega||_{D_{\rho+\delta}} \leq ||M_\rho\omega - \omega||_{D_{\rho+\sigma}}$$

for all $\sigma < \delta$, and we conclude that $||M_\rho\omega - \omega||_{D_{\rho+\delta}} = 0$ for any $\delta > 0$. Thus $M_\rho\omega = \omega$ almost everywhere in $D_{\rho+\delta}$ for any $\delta > 0$ and hence in D_ρ. Since $M_\rho\omega \in C^1(D_\rho)$, we have proved that $\omega \in C^1(D_\rho)$ for any $\rho > 0$; hence $\omega \in C^1(D)$, proving Weyl's lemma.

Combining Weyl's lemma with lemma 7–2, we get

THEOREM 7–9. $\omega \in H(S)$ *if and only if* ω *is harmonic on* S.

We can now decompose an arbitrary differential $\omega \in L^2(S)$ into three mutually orthogonal components $\omega = \omega_h + \gamma + \pi$, where $\omega_h \in H$, $\gamma \in E$ and $\pi \in E^*$. We call ω_h the *projection* of ω on H or the *harmonic component* of ω. Unfortunately, we cannot say that γ and π are exact and coexact components of ω, since all we know is that they are limits in norm of exact and coexact differentials. It would be of interest to know conditions on ω which will guarantee that γ is exact and π is coexact. With this in mind, we prove

LEMMA 7–4. *If* $f_n \in C_0^2(S)$ *and* γ, $\pi \in C^1(S) \cap L^2(S)$ *and*
  (a) $\lim_{n\to\infty} ||\gamma - df_n|| = 0$, *then* γ *is exact;*
  (b) $\lim_{n\to\infty} ||\pi - *df_n|| = 0$, *then* π *is coexact.*

In other words, if $\gamma \in C^1 \cap E$, *then* γ *is exact, whereas if* $\pi \in C^1 \cap E^*$, *then* π *is coexact.*

It is sufficient to prove (a), for $\pi = \lim_{n\to\infty} *df_n$ means $*\pi = \lim_{n\to\infty} df_n$ while $*\pi = df$ means $\pi = *df$. If $\gamma \in E$, then $\gamma \in E^{*\perp}$, and since $\gamma \in C^1$, lemma 7–1 allows us to say that $d\gamma = 0$. To show that γ is exact, we have to show merely that the period of γ over an arbitrary closed curve $C = (\alpha, I)$ is zero. We may subdivide I into intervals $I_k: t_{k-1} \leq t \leq t_k$, with $0 = t_0 < t_1 < \cdots < t_n = 1$ such that each $\alpha(I_k)$ lies in a single parametric disk D_k. We then join $\alpha(t_{k-1})$ to $\alpha(t_k)$ by a straight line segment L_k in D_k. Let L be the closed curve $L_1 L_2 \ldots L_n$; then from the definition of the line integral of a closed differential, we have $\int_L \gamma = \int_C \gamma$. The curve L is now piecewise analytic and has at most a finite number of self-intersections. Thus we may decompose L into a finite number of simple closed curves, and if we show that the period of γ over each of these is zero, then γ is exact.

We therefore assume that L is a piecewise analytic simple closed curve. Since L is two-sided, we may cover it by a finite number of parametric disks to get a region G containing L where G is divided into two components by L, say G^+ to the right of L and G^- to the left of L. We call G a *strip* about L. We define a real-valued function f on S as follows:

$$f(P) = \begin{cases} 1, & \text{for } P \in G^- \cup L, \\ 0, & \text{for } P \in S - G, \end{cases} \qquad f \in C^2(G).$$

Such a function f can be constructed by covering L by a finite number of rectangles, each lying interior to G. Let $\{e_i\}$ be a partition of unity relative to these rectangles. Then $g = \sum e_i$ is 1 on L and 0 on $S - G$. We now define $f = g$ in G^+, $f = 1$ in $G^- \cup L$, and $f = 0$ in $S - G$. In G^-, $df = 0$ and in $S - G$, $df = 0$, so even though f has a jump of 1 across the boundary of G^- and $S - G$, df is continuous and differentiable there. We can define a differential $\eta_L \in C_0^1(S)$ as

$$\eta_L = \begin{cases} df, & \text{in } G, \\ 0, & \text{in } S - G. \end{cases}$$

From its definition, it is clear that $d\eta_L = ddf = 0$ in G and $d\eta_L = 0$ in $S - G$, so η_L is closed and the carrier of η_L is contained in G^+. G is a regular region. For $\gamma \in E \cap C^1$,

$$(\gamma, *\eta_L) = \iint_S \gamma \eta_L = \iint_{G^+} \gamma \eta_L = \iint_{G^+} \gamma\, df = \int_{\partial G^+} f\gamma - \iint_{G^+} f\, d\gamma = \int_L \gamma,$$

since ∂G^+ consists of L and a piecewise analytic curve on which f vanishes. Since $\gamma \in E$ and $*\eta_L$ is co-closed, $*\eta_L \in E^\perp$ and $(\gamma, *\eta_L) = 0$. Therefore $\int_L \gamma = 0$ and γ is exact.

If we have a decomposition of ω into $\omega = \omega_h + df + *dg$, $f, g \in C^2(S)$, then $d\omega = d*dg = \Delta g$. If $\omega = p\, dx + q\, dy$ locally, $\Delta g = ((\partial q/\partial x) - (\partial p/\partial y))\, dx\, dy$ locally, that is, g must be a solution of the equation

$$\frac{\partial^2 g}{\partial x^2} + \frac{\partial^2 g}{\partial y^2} = \frac{\partial q}{\partial x} - \frac{\partial p}{\partial y}.$$

We next find some sufficient conditions for such an equation to have a solution locally.

LEMMA 7–5. *If* $\varphi(x, y) \in C^2$ *and has compact carrier in the* (x, y)-*plane, the equation*

$$\frac{\partial^2 \psi}{\partial x^2} + \frac{\partial^2 \psi}{\partial y^2} = \varphi(x, y)$$

has a solution $\psi \in C^2$.

We shall show that

$$\psi(x, y) = -\frac{1}{2\pi} \int_{-\infty}^{\infty} \int_{-\infty}^{\infty} \log \sqrt{\xi^2 + \eta^2} \; \varphi(\xi + x, \eta + y) \, d\xi \, d\eta.$$

This integral is convergent, since near $(0, 0)$ the integrand behaves like $(\log r) \; \varphi r \, dr \, d\theta$ and $r \log r \to 0$ as $r \to 0$ ($x = r \cos \theta,\, y = r \sin \theta$). To show that $\psi \in C^2$, we compute its difference quotient

$$\frac{\psi(x + h, y) - \psi(x, y)}{h} = -\frac{1}{2\pi} \int_{-\infty}^{\infty} \int_{-\infty}^{\infty}$$

$$\log \sqrt{\xi^2 + \eta^2} \; \frac{\varphi(\xi + x + h, \eta + y) - \varphi(\xi + x, \eta + y)}{h} \, d\xi \, d\eta,$$

and since the difference quotient under the integral sign converges boundedly to $\partial \varphi / \partial x$, we have

$$\frac{\partial \psi}{\partial x} = -\frac{1}{2\pi} \int_{-\infty}^{\infty} \int_{-\infty}^{\infty} \log \sqrt{\xi^2 + \eta^2} \; \frac{\partial}{\partial x} \varphi(\xi + x, \eta + y) \, d\xi \, d\eta.$$

Since $\partial \varphi / \partial x$ is continuous, $\partial \psi / \partial x$ is also continuous. We can similarly show that $\partial \psi / \partial y$, $\partial^2 \psi / \partial x^2$, $\partial^2 \psi / \partial y^2$ all exist and are continuous and if $\Delta_{xy} = \partial^2 / \partial x^2 + \partial^2 / \partial y^2$,

$$\Delta_{xy} \psi = -\frac{1}{2\pi} \int_{-\infty}^{\infty} \int_{-\infty}^{\infty} \log \sqrt{\xi^2 + \eta^2} \; \Delta_{xy} \varphi(x + \xi, y + \eta) \, d\xi \, d\eta.$$

We show that the integral on the right side is simply $\varphi(x, y)$. Now $\Delta_{xy} \varphi(x + \xi, y + \eta) = \Delta_{\xi\eta} \varphi(x + \xi, y + \eta)$, and in polar coordinates $\xi = r \cos \theta$, $\eta = r \sin \theta$, and

$$\Delta_{\xi\eta} = \frac{\partial^2}{\partial r^2} + \frac{1}{r} \frac{\partial}{\partial r} + \frac{1}{r^2} \frac{\partial^2}{\partial \theta^2},$$

so that

$$\Delta_{xy} \psi = -\frac{1}{2\pi} \iint_{0 \le r < \infty} \log r \left[\frac{\partial^2 \varphi}{\partial r^2} + \frac{1}{r} \frac{\partial \varphi}{\partial r} + \frac{1}{r^2} \frac{\partial^2 \varphi}{\partial \theta^2} \right] r \, dr \, d\theta.$$

If the carrier of $\varphi(x, y)$ is contained in $x^2 + y^2 < R^2$, then the carrier of $\varphi(x + \xi, y + \eta)$ is contained in $r < 2R$ for any (x, y) in $x^2 + y^2 < R^2$; thus

$$\Delta_{xy}\psi(x, y) = \lim_{\epsilon \to 0}$$

$$-\frac{1}{2\pi} \iint_{\epsilon < r < 2R} \left\{ \frac{\partial}{\partial r}\left[r \log r \frac{\partial \varphi}{\partial r} - \varphi \right] + \frac{\partial}{\partial \theta}\left(\frac{\log r}{r} \frac{\partial \varphi}{\partial \theta} \right) \right\} dr \, d\theta.$$

Application of Stokes' theorem yields

$$\Delta_{xy}\psi(x, y) = \lim_{\epsilon \to 0} -\frac{1}{2\pi} \int_{r=\epsilon} -\frac{\log r}{r} \frac{\partial \varphi}{\partial \theta} dr + \left[r \log r \frac{\partial \varphi}{\partial r} - \varphi \right] d\theta,$$

since $\varphi = 0$ in a neighborhood of $r = 2R$. On the circle $r = \epsilon$, $dr = 0$ and we may write

$$\Delta_{xy}\psi(x, y) = \lim_{\epsilon \to 0} -\frac{1}{2\pi} \int_{r=\epsilon} \left[r \log r \frac{\partial \varphi}{\partial r} - \varphi \right] d\theta.$$

Moreover,

$$\left| \frac{\partial \varphi}{\partial r} \right| \leq \sqrt{\left(\frac{\partial \varphi}{\partial x} \right)^2 + \left(\frac{\partial \varphi}{\partial y} \right)^2},$$

which is bounded, and $\lim_{\epsilon \to 0} r \log r = 0$; consequently,

$$\Delta_{xy}\psi(x, y) = \lim_{\epsilon \to 0} \frac{1}{2\pi} \int_{r=\epsilon} \varphi(x + r \cos \theta, y + r \sin \theta) \, d\theta = \varphi(x, y),$$

proving lemma 7–5. We next prove

LEMMA 7–6.   *If $\omega \in C^3(S)$, then locally $\omega = df + *dg$ where $f, g \in C^2$ locally.*

About a point P_0 on S, select a parametric disk D: $|z| < 3$. We first construct a function

$$t(r) = \begin{cases} 0, & 0 \leq r < 1, \\ (1 - r)^4 (2 - r)^4, & 1 < r \leq 2, \\ 0, & r > 2. \end{cases}$$

Here $t \in C^3$ and $t(r) \geq 0$ for $r \geq 0$. We then define for $r \geq 0$,

$$u(r) = \int_0^r t(r)\, dr.$$

The function $u \in C^4$ is zero for $0 \le r \le 1$, increases between 1 and 2, and is constant for $r > 2$. Finally, we set

$$s(x, y) = 1 - \frac{u(\sqrt{x^2 + y^2})}{u(2)};$$

$s \in C^4$ in the whole (x, y)-plane; $s(x, y) = 1$ in $x^2 + y^2 < 1$, decreases to zero in $1 < x^2 + y^2 < 4$, and is equal to zero for $x^2 + y^2 \ge 4$. In D, $s\omega$ is a differential in C^3 which is equal to ω in $x^2 + y^2 < 1$ and has compact carrier. If we show that $\gamma = s\omega = df + *dg$ in D, then $\omega = df + *dg$ in $x^2 + y^2 < 1$, which will prove the lemma. If $\gamma = p\, dx + q\, dy$, then $d\gamma = ((\partial q/\partial x) - (\partial p/\partial y))\, dx\, dy$. The function $(\partial q/\partial x) - (\partial p/\partial y) \in C^3$ and has compact carrier in D and hence in the whole complex plane, so by lemma 7–4, we can find a function $g \in C^2$ such that

$$\frac{\partial^2 g}{\partial x^2} + \frac{\partial^2 g}{\partial y^2} = \frac{\partial q}{\partial x} - \frac{\partial p}{\partial y},$$

or $d* dg = d\gamma$. Thus $d(\gamma - *dg) = 0$ and $\gamma - *dg$ is a closed differential which is locally exact; in other words, there is a function $f \in C^2$ such that $\gamma - *dg = df$, proving lemma 7–6. We have now arrived at the decomposition for which we have searched. We have

THEOREM 7–10.　*If $\omega \in L^2(S) \cap C^3(S)$, then $\omega = \omega_h + df + *dg$, where $f, g \in C^2(S)$ and $\omega_h \in H$. This decomposition is unique.*

Indeed, Theorems 7–8 and 7–9 give us the decomposition $\omega = \omega_h + \gamma + \pi$, $\omega_h \in H$, $\gamma \in E$, $\pi \in E^*$. Locally, $\omega = df + *dg$, by lemma 7–6. Thus in a neighborhood D of any point, $\omega_h + \gamma - df = -\pi + *dg$. In D, we set $\theta = \omega_h + \gamma - df = -\pi + *dg$, and prove that θ is harmonic in D by means of Weyl's lemma. Let $h \in C_0^2(D)$; then $(\theta, dh)_D = -(\pi, dh)_D + (*dg, dh)_D$. We can extend the function h by setting $h = 0$ in $S - D$. Then $(\pi, dh)_D = (\pi, dh)_S = 0$ because $\pi \in E^*(S)$ and $dh \in E(S)$. Furthermore,

$$(*dg, dh)_D = - \iint_D (dg)(\overline{dh}) = - \iint_D \bar{h}\, ddg = 0,$$

so that $(\theta, dh)_D = 0$. Moreover, $(\theta, *dh)_D = (\omega_h, *dh)_S + (\gamma, *dh)_S - (df, *dh)_D$, and since $\omega_h \in H$, $\gamma \in E$, $*dh \in E^*$, we have $(\omega_h, *dh)_S = 0$ and $(\gamma, *dh)_S = 0$. As before,

$$(df, *dh)_D = (*df, dh)_D = 0.$$

Thus $(\theta, *dh)_D = 0$ and θ is harmonic. Since $\gamma = df - \theta - \omega_h$ and $\pi = *dg - \theta$, and all the differentials on the right sides are in C^1, we conclude that γ and π are also in C^1. Lemma 7–4 informs us that γ is exact and π is coexact, giving us the desired decomposition.

An arbitrary exact differential $\omega = dh$, $\omega \in C^1 \cap L^2$, is closed and hence belongs to $E^{*\perp} = E \oplus H$. The totality of exact differentials in $C^1 \cap L^2$ forms a linear subset of L^2 which is not necessarily closed. Let $\widetilde{E}$ denote the closure in L^2 of the vector space of exact differentials in $C^1 \cap L^2$. Then $\widetilde{E} \subset E \oplus H$, and its orthogonal complement in $E \oplus H$ will be denoted by $\widetilde{H}$, so that $\widetilde{E} \oplus \widetilde{H} = E \oplus H$, while $E \subset \widetilde{E}$ and $\widetilde{H} \subset H$. Thus we have

THEOREM 7–11. *Any $\omega \in C^3 \cap L^2$ can be decomposed into three components*

$$\omega = \omega_0 + df + *dg, \qquad f,g \in C^2,$$

with $df \in \widetilde{E}$, $*dg \in E^*$, $\omega_0 \in \widetilde{H}$.

PROBLEMS

1. Show that the regular harmonic differentials on the compact Riemann surface S form a group $H(S)$ under addition. Prove that $H(S)$ is isomorphic to the first deRham cohomology group $H_1^*(S)$ defined in problem 4 of Chapter 6, i.e., if ω is a closed differential, there exists one and only one harmonic differential differing from ω by an exact differential. This is the *Hodge theorem* for compact Riemann surfaces (Ref. 23).

2. An n-cochain ($n = 0, 1, 2$) is a complex-valued function defined on all simplicial n-chains in $C^n(S_\Delta)$ with the property that $f(\alpha_1 c_1^n + \alpha_2 c_2^n) = \alpha_1 f(c_1^n) + \alpha_2 f(c_2^n)$ for all complex numbers α_i and all $c_i^n \in C^n(S_\Delta)$. Show that the set of all n-cochains forms a group $C_n(S_\Delta)$ under the addition operation $(f + g)(c^n) = f(c^n) + g(c^n)$.

3. We define the coboundary operator δ on $C_n(S_\Delta)$ so that for all $f \in C_n(S_\Delta)$ we shall have $\delta f \in C_{n+1}(S_\Delta)$; namely, $(\delta f)(c^{n+1}) = f(\partial c^{n+1})$. Show that δ defines a homomorphism from $C_n(S_\Delta)$ into $C_{n+1}(S_\Delta)$, with the property that $\delta \delta f = 0$.

4. Let $Z_n(S_\Delta)$ be the kernel of the homomorphism δ and let $B_n(S_\Delta)$ be the image of $C_{n-1}(S_\Delta)$ under δ. Prove that $B_n(S_\Delta)$ is a subgroup of $Z_n(S_\Delta)$. We call the elements of $Z_n(S_\Delta)$ n-cocycles, and the elements of $B_n(S_\Delta)$ n-coboundaries. Define the nth simplicial cohomology groups of S_Δ as

$$H_n(S_\Delta) = \frac{Z_n(S_\Delta)}{B_n(S_\Delta)}.$$

5. Show that the value of every 1-cocycle on any 1-cycle is completely determined by its values on the homology basis $\mathbf{a}_1$, $\mathbf{b}_1$, $\ldots$, $\mathbf{a}_g$, $\mathbf{b}_g$ for S. Prove also that a 1-cochain is a coboundary if and only if it vanishes on all 1-cycles.

6. Using the pairing $(C^n(S_\Delta),\, D_n^*(S)) \to K$ (problem 2, Chapter 6), observe that to each differential $\omega^n \in D_n^*(S)$ corresponds a 1-cocycle $h[\omega^n]$ defined as follows: $(h[\omega^n])(c^n) = (c^n, \omega^n)$. Prove that h defines a homomorphism from $D_n^*(S)$ into $C_n(S_\Delta)$. Show furthermore that $\delta(h[\omega^n]) = h[d\omega^n]$, that is, that $(h[\omega^n])(\partial c^{n+1}) = (h[d\omega^n])(c^{n+1})$ for all $c^{n+1} \in C^{n+1}(S_\Delta)$, is the equivalent of problem 3 of Chapter 6. Consequently h takes every closed differential into a cocycle and every exact differential into a coboundary. Show that h therefore induces a homomorphism $\tilde{h}$ of $H_1^*(S)$ into $H_1(S_\Delta)$.

7. Show that the orthogonality of the pairing $(H^1(S_\Delta),\, H_1^*(S)) \to K$ (problem 7, Chapter 6) implies that the homomorphism $\tilde{h}$ is an isomorphism.

8. By constructing the differentials $\pi(\mathbf{a}_i)$ with period 1 on $\mathbf{a}_i$ and 0 on all other $\mathbf{a}_j$, $j \neq i$, and all $\mathbf{b}_j$, and similarly $\pi(\mathbf{b}_i)$ with period 1 on $\mathbf{b}_i$ and 0 on all other $\mathbf{b}_j$, $j \neq i$, and all $\mathbf{a}_j$, show that $\tilde{h}$ maps $H_1^*(S)$ onto $H_1(S_\Delta)$. Thus h is an isomorphism of $H_1^*(S)$ onto $H_1(S_\Delta)$, and both are then isomorphic to the vector space over the complex number field with basis $\pi(\mathbf{a}_i)$, $\pi(\mathbf{b}_i)$, $i = 1, 2, \ldots, g$. This is the *deRham theorem* for compact Riemann surfaces (Ref. 39). From the Hodge theorem (problem 1) we conclude that $H_1(S_\Delta)$, $H_1^*(S)$, and $H(S)$ are all isomorphic groups.

CHAPTER 8

EXISTENCE OF HARMONIC AND ANALYTIC DIFFERENTIALS

8–1 Existence theorems. We shall now concern ourselves with the proofs of the existence of harmonic and analytic differentials with prescribed singularities on an arbitrary Riemann surface. This problem was first formulated in its full generality and "solved" by Riemann in 1851. Weierstrass showed in 1870 by means of an example that Riemann's use of the so-called Dirichlet principle was unsound. This led to the invention of numerous other methods of attacking the existence problem. For compact surfaces, the problem was solved in 1870 by Schwarz using the alternating process and by C. Neumann using the method of arithmetic means, both of these being combinatorial methods. Poincaré introduced the *méthode de balayage* (method of sweeping out) to obtain the existence of harmonic functions in the year 1883. It was not until 1900 that Hilbert salvaged Riemann's original method of proof based upon the Dirichlet principle. In the same year Osgood proved by potential-theoretic means the Riemann mapping theorem for a general simply connected region of the plane.

The related problem of uniformization (see Sections 1–6, 9–1, and 9–2) was solved in 1882 by F. Klein for algebraic functions. In 1883, Poincaré solved the uniformization problem when the analytic function $w = f(z)$ omits at least three values in its range. Klein based his existence proofs on the results of Schwarz and Neumann, while Poincaré constructed the uniformizing functions analytically as θ-series. Finally, the general uniformization theorem was proved by Koebe in 1908 by purely function-theoretic methods.

The introduction of subharmonic functions led to the Perron process for proving the existence of harmonic functions in 1928. The method of orthogonal projections, a modern version devised by H. Weyl in 1940 of Riemann's original method, is to be used to prove the existence theorems in this chapter.

We shall first consider the problem of finding an everywhere regular harmonic or analytic differential on a Riemann surface S. To this end, we prove the following decomposition theorem for closed differentials.

LEMMA 8–1. *Let* $\omega \in C^1(S) \cap L^2(S)$ *and* $d\omega = 0$. *Then* $\omega = \omega_h + df$, $\omega_h \in H$, *and* $f \in C^2(S)$.

We have shown in Theorems 7–8 and 7–9 that $\omega = \omega_h + \gamma + \pi$, where $\gamma \in E$ and $\pi \in E^*$. Since $d\omega = 0$, $\omega \in E^{*\perp}$, so $(\omega, \pi) = (\pi, \pi) = 0$; hence $\pi = 0$ and $\omega = \omega_h + \gamma$. Since $\omega_h \in C^1$ and $\omega \in C^1$, we conclude that $\gamma = C^1 \cap E$ or $\gamma = df, f \in C^2$.

Thus one way to find an everywhere finite harmonic differential on S is to look for a closed differential on S with nonzero periods and decompose it into its harmonic and exact components. Since the exact component has zero periods, the harmonic component will have the same periods as the closed differential and hence cannot vanish identically on S. We then have the following statement:

If one can construct a closed differential $\omega \in C^1 \cap L^2$ on S which is not exact, then there exists an everywhere regular harmonic differential ω_h on S with the same periods as ω. If we can find a simple closed piecewise analytic curve C on S which does not separate S (that is, $S - |C|$ is connected), we can construct a closed differential $\omega \in C^1 \cap L^2$ with nonvanishing period over C. Indeed, let D be a parametric disk about a point P_0 on C in which C appears as the real axis. Then in D, we can select two points P' and P'' which are separated locally by C (say $i/2$ and $-i/2$). We know that P' and P'' can be joined in $S - |C|$ by a simple curve which may be taken to be piecewise analytic. P' and P'' can be joined to P_0 with a straight line in D to give us a simple closed piecewise analytic curve L on S which crosses C at only one point. We construct the differential $\omega = \eta_L$ using a strip about L which crosses C in D (see lemma 7–4). Then ω is closed and $\int_C \omega = \int_C df = 1$, since f increases from 0 to 1 as we cross the strip and $df = 0$ outside the strip. By lemma 8–1, ω can be projected into its harmonic component, which has the same period as ω on C. Since ω_h is an everywhere regular harmonic differential ω_h, then $\omega_h + i*\omega_h$ is an everywhere regular analytic differential and we have proved

THEOREM 8–1. *If there is a simple closed piecewise analytic curve C which does not separate S, then there is an everywhere regular harmonic differential ω on S which has nonzero period on C and an everywhere regular analytic differential $\omega + i*\omega$.*

The differentials constructed in Theorem 8–1 have nonzero periods and hence are not exact and do not lead us to single-valued harmonic functions or analytic functions when integrated. Since we shall be interested in finding functions on S as well as differentials, we shall investigate the possibility of finding an everywhere regular harmonic function on S. In general, this is not possible, as the following lemma shows.

LEMMA 8–2. *On a compact Riemann surface S, a differential ω which is harmonic and exact vanishes identically.*

Since $\omega = df$ and since f has compact carrier (S is compact), we have $\omega \in E$ and $\omega \in H$; but since $E \perp H$, $\omega \equiv 0$.

Therefore, to prove a general existence theorem for exact harmonic differentials on an arbitrary S, we must give up our quest for everywhere regular differentials and admit certain singularities.[†] Let D be a parametric disk about an arbitrary point P_0 on S in which the local coordinate is $\varphi(P) = z$, $\varphi(P_0) = 0$, $|z| < 3$. Then let θ be the differential $\theta = d(1/z^n) = -(n/z^{n+1})\, dz$, $n \geq 1$, defined in D. We shall prove

THEOREM 8–2. *There exists a unique differential ω satisfying the following conditions:*
(a) *ω is harmonic in $S - P_0$ and exact;*
(b) *$\omega - \theta = \omega + (n/z^{n+1})\, dz$, $n \geq 1$, is harmonic in a neighborhood N of P_0;*
(c) *$\|\omega\|^2_{S-\bar{N}} = \iint_{S-\bar{N}} \omega * \bar{\omega} < \infty$;*
(d) *for any function $h \in C^2(S)$ with the two properties $\|dh\| < \infty$ and $h \equiv 0$ in a neighborhood of P_0, we have $(\omega, dh) = 0$.*

To construct ω, we call forth the function $s(x, y)$ defined in lemma 7–6 and set $\rho(z) = \rho(x + iy) = s(x, y)$ in D. Then $d(\rho(z)/z^n) = \theta$ in $|z| < 1$, $d(\rho(z)/z^n) = 0$ in $|z| > 2$, and $d(\rho(z)/z^n) \in C^3$ in $|z| > 0$. We extend $d(\rho(z)/z^n)$ to a differential ψ on S by setting

$$\psi = \begin{cases} d\left(\dfrac{\rho(z)}{z^n}\right), & \text{in } D, \\ 0, & \text{in } S - D. \end{cases}$$

Since θ is analytic in $D - P_0$, $*\theta = -i\theta$ or $i*\theta = \theta$. Moreover, $\psi = \theta$ in $|z| < 1$, so $\psi - i*\psi \equiv 0$ in $|z| < 1$ and in $S - D$. Thus

$$\psi - i*\psi \in C^3(S) \cap L^2(S)$$

and by Theorem 7–11 may be decomposed into harmonic, exact, and coexact components:

$$\psi - i*\psi = \omega_0 + df + *dg,$$

where $f, g \in C^2$, $df \in \widetilde{E}$, $*dg \in E^*$, and $\omega_0 \in \widetilde{H}$. Let us define

$$\omega = \psi - df = i*\psi + \omega_0 + *dg.$$

[†]It can be shown that on noncompact Riemann surfaces, there always exist everywhere regular exact harmonic differentials and also exact holomorphic differentials which do not vanish identically. See, for example, Behnke and Sommer, Ref. 6, p. 565.

We shall prove that ω satisfies (a) through (d).

(a) From its definition, $\omega \in C^1(S - P_0)$ and $d\omega = d\psi - ddf = 0$, since ψ is exact in $S - P_0$, while $d*\omega = -i\,d\psi + d*\omega_0 - ddg = 0$ in $S - P_0$ since ω_0 is harmonic. Thus ω is harmonic in $S - P_0$. The fact that both ψ and df are exact means that ω is also exact in $S - P_0$.

(b) In $|z| < 1$, $\psi = i*\psi = \theta$, so that $\omega - \theta = -df = \omega_0 + *dg$, which is in C^1. Then $d(\omega - \theta) = -ddf = 0$ and

$$d*(\omega - \theta) = d*\omega_0 - ddg = 0,$$

proving that $\omega - \theta$ is harmonic in N: $|z| < 1$ about P_0.

(c) $\|\omega\|_{S-\bar{N}} = \|\psi - df\|_{S-\bar{N}} \leq \|\psi\|_{S-\bar{N}} + \|df\|_{S-\bar{N}}$. $\|\psi\|_{S-\bar{N}} < \infty$ from the definition of ψ, and $\|df\|_{S-\bar{N}} \leq \|df\|_S < \infty$ because $df \in \widetilde{E} \subset L^2$.

(d) $(\omega, dh) = i(*\psi, dh) + (\omega_0, dh) + (*dg, dh)$. Since $dh \in \widetilde{E}$ while $\omega_0 \in \widetilde{H}$ and $*dg \in E^*$, we know that $(\omega_0, dh) = 0$ and $(*dg, dh) = 0$. If $h \equiv 0$ in a neighborhood of P_0, we know that $h \equiv 0$ in $|z| \leq \delta$, $\delta > 0$. Let G represent the annulus $\delta < |z| < 2$. We have

$$(*\psi, dh) = -\iint_G \psi\,dh = \iint_G h\,d\psi + \int_{\partial G} h\psi = 0$$

since $d\psi = 0$, and $\psi = 0$ on $|z| = 2$ while $h = 0$ on $|z| = \delta$, proving (d).

All that remains unproved is the uniqueness of ω satisfying (a) through (d). Suppose that there were another differential ω_1 satisfying (a) through (d). Then $\omega - \omega_1 \in C^1 \cap L^2$ on S, since the singularities at P_0 cancel under the subtraction. Since each is exact, $\omega - \omega_1 = dh$, where h is harmonic on S. We define a new function g on S as

$$g = \begin{cases} \rho(z)h(z), & \text{in } D, \\ 0, & \text{in } S - D. \end{cases}$$

Then $g \in C_0^2(S)$ and $g = h$ in N: $|z| < 1$. Moreover, $\|d(h - g)\| \leq \|dh\|_{S-\bar{N}} + \|dg\|_{S-\bar{N}} \leq \|\omega\|_{S-\bar{N}} + \|\omega_1\|_{S-\bar{N}} + \|dg\| < \infty$. Therefore, according to (d), $(\omega - \omega_1, d(h - g)) = 0$. We then have

$$\|\omega - \omega_1\|^2 = (\omega - \omega_1, dh)$$
$$= (\omega - \omega_1, d(h - g)) + (\omega - \omega_1, dg) = 0,$$

because $dg \in E$ and $\omega - \omega_1 \in H$, proving the uniqueness.

Directly from Theorem 8–2, we can deduce the existence of several other harmonic and analytic differentials which will be of interest. First, once ω

has been found in Theorem 8–2, $2^{-1}(\omega + \bar{\omega}) = \gamma$ is an exact real harmonic differential with the singularity $\mathrm{Re}\, d(1/z^n)$ at P_0 which also satisfies conditions (c) and (d), while $(2i)^{-1}(\omega - \bar{\omega})$ is an exact real harmonic differential with the singularity $\mathrm{Im}\, d(1/z^n)$ at P_0 which satisfies (c) and (d), where in both cases h in (d) can be restricted to be real.

If γ is an exact real harmonic differential with singularity $\mathrm{Re}\, d(1/z^n)$ at P_0, then $*\gamma$ is a real harmonic differential with the singularity $\mathrm{Im}\, d(1/z^n)$, which is not, in general, exact. The differential $\omega = \gamma + i*\gamma$ is an analytic differential on S with singularity $d(1/z^n)$ at P_0 whose real part is exact and satisfies (c) and (d) of Theorem 8–2.

Finally, since ω in Theorem 8–2 is exact, $\omega = df$, where f is a function on S which is harmonic in $S - P_0$ with the singularity $1/z^n$ at P_0, and df satisfies (c) and (d). We leave the question of finding exact analytic differentials (analytic functions) with prescribed singularities on S until Chapter 10. We shall summarize these remarks in

COROLLARY 8–1.   *On an arbitrary Riemann surface S, there exists, for $n \geq 1$,*

(i)   *an exact harmonic differential with singularity $d(1/z^n)$ at P_0,*

(ii) *an exact real harmonic differential with singularity $\mathrm{Re}\, d(1/z^n)$ [or $\mathrm{Im}\, d(1/z^n)$] at P_0,*

(iii) *a harmonic function with singularity $1/z^n$ at P_0,*

(iv) *an analytic differential with singularity $d(1/z^n)$ at P_0 and exact real part.*

The Dirichlet principle, which forms the basis for many existence proofs, states, in general, that the harmonic function minimizes a certain integral within a certain class of functions. If $f \in C^1(S) \cap L^2(S)$, the norm of df is

$$||df||_S^2 = \iint\limits_S df*\overline{df},$$

where locally $df*\overline{df} = |\partial f/\partial x|^2 + |\partial f/\partial y|^2$. The integral $\iint_S df*\overline{df}$ is called the *Dirichlet integral* of f on S. Let us select a point P_0 and specify a singularity $1/z^n$ in a disk D about P_0. We have shown that there is a harmonic function f on S with singularity $1/z^n$ at P_0 satisfying $||df||_{S-\bar{N}} < \infty$ and $(df, dh) = 0$ for all $h \in C^2(S)$, $||dh|| < \infty$, $h \equiv 0$, in a neighborhood N of P_0. If we vary f by adding to it any h satisfying the above conditions, then $f + h - 1/z^n \in C^2(D)$ and $f + h \in C^2(S - D)$. We see that

$$||d(f + h)||_{S-\bar{N}}^2 = (df + dh, df + dh)_{S-\bar{N}}$$

$$= ||df||_{S-\bar{N}}^2 + ||dh||_{S-\bar{N}}^2 + (df, dh) + (\overline{df, dh}).$$

Since $(df, dh) = 0$, we have proved that

$$\|d(f + h)\|^2_{S-\bar{N}} = \|df\|^2_{S-\bar{N}} + \|dh\|^2_{S-\bar{N}} \geq \|df\|^2_{S-\bar{N}}.$$

Thus the harmonic function f minimizes the Dirichlet integral over $S - \bar{N}$ in the class of all functions $f + h$. This fact is called the *Dirichlet principle.*

The singularities $d(1/z^n) = -(n/z^{n+1})\, dz$, $n \geq 1$, all have residues zero, so all the differentials so far constructed on S have residues equal to zero on S. We should now like to find a differential that has a singularity dz/z. But we cannot arbitrarily specify the point and the residue, for we have shown that in the case of a compact surface the sum of the residues must be zero. To get around this difficulty, we shall look for a differential which has two singular points, each having nonzero residues whose sum is zero. To be specific, let D be a parametric disk with local parameter $\varphi(P) = z$, $|z| < 3$, and let N be the disk $|z| < 1$ in D. We shall select two points A and B on N with $\varphi(A) = a$, $\varphi(B) = b$. Then

$$(z - a)^{-1}\, dz - (z - b)^{-1}\, dz = \theta$$

is an analytic differential in D except at $z = a$ and $z = b$. Since $\theta = d \log [(z - a)/(z - b)]$ and since $\log [(z - a)/(z - b)]$ is single-valued in $|z| > 1$, θ is exact in $|z| > 1$. We may now proceed just as in Theorem 8–2 to prove

THEOREM 8–3. *There exists a unique differential ω on S satisfying the following conditions:*
  (a) *ω is harmonic in $S - (A \cup B)$,*
  (b) *$\omega - \theta$ is harmonic in N,*
  (c) *$\|\omega\|_{S-\bar{N}} < \infty$,*
  (d) *if $h \in C^2(S)$, $\|dh\| < \infty$, and $h \equiv 0$ in N, then $(\omega, dh) = 0$,*
  (e) *ω is exact in $S - N$ and has the same periods in N as θ.*

Again set

$$\psi(P) = \begin{cases} d\left(\rho(z) \log \dfrac{z - a}{z - b}\right), & P \in D, \quad z = \varphi(P), \\ 0, & P \in S - D, \end{cases}$$

and observe that $\psi - i{*}\psi \equiv 0$ in $N: |z| < 1$ and is in $C^1(S) \cap L^2(S)$. We decompose $\psi - i{*}\psi$ into its three components $\psi - i{*}\psi = \omega_0 + df + {*}dg$, $\omega_0 \in \widetilde{H}$, $f,g \in C^2(S)$, $df \in \widetilde{E}$, and ${*}dg \in E^*$, and define $\omega = \psi - df = i{*}\psi + \omega_0 + {*}dg$. The proofs of (a), (b), (c), and (d) are exactly the same as in Theorem 8–2. For (e), we observe that ψ is exact in $S - \bar{N}$ and $\omega = \psi - df$, so ω is also exact in $S - \bar{N}$. In N, $\psi = \theta$, so ω and θ have the same periods. To prove the uniqueness, observe that if ω_1 were another differential satisfying (a) through (e), then $\omega - \omega_1$ would be exact and harmonic on S with no singularities, and the proof follows as in Theorem 8–2.

Once again, $2^{-1}(\omega + \bar\omega) = \gamma$ and $(2i)^{-1}(\omega - \bar\omega)$ are real harmonic differentials which have the singularities $d \log |(z - a)/(z - b)|$ and $d \arg (z - a)/(z - b)$, respectively. We may note that even though $\log [(z - a)/(z - b)]$ is not single-valued in N, $\log |(z - a)/(z - b)|$ is single-valued, and consequently, according to (e), γ is exact on S. Thus we can find a real harmonic function on S which has the singularities $\log |(z - a)/(z - b)|$ at A and B. Finally, $\gamma + i*\gamma = \omega$ is an analytic differential with singularity $\log [(z - a)/(z - b)]$ at A and B and an exact real part.

The requirement that A and B lie in the same parametric disk may now be relaxed. If A and B are any two points on S, they may be joined by a curve $C = (\alpha, I)$, $\alpha(0) = A$, $\alpha(1) = B$. We may subdivide C into arcs $C_k = (\alpha, I_k)$, I_k: $t_k \le t \le t_{k+1}$, and $0 = t_0 < t_1 < \cdots < t_n = 1$, such that each C_k lies in a parametric disk D_k with local parameter $\varphi_k(P) = z_k$, $|z_k| < 1$. We may construct a harmonic differential γ_k, $k = 0, 1, \ldots, n - 1$, which has the singularity $d \log [(z_k - p_k')/(z_k - p_k)]$ in the disk D_k according to Theorem 8–3, where $\alpha(t_k) = P_k$ and $\varphi_k(P_k) = p_k$, and $\varphi_k(P_{k+1}) = p_k'$. The point P_k lies in the disks D_{k-1} and D_k, so γ_{k-1} and γ_k both have singularities at P_k: γ_{k-1} with residue $+1$ and γ_k with residue -1. We have seen that under the change of coordinate from z_{k-1} to z_k, the residue and order of the pole remain the same. Hence $-\gamma_{k-1}$ and γ_k have the same singular parts at P_k, and $\gamma_{k-1} + \gamma_k$ has no singularity at P_k. Thus $\omega = \gamma_0 + \gamma_1 + \cdots + \gamma_{n-1}$ is harmonic on $S - (A \cup B)$ and has the singularity $-(1/z) \, dz$ at A and $(1/z) \, dz$ at B. If we begin with real harmonic functions f_k having singularities $\log |(z_k - p_k')/(z_k - p_k)|$ at P_k and P_{k+1}, the function $f = f_0 + f_1 + \cdots + f_{n-1}$ is harmonic on $S - (A \cup B)$ and has the singularity $-\log |z|$ at A and $\log |z|$ at B, expressed in local coordinates about A and about B. We may summarize these results as follows:

COROLLARY 8–2. *If A and B are any two points on a Riemann surface S, then there exist*

(i) *a harmonic or analytic differential on S with singularity $-dz/z$ at A and dz/z at B,*

(ii) *a real harmonic function on S having singularity $-\log |z|$ at A and $\log |z|$ at B.*

Finally, we can construct a harmonic or analytic differential which has prescribed residues at prescribed points so long as the sum of the residues is equal to zero. In fact, let $P_1, P_2, \ldots, P_n$ be arbitrary distinct points on S and let $c_1, c_2, \ldots, c_n$ be arbitrary nonzero complex numbers with

$c_1 + c_2 + \cdots + c_n = 0$. Let Q be a point on S different from the P_i, $i = 1, \ldots, n$. Then construct an analytic differential ω_i, $i = 1, 2, \ldots, n$, which has residue $+1$ at P_i and residue -1 at Q, as given in corollary 8–2. Then $\omega = c_1\omega_1 + c_2\omega_2 + \cdots + c_n\omega_n$ has a pole of order 1 at P_i with residue c_i, $i = 1, 2, \ldots, n$, and has a pole of order 1 with residue $\sum_{i=1}^{n} c_i = 0$ at Q. Thus ω is regular at Q and gives us the desired differential. We have proved

COROLLARY 8–3. *If $P_1, P_2, \ldots, P_n$ are arbitrary distinct points on S and $c_1, c_2, \ldots, c_n$ are arbitrary nonzero complex numbers with $c_1 + c_2 + \cdots + c_n = 0$, then there is an analytic (or harmonic) differential on S which has poles of order 1 at P_i with residues c_i, $i = 1, 2, \ldots, n$, and is otherwise regular.*

Another type of existence problem that should be mentioned in connection with orthogonal projections is the boundary-value problem for harmonic functions. Let G be a region with compact closure on a Riemann surface S. The region G will be called a *Jordan region* if its boundary $\partial G = \overline{G} - G$ consists of n connected components $C_1, C_2, \ldots, C_n$, each of which is a Jordan curve, i.e., the topological image of a circle. (The regular regions defined in Chapter 6 are examples of Jordan regions.) Let f be a real-valued function defined in $\overline{G}$ which is of class C^2 in G, continuous in $\overline{G}$, and with $\|df\|_G < \infty$. The boundary-value problem asks for a harmonic function h in G such that $\lim_{p \to \partial G} (h(p) - f(p)) = 0$, that is, a harmonic function h with the same boundary values as f.

The differential df is closed so that $df \in E^{*\perp}$, and according to lemma 7–1, $df = \omega + \gamma$, where ω is harmonic and γ is in E for the region G. However, ω and df are both in C^1, so $\gamma \in C^1 \cap E$, and from lemma 7–4, we conclude that $\gamma = dg$ for $g \in C^2(G)$. Then $\omega = d(f - g)$ is also exact, and we define the harmonic function h as $h = f - g$. We know that g satisfies the property that there exists a sequence of functions $g_n \in C_0^2(G)$ with $\|dg_n - dg\|_G \to 0$. We must deduce from the fact that each g_n vanishes in some neighborhood of the boundary the fact that g itself tends to zero (actually a constant which we subtract away) as we approach the boundary, and hence $h - f \to 0$. This would solve the boundary-value problem. We shall not give the proof here but rather refer to the interesting proof due to P. Lax which is presented in Schiffer and Spencer's recent book (Ref. 42). In their book is also presented a discussion of various important domain functions on finite Riemann surfaces (i.e., surfaces obtained from a compact surface by removing a finite number of topological disks). The authors extend to finite Riemann surfaces the study of the Bergman kernel function and related domain functions, a study which had already yielded a wealth of interesting results in the case of schlicht domains (see Bergman, Ref. 8).

8–2 Countability of a Riemann surface. We now have the apparatus at hand to prove that every Riemann surface has a countable base. This result will also follow from the triangulability of the surface to be proved independently in Chapter 9, but the proof given here is also of interest. We have shown in Chapter 2 that it is sufficient to prove that the Riemann surface is metrizable and separable.

To show these things, we select a point P_0 on S and construct the exact real harmonic differential ω satisfying conditions (a) through (d) with singularity Re $d(1/z)$ at P_0, as in Theorem 8–2. If N is the disk $|z| < 1$ in a parametric disk $D_0 : |z| < 2$ about P_0, we show how to define a metric on $S - N$. Let $\gamma = \omega + i{*}\omega$ be the analytic differential with real part ω and $|\gamma|$ be the absolute value of γ. If P and Q are two points of $S - \overline{N}$, and $C = (\alpha, I)$, $\alpha(0) = P$, $\alpha(1) = Q$, is a piecewise differentiable curve, $\int_C |\gamma|$ is a positive number. We define $d(P, Q) = $ g.l.b. $\int_C |\gamma|$ for all piecewise differentiable curves C joining P and Q on $S - \overline{N}$. Then since $\int_{C^{-1}} |\gamma| = \int_C |\gamma|$, we have $d(P, Q) = d(Q, P)$. Clearly, $d(P, P) = 0$, and if $P \neq Q$, we can put a parametric disk $D : |z| < r$, $r > 0$, about P so that Q is not in D. In D, $\gamma = df$ for some analytic function $f(z) = a_0 + a_n z^n + a_{n+1} z^{n+1} + \cdots$, $a_n \neq 0$. Then $f'(z) = n a_n z^{n-1} + (n + 1) a_{n+1} z^n + \cdots = n a_n z^{n-1} \varphi(z)$, where $\varphi(z)$ is an analytic function in D with $\varphi(0) = 1$. Thus $|\varphi(z)| > \frac{1}{2}$ in some $|z| < r_1 < r$, $r_1 > 0$, and if z_1 is the first intersection point of C with $z = r_1$, and C_1 is the part of C from $z = 0$ to $z = z_1$, we have

$$\int_C |\gamma| \geq \int_{C_1} |f'(z)||dz| \geq \int_{C_1} \tfrac{1}{2} n |a_n||z^{n-1}||dz| \geq \tfrac{1}{2} n |a_n| \left| \int_{C_1} z^{n-1}\, dz \right|$$

$$= \tfrac{1}{2}|a_n| r_1^n > 0,$$

so that $d(P, Q) \geq (\frac{1}{2})|a_n| r_1^n > 0$. Finally, if P, Q, and R are any three points of $S - \overline{N}$, and if C_{PQ} joins P to Q, C_{QR} joins Q to R, then $C_{PQR} = C_{PQ} C_{QR}$ joins P to R and

$$\int_{C_{PQR}} |\gamma| = \int_{C_{PQ}} |\gamma| + \int_{C_{QR}} |\gamma|.$$

As C_{PQ} and C_{QR} vary through all curves joining P to Q and Q to R, C_{PQR} goes through a subclass of the curves joining P to R, so that $d(P, R) \leq d(P, Q) + d(Q, R)$. Thus $d(P, Q)$ is a metric on $S - \overline{N}$, and it remains to show that the topology is preserved.

We show that each sphere about an arbitrary point P' contains a parametric disk about P', and vice versa. Let D be a parametric disk about P' with local parameter $\varphi(P) = z$, $\varphi(P') = 0$, and $|z| < 1$. As before,

$\gamma = df$, where f is an analytic function in D. We have seen that for some $r_1 > 0$, $|f'(z)| \geq n|a_n z^{n-1}|\frac{1}{2}$, so that if $\varphi(Q) = \zeta$ with $|\zeta| < r_1$,

$$d(P', Q) \geq \tfrac{1}{2}|a_n||\zeta|^n.$$

On the other hand, if $|f'(z)| < K$ in $|z| < r_1$, we have

$$d(P', Q) \leq \int_0^{|\zeta|} |f'(z)||dz| \leq K|\zeta|,$$

so that for $\varphi(P') = 0$, $\varphi(Q) = \zeta$,

$$\tfrac{1}{2}|a_n||\zeta|^n \leq d(P', Q) \leq K|\zeta|.$$

Therefore, any sphere $d(P', Q) < R$ contains a disk $|\zeta| < R/K$, whereas any disk $|\zeta| < \rho$ contains the sphere $d(P', Q) < \frac{1}{2}|a_n|\rho^n$, showing that the metric gives $S - \overline{N}$ the same topology as its locally euclidean structure.

The proof that $S - \overline{N}$ is separable proceeds as follows. According to Theorem 8–2, $\|\gamma\|^2_{S-\overline{N}} = \iint_{S-\overline{N}} \gamma * \bar\gamma < \infty$ and locally $\gamma * \bar\gamma = |f'(z)|^2 \, dx \, dy$ is a positive differential. From the definition of the integral over $S - \overline{N}$, there is a sequence $\{G_n\}$ of regions G_n with compact closures in $S - \overline{N}$, such that $\iint_{S-\overline{N}} \gamma * \bar\gamma = \lim_{N\to\infty} \iint_{G_n} \gamma * \bar\gamma$. Each set $\overline{G}_n$ may be covered by a finite number of parametric disks in which the points with rational real and imaginary parts form a countable dense set. Then the set $G = \cup_{n=1}^{\infty} G_n$ also contains a countable dense set of points K, since the countable union of countable sets is countable and each point of G is in some G_n and is hence the limit of points of the countable dense set in G_n, so that $\overline{K} = G$. We prove next that $S - \overline{N} \subset \overline{K}$. Otherwise, there is a point P in $S - \overline{N}$ which is not in $\overline{K}$. This means that there is a neighborhood D of P $(D \subset S - \overline{N})$ which contains no points of G and hence no points of any G_n. The analytic differential γ cannot vanish identically in D; for locally $\gamma = p(z) \, dz$, where p is an analytic function, and if p vanishes in D, by analytic continuation, $\gamma \equiv 0$ on S, which contradicts its having the specified singularity. Therefore $\iint_D \gamma * \bar\gamma = \delta > 0$. We may select a G_n such that $\iint_{G_n} \gamma * \bar\gamma > \iint_{S-\overline{N}} \gamma * \bar\gamma - \delta/2$. Then we join a point in G_n to P with a curve C and cover C with a finite number of parametric disks $D_1, D_2, \ldots, D_k$, each in $S - \overline{N}$, and set $G' = G_n \cup D \cup D_1 \cup \cdots \cup D_k$. G' is a region with compact closure in $S - \overline{N}$ and

$$\iint_{G'} \gamma * \bar\gamma \geq \iint_{G_n} \gamma * \bar\gamma + \iint_D \gamma * \bar\gamma \geq \iint_{S-\overline{N}} \gamma * \bar\gamma + \frac{\delta}{2},$$

which contradicts the definition of $\iint_{S-\bar{N}} \gamma * \bar{\gamma}$. Therefore K is a countable dense set in $S - \bar{N}$, so $S - \bar{N}$ is a separable metrizable manifold and hence has a countable covering by parametric disks. If we add the disk D_0 about P_0, we get a countable covering by parametric disks for S itself. Therefore,

THEOREM 8–4. *Every Riemann surface S has a countable base.*[†]

PROBLEMS

1. Let $p' = h(p)$ be a homeomorphism (the identity mapping, for example) of a Riemann surface S onto a surface S'. We introduce the following structure on S': When $\varphi(p) = z$ is a local parameter about $p_0 = \varphi^{-1}(0)$, then as local parameter about $p_0' = h(p_0)$, we define $\psi(p') = \overline{\varphi(h^{-1}(p'))} = \bar{z}$, the complex conjugate of z. Prove that S' is a Riemann surface. S' is called the *conjugate surface* of S and p' the *point conjugate* to p.

2. Let G be a Jordan region with compact closure on a Riemann surface S. Assume that each point $p_0 \in C_i$, $i = 1, 2, \ldots, n$ (the n boundary components of the region G), has about it a parametric disk N of S such that $N \cap G$ can be mapped one-to-one and conformally by a function $z = \chi(p)$ into a region in the upper half-plane $\text{Im}(z) > 0$, with $\chi(p_0) = 0$ and the segment of C_i in N going one-to-one continuously into a segment of the real axis.[††] From G and its conjugate G', we now form the *double* $\widetilde{G}$ of G by identifying conjugate boundary points. As local parameter about the identified boundary points p_0 and p_0', we take

$$\zeta = \begin{cases} \chi(p), & p \in G, \\ \overline{\chi(h^{-1}(p))}, & p \in G'. \end{cases}$$

Prove that $\widetilde{G}$ is a compact Riemann surface.

3. By constructing on $\widetilde{G}$ a harmonic differential all of whose singularities are in G', prove that there exist infinitely many independent single-valued regular harmonic functions on G.

4. Let $h(p; q, q')$ be the real harmonic function which has singularity $-\log|z|$ at q and $+\log|z|$ at q', the conjugate of q on G. Then set

$$g(p; q) = \tfrac{1}{2}(h(p; q, q') - h(p'; q, q')).$$

[†] The proof presented here is similar to that in Nevanlinna (Ref. 35, pp. 145–148).

[††] This is always possible, and the proof appears in most books on conformal mapping; e.g., C. Carathéodory, Ref. 12.

Show that $g(p; q)$ has the following properties:

(a) $g(p; q)$ is regular harmonic in the variable p in $G - q$;
(b) $g(p; q)$ has singularity $-\log |z|$ at $p = q$;
(c) $g(p; q)$ is continuous in $\overline{G} - Q$ and $g(p; q) = 0$ for $p \in \partial G$.

The function $g(p; q)$ is called the *Green's function* of G with singularity at q.

5. If the boundary curves of G are all analytic curves and u is harmonic in $\overline{G}$, prove that

$$u(q) = -\frac{1}{2\pi} \int\limits_{p \in \partial G} u(p) * d_p g(p; q),$$

where $d_p g$ denotes the differential of g with respect to the variable p.

CHAPTER 9

UNIFORMIZATION

9–1 Schlichtartig surfaces. On a Riemann surface S, each point has a neighborhood which is the conformal image of a plane disk. This gives us a system of local coordinates in the neighborhood of this point. In general, this local system cannot be extended to a coordinate system over the whole surface, assigning in a one-to-one conformal fashion a complex number to each point on the surface. Such a "coordinate system in the large" would give us a one-to-one conformal mapping of S onto a region in the plane and, conversely, such a mapping would supply us with the desired global coordinate system.

When we look for such a mapping, we must first ask whether the mapping is topologically possible. According to the Jordan curve theorem, any plane region is schlichtartig, and since this is a topological property, any surface S which is mapped conformally onto a plane region must enjoy this property. We shall see in this section that the schlichtartigness of S is also sufficient, for every schlichtartig Riemann surface can be mapped in a one-to-one conformal fashion onto a plane region.†

In Chapter 8, we established the existence of a real-valued function U on S enjoying the following properties:

(a) U is harmonic on $S - P_0$, where P_0 is a fixed point on S,

(b) $U - \operatorname{Re}(1/z)$ is harmonic in a neighborhood N of P_0,

(c) $\|dU\|_{S-\bar{N}} = \iint_{S-\bar{N}} dU * dU < \infty$,

(d) for any real function $h \in C^2(S)$ with $\|dh\| < \infty$ and $h \equiv 0$ in a neighborhood of P_0, we have $(dU, dh) = 0$.

We saw that U was the harmonic function that minimized the Dirichlet integral over $S - \bar{N}$ in the class of functions $U + h$. The differential $dU + i*dU$ is analytic on S with singularity $d(1/z)$ at P_0. Even though dU is exact, there is no *a priori* reason for $*dU$ to be exact. We shall prove that this is the case when S is schlichtartig.

We must show that $\int_C *dU = 0$ for every closed curve C in $S - P_0$, for U is harmonic in $S - P_0$, which means that $d* dU = 0$ or $*dU$ is

---

†The proof given here is the original proof due to Koebe (Ref. 29, pp. 192–253). Many other proofs have been given; notable among these is the very simple proof using the Green's function by M. Heins (Ref. 21).

closed. By subdividing C so that each segment lies in a single parametric disk and then replacing each segment by a straight line segment in that disk, we obtain a piecewise analytic curve on which $*dU$ has the same period as on C. If we show that on each simple closed curve composing this piecewise analytic curve $*dU$ has zero period, we shall have proved that $*dU$ has no periods. Let us assume, then, that C is a simple closed piecewise analytic curve on S. Since S is schlichtartig, C divides S into two components S' and S'', of which we assume that S'' contains P_0. We cover C with a finite number of parametric disks, none of which contain P_0 in their closures. The part of the union of these disks which lies in S'' we shall call G. Then define a function h on S as follows:

$$h(P) = \begin{cases} 1, & \text{for } P \in S', \\ 0, & \text{for } P \in S'' - G, \end{cases}$$

such that $h \in C^2(S)$. The function h satisfies the conditions in (d), so that $(dU, dh) = 0$. This means, however, that

$$0 = (dU, dh) = \iint_G dU*dh = \iint_G dh*dU$$

$$= \int_{\partial G} h*dU - \iint_G h\,d*dU = \int_C *dU,$$

since $d*dU = 0$, and ∂G consists of two components, with $h = 1$ on C and $h = 0$ on $\partial G - C$. This proves that $*dU$ is exact, say $*dU = dV$, and we have found an analytic function $f = U + iV$ on S which has the singularity $1/z$ at P_0 and whose real part satisfies (c) and (d). The function $w = f(P)$ gives us a conformal mapping of S into the extended complex w-plane which is one-to-one, giving us the sought-for mapping of S. We proceed to show that $w = f(P)$ is one-to-one.

We first show that if P_1 and P_2 are any two points on S different from P_0, and at which $df \neq 0$, we have $f(P_1) \neq f(P_2)$. Assume the contrary, that $f(P_1) = f(P_2) = U_1 + iV_1$. The level curves $U = U_1$ and $V = V_1$ divide S into regions in each of which one of the following four sets of inequalities holds:

(1) $\qquad\qquad U > U_1, \qquad V > V_1,$

(2) $\qquad\qquad U > U_1, \qquad V < V_1,$

(3) $\qquad\qquad U < U_1, \qquad V > V_1,$

(4) $\qquad\qquad U < U_1, \qquad V < V_1.$

Since $df \neq 0$ at P_1 (or P_2), locally f^{-1} yields a one-to-one conformal mapping of a neighborhood of (U_1, V_1) onto a neighborhood of P_1 (or P_2), and only one line $U = U_1$ and one line $V = V_1$ pass through P_1 (or P_2), and these two lines intersect orthogonally. Thus the neighborhood of P_1 (or P_2) is divided into four regions by $U = U_1$, $V = V_1$. The same is true in a neighborhood of P_0, for f maps a neighborhood of P_0 one-to-one and conformally onto a neighborhood of $w = \infty$ on the w-sphere, and this neighborhood of $w = \infty$ is divided into four parts by the lines $U = U_1$ and $V = V_1$.

We prove that each of the regions into which S is divided by $U = U_1$ and $V = V_1$ has P_0 as a boundary point, and hence S is divided into only four regions by these level curves. Assume the contrary, and let G be a region on S bounded by $U = U_1$ and $V = V_1$ which does not have P_0 as a boundary point. For the real variable t in $-\infty < t < \infty$, set

$$\varphi(t) = \frac{2}{\pi} \arctan t^3, \qquad -1 < \varphi(t) < 1,$$

$$\psi(t) = \frac{t^4}{1 + t^4}, \qquad 0 \le \psi(t) < 1.$$

Then

$$\varphi'(t) = \frac{6}{\pi} \frac{t^2}{1 + t^6}, \qquad 0 \le \varphi'(t) < 2,$$

$$\psi'(t) = \frac{4t^3}{(1 + t^4)^2}, \qquad 0 \le |\psi'(t)| < 2.$$

We set

$$g(P) = \begin{cases} 0, & \text{for } P \in S - G, \\ \varphi(U(P) - U_1)\psi(V(P) - V_1), & \text{for } P \in G. \end{cases}$$

Then g has the following properties:

(1) $g \in C^2(S)$,
(2) $g \equiv 0$ in a neighborhood of P_0,

Properties (1) and (2) of g show that if $||dg|| < \infty$, then $(dU, dg) = 0$ by (d). But we shall compute these explicitly by taking an arbitrary region $R \subset G$ with compact closure on S and a partition of unity $\{e_i\}$ on $\overline{R}$ such that $\sum_{i=1}^{n} e_i \equiv 1$ on R and $e_i \in C^2(R)$. Then if (x_i, y_i) is the local coordinate in the neighborhood N_i where $e_i > 0$,

$$(dU, dg) = \underset{R \subset G}{\text{l.u.b.}} \sum_{i=1}^{n} \iint_{N_i} \left(\frac{\partial U}{\partial x_i} \frac{\partial g}{\partial x_i} + \frac{\partial U}{\partial y_i} \frac{\partial g}{\partial y_i} \right) e_i \, dx_i \, dy_i,$$

$$||dg||^2 = \underset{R \subset G}{\text{l.u.b.}} \sum_{i=1}^{n} \iint_{N_i} \left[\left(\frac{\partial g}{\partial x_i} \right)^2 + \left(\frac{\partial g}{\partial y_i} \right)^2 \right] e_i \, dx_i \, dy_i.$$

But in G,

$$\frac{\partial g}{\partial x_i} = \varphi'(U - U_1)\psi(V - V_1)\frac{\partial U}{\partial x_i} + \varphi(U - U_1)\psi'(V - V_1)\frac{\partial V}{\partial x_i}$$

$$= \varphi'(U - U_1)\psi(V - V_1)\frac{\partial U}{\partial x_i} - \varphi(U - U_1)\psi'(V - V_1)\frac{\partial U}{\partial y_i}$$

and

$$\frac{\partial g}{\partial y_i} = \varphi'(U - U_1)\psi(V - V_1)\frac{\partial U}{\partial y_i} + \varphi(U - U_1)\psi'(V - V_1)\frac{\partial V}{\partial y_i}$$

$$= \varphi'(U - U_1)\psi(V - V_1)\frac{\partial U}{\partial y_i} + \varphi(U - U_1)\psi'(V - V_1)\frac{\partial U}{\partial x_i}.$$

Therefore,

$$\left(\frac{\partial g}{\partial x_i} \right)^2 + \left(\frac{\partial g}{\partial y_i} \right)^2 = (\varphi'^2\psi^2 + \varphi^2\psi'^2) \left[\left(\frac{\partial U}{\partial x_i} \right)^2 + \left(\frac{\partial U}{\partial y_i} \right)^2 \right]$$

$$< 8 \left[\left(\frac{\partial U}{\partial x_i} \right)^2 + \left(\frac{\partial U}{\partial y_i} \right)^2 \right],$$

so that $||dg||^2 < 8||dU||_G^2 < \infty$. Furthermore,

$$\frac{\partial U}{\partial x_i} \frac{\partial g}{\partial x_i} + \frac{\partial U}{\partial y_i} \frac{\partial g}{\partial y_i} = \varphi'\psi \left[\left(\frac{\partial U}{\partial x_i} \right)^2 + \left(\frac{\partial U}{\partial y_i} \right)^2 \right]$$

and $\varphi' > 0$, $\psi > 0$, $(\partial U/\partial x_i)^2 + (\partial U/\partial y_i)^2 > 0$ (except possibly at isolated points) in G, so that $(dU, dg) > 0$. This contradiction to (d) tells us that S is divided into four regions by $U = U_1$, $V = V_1$, each region having P_0, P_1, and P_2 on its boundary. Label these regions as

$$
\begin{array}{lll}
\text{I:} & U > U_1, & V > V_1, \\
\text{II:} & U < U_1, & V > V_1, \\
\text{III:} & U < U_1, & V < V_1, \\
\text{IV:} & U > U_1, & V < V_1.
\end{array}
$$

We can join P_1 to P_2 by an arc C_1 lying entirely in I and also by an arc C_2 lying entirely in III, except for their end points. By covering C_1 by a finite number of parametric disks and replacing segments of C_1 by straight line segments in these disks, we can make C_1 (and C_2) piecewise analytic, and by throwing away closed curves in C_1, we can make C_1 have no self-intersections. Thus $C_1C_2 = C$ is a simple closed piecewise analytic curve and hence must divide S into two parts D_1 and D_2, because S is schlichtartig. One of these parts, say D_1, contains the point P_0. There are points of the regions II and IV in the neighborhood of P_0, so II and IV are both completely contained in D_1. Otherwise if II (or IV) meets D_1 and D_2, we have II $= (D_1 \cap \text{II}) \cup (D_2 \cap \text{II})$ and we have divided II into two disjoint open sets. In the neighborhood of P_1, we see that points of II lie on one side of C and the points of IV on the other side of C, so that both cannot be contained in D_1. This contradiction proves that f takes on different values at P_1 and P_2.

This shows, moreover, that df cannot vanish at any point of S, for if $df = 0$ at some point P_1, in the local coordinate z about P_1, $f(z) = a_n z^n + a_{n+1} z^{n+1} + \cdots$, $a_n \neq 0$, $n > 1$. But in the neighborhood of $z = 0$, f takes on each value n times at n distinct points of S, which is a contradiction to what was just demonstrated. Thus we conclude that $w = f(z)$ maps S one-to-one and conformally onto a region S' on the w-sphere which contains $w = \infty$ in its interior.

We next prove that S' is bounded by straight line segments parallel to the real axis (some of which may degenerate to single points). Assume the contrary to be true, so that a component C of the boundary of S' joins the points (U_1, V_1) and (U_2, V_2), with $V_1 < V_2$. Extending the lines $V = V_1$ and $V = V_2$ to the right from C, we eventually go far enough so that the whole segment of $U = U_3$ between $V_1 < V < V_2$ lies entirely within S'. (This is certainly possible, since S' contains a neighborhood of ∞.) Designate by G' the region bounded on the right by

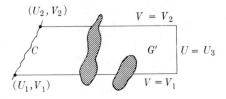

FIGURE 9–1.

$U = U_3$, above by $V = V_2$ and components of the boundary of S', and below by $V = V_1$ and pieces of the boundary of S' (Fig. 9–1). Define the function g in S' as follows:

$$g(U, V) = \begin{cases} 0, & \text{for } (U, V) \in S' - G', \\ (U - U_3)^3 (V - V_1)^3 (V - V_2)^3, & \text{for } (U, V) \in G'. \end{cases}$$

We note that $g \in C^2$ in S' and $g \equiv 0$ in a neighborhood of $w = U +$

$iV = \infty$. The one-to-one conformal mapping $w = f(P)$ of S onto S' enables us to use $w = U + iV$ as a local parameter on S, and g is then defined on S with the properties $g \equiv 0$ in a neighborhood of P_0, and $\|dg\| < \infty$. Then

$$(dU, dg) = \iint\limits_{S'} \left(\frac{\partial U}{\partial U} \frac{\partial g}{\partial U} + \frac{\partial U}{\partial V} \frac{\partial g}{\partial V} \right) dU\, dV = \iint\limits_{S'} \frac{\partial g}{\partial U} dU\, dV < 0,$$

since $\partial g/\partial U = 3(U - U_3)^2(V - V_1)^3(V - V_2)^3$ is always negative in $V_1 < V < V_2$, $U < U_3$. But again we have a contradiction to (d), proving that the boundary components must be horizontal line segments or points. We call a region on the extended plane which contains ∞ in its interior and whose boundary consists of parallel line segments (or points) a *(rectilinear) slit region*. We have therefore proved

THEOREM 9–1. *Every schlichtartig Riemann surface can be mapped one-to-one and conformally onto a slit region whose slits are parallel to the real axis.*

This mapping provides us with a coordinate system in the large on S. It should be mentioned that there may be infinitely many such line segments (slits) in the boundary of S' and that these are not necessarily isolated sets; i.e., points on one slit may be limit points of points on different slits.

When S is simply connected, the boundary of the slit region S' can contain at most one component. There are three cases which can occur:

    (1) S' is the whole sphere (*elliptic case*),
    (2) S' is the whole sphere with one point removed (*parabolic case*),
    (3) S' is the sphere with a slit of positive length parallel to the real axis cut out of it (*hyperbolic case*).

The fact that a given simply connected Riemann surface S can be mapped onto a particular one of these three surfaces is characteristic of the surface and does not depend upon the particular mapping we set up. We shall prove that it is possible to map S onto only one of these three domains.

First we shall transform each of these domains into canonical regions. (1) The whole sphere is kept as a canonical region. (2) The sphere punctured at $w = c$ can always be transformed into the whole finite plane $|w'| < \infty$ by the linear fractional transformation $w' = 1/(w - c)$. (3) The w-sphere cut along a horizontal line segment of length L and center $w = c$ is mapped onto the w_1-sphere cut along the real axis from $w_1 = -2$ to $w_1 = 2$ by the linear mapping $w_1 = (4/L)(w - c)$. Then the mapping $w_1 = w_2 + (1/w_2)$ maps this slit region onto the interior of the unit disk $|w_2| < 1$, which is the third canonical region.

If S could be mapped onto two of the three types of regions (1), (2), or (3), we could find a mapping from one canonical region to another. We shall now prove that such a mapping is impossible.

(i) The whole sphere cannot be mapped conformally and one-to-one onto either the entire finite plane or the unit disk for purely topological reasons; for the sphere is compact and the others are not.

(ii) The topological mapping $w' = w/(1 - |w|)$ maps the unit disk homeomorphically onto the whole finite plane, so such a conformal mapping cannot be excluded on purely topological grounds. On the other hand, a one-to-one conformal mapping of $|w| < \infty$ onto $|w'| < 1$ would imply the existence of an everywhere regular, bounded analytic function in the whole w-plane which would necessarily be a constant by Liouville's theorem.

We therefore classify a simply connected Riemann surface as

(1) *elliptic* if it is conformally equivalent to the whole sphere,

(2) *parabolic* if it is conformally equivalent to the whole finite plane,

(3) *hyperbolic* if it is conformally equivalent to the unit disk.

We have already topologically classified compact Riemann surfaces, which are triangulable, according to their genus g. The only such surface which is simply connected is the surface of genus zero, which we saw was topologically a sphere. Since the compactness is preserved, we have now shown that compact surfaces of genus zero are also conformally equivalent to a sphere.

Now what does our mapping theorem tell us about simply connected regions on the sphere? The whole sphere is elliptic and the sphere with one point removed is parabolic. If the surface S is a simply connected region on the sphere whose boundary consists of at least two points, say $w = a$ and $w = b$, then S is hyperbolic. For then the boundary consists at least of a connected component joining the two points a and b. If there is a point $w = c$ exterior to S, $w_1 = 1/(w - c)$ maps S into a bounded region of the w_1-plane. Otherwise the simple connectivity of S implies that $w_1 = \sqrt{(w - a)/(w - b)}$ is single-valued in S (once a branch has been fixed at one point) and maps S onto a region S_1 having the property that if $w_1 = -c$ is an interior point of S_1, $w_1 = c$ is an exterior point. Then S_1 can be mapped onto a bounded region of the plane. But again Liouville's theorem excludes the possibilities that S is parabolic or elliptic. This is precisely the *Riemann mapping theorem:*

THEOREM 9–2. *Any simply connected plane region with at least two boundary points is conformally equivalent to the unit disk.*

9–2 Universal covering surfaces. The universal covering surface $\hat{S}$ of an arbitrary Riemann surface S is simply connected. Consequently, there is a conformal one-to-one mapping $w = f(\hat{P})$ of $\hat{S}$ onto one of the three canonical regions G. We have also defined a conformal projection mapping π of $\hat{S}$ onto S. Therefore, there has been defined a single-valued mapping $P = \pi(f^{-1}(w)) = F(w)$ of G onto S which is conformal but not one-to-one, for several points in G may map into the same point P on S. But $w = F^{-1}(P)$ is just the uniformizing parameter for which we sought, for two different values of P determine different values of w, and we may use w as a parameter over all of S (remembering that F^{-1} is not single-valued).

If $g(P)$ is any multiple-valued analytic function which is regular at every point of S, then the composite function $g(F(w))$ is a single-valued function of w in G. This follows immediately from the monodromy theorem, because G is simply connected and $g \circ F$ is regular in G and must be single-valued. Thus we say that the mapping $P = F(w)$ "uniformizes" any function on S. The existence of the function $P = F(w)$ from G to S such that any multiple-valued analytic function g on S becomes a single-valued analytic function $g(F(w))$ of w in G is the content of the *general uniformization theorem* due to Klein, Poincaré, and Koebe.

In how many ways can the surface $\hat{S}$ be mapped onto the canonical region G? If f and g both map $\hat{S}$ onto G, then $f \circ g^{-1}$ maps G onto itself. Thus our problem is to study the conformal mappings of G onto itself.

(1) *If G is the whole sphere* (elliptic case) *the only one-to-one conformal self-mappings of G are the linear functional transformations,*

$$w = (az + b)/(cz + d), \qquad ad - bc \neq 0.$$

These mappings form a six-real-parameter group of transformations.

(2) *When G is the finite plane* (parabolic case), *the only one-to-one conformal self-transformations of G are the entire linear transformations $w' = aw + b$, $a \neq 0$, which form a four-real-parameter group.*

(3) *When G is the unit disk* (hyperbolic case), *its one-to-one conformal self-mappings consist of the linear fractional transformations*

$$w' = e^{i\theta} (w - a)/(1 - \bar{a}w),$$

θ *real,* $|a| < 1$, *which form a three-real-parameter group.*

To prove these statements, we first observe that the only entire function f which yields a one-to-one conformal mapping of the plane onto itself is a linear function $w' = aw + b$, $a \neq 0$. For the entire function has a power-series expansion about the origin $\sum_{n=0}^{\infty} a_n w^n$ having an infinite radius of convergence. If there are an infinite number of the $a_n \neq 0$, $w = \infty$ is an essential singularity. By the Casorati-Weierstrass theorem, w comes arbitrarily close to every value in every neighborhood of $w = \infty$. But this contradicts the one-to-oneness of $w' = f(w)$; for $f(0) = c$, $c \neq \infty$, and the image of $|w| < \epsilon$ covers a neighborhood of $w' = c$, so that w' cannot come close to c near $w = \infty$. Thus $w' = a_0 + a_1 w + \cdots + a_n w^n$, $a_n \neq 0$. If $n > 1$, w' assumes each value n times, again a contradiction. Hence $w' = a_0 + a_1 w$, $a_1 \neq 0$.

(1) Now in the elliptic case, suppose that $w' = f(w)$ mapping G onto itself has $f(\infty) = k \neq \infty$. Then $w'' = 1/(w' - k) = 1/(f(w) - k)$ takes $w = \infty$ into $w'' = \infty$ and is an entire function giving a one-to-one mapping of the w-plane. But then $w'' = a_0 + a_1 w$, $a_1 \neq 0$, or

$$1/(w' - k) = a_0 + a_1 w.$$

Hence $w' = (aw + b)/(cw + d)$, where $a = ka_1$, $b = ka_0 + 1$, $c = a_1$, and $d = a_0$, while $ad - bc = -a_1 \neq 0$. If $f(\infty) = \infty$, we have directly that $w' = a_0 + a_1 w$.

(2) In the parabolic case, $w' = f(w)$ is an entire function giving us a one-to-one mapping. Hence $w' = aw + b$, $a \neq 0$.

(3) When G is the disk $|w| < 1$, let $f(a) = 0$. Then

$$w'' = (w - a)/(1 - \bar{a}w) = g(w)$$

maps $|w| < 1$ one-to-one and conformally onto $|w''| < 1$, with $w = a$ going into $w'' = 0$. The composite function $w' = f(g^{-1}(w''))$ maps $|w''| < 1$ conformally and one-to-one onto $|w'| < 1$, with 0 going into 0. We now use the reasoning of Schwarz' lemma: w'/w'' is a regular function of w'' in $|w''| < 1$, and on $|w''| = r < 1$ we have $|w'/w''| \leq 1/r$. Thus by the maximum principle, $|w'/w''| \leq 1/r$ in $|w''| < r$, which holds for all $r < 1$. Thus $|w'/w''| \leq 1$ in $|w''| < 1$. The same applied to w''/w' yields $|w''/w'| \leq 1$ in $|w'| < 1$. Combining these yields $|w'/w''| \equiv 1$, which is possible only when $w' = e^{i\theta} w''$, for a real constant θ. Therefore $w' = e^{i\theta}(w - a)/(1 - \bar{a}w)$.

We summarize our results in the following theorem:

THEOREM 9–3. *The uniformizing function is always determined uniquely up to a linear fractional transformation.*

The covering transformations of $\hat{S}$ are one-to-one conformal mappings of $\hat{S}$ onto itself. Let $w = g(\hat{P})$ be a mapping of $\hat{S}$ onto its canonical plane region G and let $\hat{Q} = f(\hat{P})$ be a covering transformation of $\hat{S}$. Then $w' = g \circ f \circ g^{-1}(w)$ is a map of G onto itself and must be a linear fractional transformation. The group of covering transformations of $\hat{S}$ corresponds to a group Γ of linear fractional transformations of G. The group Γ is therefore isomorphic to the fundamental group $\mathfrak{F}$ of S. With the exception of the identity transformation, no mapping in Γ has a fixed point (a point mapping into itself) in G, for this is indeed true of the covering transformations which shift the "sheets" of the covering surface. In the elliptic case, we note that every one-to-one conformal mapping of the sphere onto itself has at least one fixed point determined by solving the equations $z = (az + b)/(cz + d)$, so that the identity is the only element in Γ. Thus $\hat{S}$ is a one-sheeted covering surface of S which must then be the same Riemann surface as S. We have therefore proved

THEOREM 9–4. *A Riemann surface which has an elliptic covering surface must be conformally equivalent to a sphere.*

The points $\hat{P}_1$, $\hat{P}_2$, ... on $\hat{S}$ lying over the point P on S map into the points w_1, w_2, ... in G. The covering transformations of $\hat{S}$ interchange these points $\hat{P}_i \to \hat{P}_j$ so that the linear fractional transformations in Γ also merely interchange the points w_1, w_2, ..., and since the group of covering transformations is transitive, there is a mapping in Γ which takes any w_i into any other w_j. We say that the points w_1, w_2, ... form a set of equivalent points with respect to the group Γ. In general, a set of points Σ of G is called *equivalent with respect to* Γ if (a) for any $f \in \Gamma$ and $w \in \Sigma$, we have $f(w) \in \Sigma$, and (b) for any two points $w_1 \in \Sigma$ and $w_2 \in \Sigma$, there exists an $f \in \Gamma$ such that $w_2 = f(w_1)$.

A group Λ of transformations of G into itself is called *discontinuous* if any set Σ of equivalent points with respect to Λ has no point of accumulation in G. We now prove

THEOREM 9–5. *The group Γ of linear fractional transformations, corresponding to the covering transformations of $\hat{S}$, is discontinuous.*

For if $w_0 \in G$ is a cluster point of Σ, there is a mapping of $\hat{S}$ onto G such that $\hat{P}_0 \to w_0$. Then $\hat{P}_0$ has a neighborhood $\hat{N}$ which covers S once, and $\hat{N}$ maps into a neighborhood N of w_0. N then contains an infinite number of equivalent points, which is impossible since $\hat{N}$ covers S only once.

Now let F be any single-valued analytic function on S, regular except possibly for poles. We may take the mapping $\hat{P} = g(w)$ of $\hat{S}$ onto G and the projection $\pi(\hat{P}) = P$ of $\hat{S}$ onto S to define $P = \pi \circ g(w)$ and give us the uniformizing parameter w on S. Then $F(P) = F(\pi \circ g(w)) = H(w)$ is an analytic function of w in G which necessarily assumes the same value on each set of equivalent points Σ. If $w' = (aw + b)/(cw + d) \in \Gamma$, we have $H(w) = H((aw + b)/(cw + d))$. We see that H is an *automorphic function* relative to the group Γ.†

We can now construct a conformal model of S. From the canonical region G, we form a Riemann surface G_Γ by identifying each set of equivalent points Σ with respect to Γ to be a single point of G_Γ. There is clearly

---

†In general, let Γ be a group of conformal homeomorphisms of a region G onto itself, and F an analytic function in G. Then F is called an *automorphic function* relative to Γ if $F(g(w)) \equiv F(w)$ for all $g \in \Gamma$. See, for example, Ford, Ref. 17.

a one-to-one correspondence between the points of S and the points of G_Γ, and the mapping of S onto G gives us a conformal mapping of a neighborhood of each point P on S into a neighborhood of each point in Σ, and these neighborhoods are invariant under Γ. Thus the mapping $S \to G_\Gamma$ is one-to-one and conformal, and we may take G_Γ as a *normal form* of S. A connected subset of G which contains one and only one point from each equivalent set of points with respect to Γ is called a *fundamental domain*. The fundamental domain is essentially the image of one "sheet" of $\hat{S}$ in G.

We can now list all possible Riemann surfaces with parabolic universal covering surfaces. We ask for the possible entire linear transformations having no finite fixed points. If $w' = aw + b$, we get $w = b/(1 - a)$ as the only fixed point, and there is no finite fixed point if and only if $a = 1$. The group Γ can consist only of translations of the plane $w' = w + b$. There are only three possibilities for Γ:

(a) Γ consists only of the identity translation $w' = w$, in which case $\hat{S} = S$ and S is conformally equivalent to the finite plane (a sphere with one point removed).

(b) Γ consists of the group generated by $w' = w + b$. Thus Γ consists of all translations of the form $w' = w + nb$, $n = 0, \pm1, \pm2, \ldots$. In this case the fundamental domain is an infinite strip of width $|b|$, which contains one of its boundary edges. A model of S is then a circular cylinder of infinite length. The mapping $w = e^{2\pi iz/b}$ maps G_Γ one-to-one onto the sphere with the north and south poles removed. Therefore S is conformally equivalent to a doubly punctured sphere.

When Σ consists of the points $ma + nb$, $m, n = 0, \pm1, \pm2, \ldots$, and $a = \theta b$ for a real θ, there must be a point $c \in \Sigma$ such that $a = kc$, $b = lc$, where k and l are integers. For on the line through 0, a, and b, there must be a point $c = m_1 a + n_1 b \in \Sigma$ closest to 0 (otherwise 0 would be a cluster point of Σ). Then there is an integer k such that $|ck - a| < a$. But this says that $|(m_1 k - 1)a + n_1 kb| < c$, which is impossible unless $ck - a = 0$. Similarly, $cl = b$ and the group Γ is generated by the single translation $w' = w + c$. This leads to the next case:

(c) Γ is generated by $w' = w + a$ and $w' = w + b$, where a and b are nonzero complex numbers having different arguments $(\mathrm{Im}\,(a/b) \neq 0)$. Then Γ consists of the mappings

$$w' = w + na + mb, \qquad n, m = 0, \pm1, \pm2, \ldots.$$

The fundamental domain is obtained from the parallelogram with vertices 0, a, b, $a + b$, by taking the interior, the origin, and the interiors of the two edges meeting at the origin. To form a model of G_Γ, we identify the opposite edges of the parallelogram, topologically getting a torus. Thus G_Γ or its conformal image S must be a compact surface of genus 1. In the next chapter, we shall show that every compact Riemann surface of genus 1 has a parabolic universal covering surface of this kind.

If Γ were to be generated by more than two independent translations, the argument usually given in showing that a multiply periodic function in the plane can have no more than two independent periods shows that the lattice of equivalent points would have a finite limit point.† We have therefore proved

THEOREM 9–6. *The only Riemann surfaces with parabolic universal covering surfaces are those which are conformally equivalent to the once-punctured sphere, the doubly punctured sphere, or compact surfaces of genus 1.*

We now turn to the hyperbolic case, in which the region G is the unit disk. To make the discussion easier, we introduce a noneuclidean (N.E.) geometry into the unit disk G in which the one-to-one conformal self-mappings are the rigid motions. The N.E. points of G in this geometry will be the usual points of the w-plane interior to $|w| < 1$. An N.E. straight line will be a circular arc lying in $|w| < 1$ which is orthogonal to $|w| = 1$. (In particular, the diameters of $|w| = 1$ are included in the N.E. straight lines.) We call G the N.E. plane. The rigid motions of G, which are the linear fractional transformations of $|w| < 1$ onto itself, carry N.E. straight lines into N.E. straight lines. Through any two points w_1 and $w_2 \in G$ passes one and only one straight line; for when we move w_1 to 0, w_2 goes into a point w_2'. The diameter of $|w| < 1$ is then clearly the only N.E. line through 0 and w_2'. Moving 0 back to w_1 carries this diameter into the N.E. line through w_1 and w_2. Angles in this geometry will be taken as the ordinary euclidean angles between arcs. The rigid motions also preserve angles. The geometry so defined satisfies all the axioms of euclidean geometry except the parallel postulate, for through a given point P not on a given line L pass an infinite number of lines which do not intersect L (Fig. 9–2). This geometry therefore satisfies the axioms of Bolyai and Lobachevsky. This particular model is due to Poincaré. A more complete discussion of the N.E. geometry is presented in Carathéodory's *Conformal Repre-*

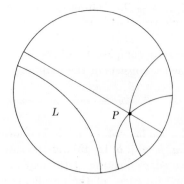

FIGURE 9–2.

†See, for example, Knopp (Ref. 27).

sentation (Ref. 12) or in his *Theory of Functions of a Complex Variable* (Ref. 13, Vol. I).

If $\hat{P}' = f(\hat{P})$ is a covering transformation of $\hat{S}$ and $w = g(\hat{P})$ is a mapping of $\hat{S}$ into G, then we have seen that $L = g \circ f \circ g^{-1} \in \Gamma$ is a rigid motion of G and Γ is a subgroup of the group of all N.E. rigid motions. If we change the uniformizing parameter w by using the mapping $w_1 = g_1(\hat{P})$ of $\hat{S}$ onto G, then $w_1 = F(w)$ is also a rigid motion in G and, represented in terms of the uniformizing parameter w_1, the covering transformation f becomes $L_1 = g_1 \circ f \circ g^{-1}$, and we get a new subgroup of rigid motions which we shall denote by Γ_1. Since $F = g_1 \circ g^{-1}$, for any $L_1 \in \Gamma_1$, we can write $L_1 = g_1 \circ f \circ g_1^{-1} = g_1 \circ g^{-1} \circ (g \circ f \circ g^{-1}) \circ g \circ g_1^{-1} = F \circ L \circ F^{-1}$ for some $L = g \circ f \circ g^{-1} \in \Gamma$. Thus L and L_1 are conjugate elements in the group of all rigid motions, and we can say that $\Gamma_1 = F\Gamma F^{-1}$; that is, Γ_1 and Γ are conjugate subgroups. Thus Γ and Γ_1 are the same groups of rigid motions, but are expressed in terms of different coordinate systems in G.

Every linear fractional transformation of the sphere has either one or two fixed points if it is not the identity. We use this information to divide the N.E. rigid motions into three types.

(1) The N.E. *rotations* have only one fixed point $w = w_0$ interior to $|w| < 1$. Then $w = 1/\overline{w}_0$ is also a fixed point and the N.E. rotation $w \to w'$ is given by

$$\frac{w' - w_0}{w' - 1/\overline{w}_0} = e^{i\theta} \frac{w - w_0}{w - 1/\overline{w}_0}, \qquad \theta \text{ real.}$$

This has the effect of mapping w_0 into 0, rotating the disk through an angle θ, and then mapping 0 back to w_0, always taking $|w| < 1$ into itself.

(2) The N.E. *translations* have two fixed points on $|w| = 1$. If they are $w = w_1$ and $w = w_2$, $|w_1| = |w_2| = 1$, then the N.E. translation is given by

$$\frac{w' - w_1}{w' - w_2} = r \frac{w - w_1}{w - w_2}, \qquad r > 0.$$

This has the effect of mapping $|w| < 1$ onto a half-plane, with $w_1 \to 0$, $w_2 \to \infty$, magnifying by a factor r, and then mapping back to the unit disk, with $0 \to w_1$, $\infty \to w_2$. Since magnification leaves 0 and ∞ fixed, w_1 and w_2 are fixed points of the motion.

(3) The N.E. *limit rotations* have just one fixed point w_1 which lies on $|w| = 1$. These transformations are given by

$$\frac{-iw_1}{w' - w_1} = \frac{-iw_1}{w - w_1} + b, \qquad b \text{ real.}$$

We may view this limit rotation as the sequence of transformations starting with an inversion taking $w_1 \to \infty$ and $|w| < 1$ into a half-plane, $\operatorname{Im} w > i/2$. Then comes a translation through b parallel to the real axis, and finally an inversion taking the half-plane back to the unit disk with $\infty \to w_1$. Since ∞ is the only fixed point of the translation, w_1 is the only fixed point of the limit rotation.

The motions in Γ do not contain any fixed points, so Γ contains no N.E. rotations. The rigid motion in Γ taking w' into w'' is unique; for if $L_1(w') = w''$ and $L_2(w') = w''$, then $F_1 \circ F_2^{-1}(w'') = w''$, and w'' is a fixed point of $F_1 \circ F_2^{-1}$; thus $F_1 \circ F_2^{-1}$ is the identity mapping, or $F_1 \equiv F_2$.

We may summarize our results as follows:

THEOREM 9-7. *To each Riemann surface S with a hyperbolic universal covering surface corresponds a uniquely defined, discontinuous group Γ of N.E. rigid motions of the N.E. plane G, containing no N.E. rotations. If we identify the equivalent points of G, we get a Riemann surface G_Γ which is conformally equivalent to S.*

If h is a conformal homeomorphism of a Riemann surface S_1 onto S_2, then there is also a conformal homeomorphism h^* of $\hat{S}_1$ onto $\hat{S}_2$ such that the projection mappings $f_1 \colon \hat{S}_1 \to S_1$ and $f_2 \colon \hat{S}_2 \to S_2$ satisfy $f_2 \circ h^* = h \circ f_1$. Then to each covering transformation $T_1 \colon \hat{S}_1 \to \hat{S}_1$ corresponds the covering transformation $T_2 = \lambda T_1 \colon \hat{S}_2 \to \hat{S}_2$ defined by $T_2 = h^* \circ T_1 \circ h^{*-1}$. That T_2 is a covering transformation is verified by noting that from $f_1 \circ T_1(p_1) = f_1(p_1)$, $p_1 \in \hat{S}_1$, follows $h \circ f_1 \circ T_1(p_1) = h \circ f_1(p_1)$, and hence $f_2 \circ h^* \circ T_1(p_1) = f_2 \circ h^*(p_1)$. If we set $h^*(p_1) = p_2$, we get $f_2 \circ (h^* \circ T_1 \circ h^{*-1})(p_2) = f_2 \circ (h^* \circ h^{*-1})(p_2)$, or simply

$$f_2 \circ T_2(p_2) = f_2(p_2),$$

and hence T_2 is a covering transformation. The mapping λ defines an isomorphism of the groups of covering transformations of S_1 onto those of S_2.

If we now let $g_2 \colon \hat{S}_2 \to G$ map $\hat{S}_2$ conformally onto G, then $g_2 \circ h^* = g_1$ maps $\hat{S}_1$ conformally onto G. To the covering transformation $T_1 \colon \hat{S}_1 \to \hat{S}_1$ corresponds the N.E. rigid motion $g_2 \circ T_2 \circ g_2^{-1}$. However,

$$g_1 \circ T_1 \circ g_1^{-1} = (g_2 \circ h^*) \circ T_1 \circ (g_2 \circ h^*)^{-1} = (g_2 \circ h^*) \circ T_1 \circ (h^{*-1} \circ g_2^{-1})$$

$$= g_2 \circ (h^* \circ T_1 \circ h_1^{*-1}) \circ g_2^{-1} = g_2 \circ T_2 \circ g_2^{-1},$$

so that both T_1 and T_2 correspond to the same N.E. rigid motion of G.

Thus the isomorphism λ induces the identity isomorphism in the group of N.E. rigid motions, and we may say that two conformally equivalent surfaces S_1 and S_2 correspond to the same group of N.E. rigid motions of G.

Conversely, if any discontinuous group Γ of rigid motions of G, not including any N.E. rotation, is given, identification of equivalent points with respect to Γ does give rise to a Riemann surface G_Γ. Therefore, we have proved

THEOREM 9–8. *Two Riemann surfaces correspond to the same group of rigid motions if and only if they are conformally equivalent.*

The study of the fundamental region is made easier by having a "distance" defined in the N.E. plane G. With this in mind, we observe that for any four points w_1, w_2, w_3, w_4 in the complex plane, the cross-ratio

$$\frac{(w_2 - w_4)(w_3 - w_1)}{(w_2 - w_1)(w_3 - w_4)}$$

is invariant under any linear fractional transformation. If the four points lie on the circumference of any circle, so that they are encountered in the given order as we go around the circumference, a linear fractional mapping can be found taking the interior of the circle onto the upper half-plane, and the four points into four consecutive points on the real axis. Then it is clear that for these points, the cross-ratio is a positive real number greater than 1.

Now let w_1 and w_2 be any two points in G: $|w| < 1$. The N.E. line through w_1 and w_2 intersects $|w| = 1$ in two points; we shall denote the one near w_1 as ∞_1 and that near w_2 as ∞_2. The cross-ratio

$$\frac{(w_1 - \infty_2)(w_2 - \infty_1)}{(w_1 - \infty_1)(w_2 - \infty_2)}$$

is real and greater than 1; hence one-half of its logarithm is a positive number which we call the N.E. *distance* between w_1 and w_2:

$$d(w_1, w_2) = \frac{1}{2} \log \frac{w_2 - \infty_1}{w_2 - \infty_2} - \frac{1}{2} \log \left(\frac{w_1 - \infty_1}{w_1 - \infty_2} \right).$$

(See Fig. 9–3.) This N.E. distance, being the logarithm of a cross-ratio, is invariant under N.E. rigid motions of G. If w_1, w_2, and w_3 lie on the same N.E. line in the given order, the points ∞_1 and ∞_2 are the same for any pair, and we have

$$d(w_1, w_3) = d(w_1, w_2) + d(w_2, w_3).$$

If $w_1 = 0$ and $w_2 = he^{i\theta}, 0 < h < 1$, we have

$$d(0, he^{i\theta}) = \frac{1}{2} \log \frac{1+h}{1-h}, \qquad (1)$$

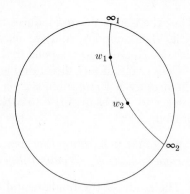

which is an increasing function of the euclidean distance from 0 to $he^{i\theta}$, which becomes infinite as h tends to 1, or the point approaches the ideal boundary of G. The locus $d(w_0, w) = k > 0$ is called an N.E. *circle* with center at w_0 and radius k. Transforming w_0 into 0 by a rigid

FIGURE 9–3.

motion takes the N.E. circle into an ordinary circle with center at the origin. Thus the N.E. circle is the image of euclidean circle under a linear fractional mapping and is itself a euclidean circle in $|w| < 1$. To get another expression for $d(w_1, w_2)$ in terms of w_1 and w_2 alone, we note that $(w - w_1)/(1 - \overline{w}_1 w)$ is a rigid motion taking $w_1 \to 0$ and $w_2 \to (w_2 - w_1)/(1 - \overline{w}_1 w_2)$, so that (1) applies, giving

$$d(w_1, w_2) = \frac{1}{2} \log \frac{1 + |(w_2 - w_1)/(1 - \overline{w}_1 w_2)|}{1 - |(w_2 - w_1)/(1 - \overline{w}_1 w_2)|}. \qquad (2)$$

Note from this that $d(w_1, w_2) = d(w_2, w_1)$.

For the N.E. distance, the triangle inequality holds:

$$d(w_1, w_3) \le d(w_1, w_2) + d(w_2, w_3), \qquad (3)$$

with equality if and only if the three points w_1, w_2, w_3 lie in order on a N.E. line. To verify this, we use a rigid motion to take $w_2 \to 0$, $w_1 \to a > 0$, and $w_3 \to be^{i\beta}$, $b > 0$. Then (3) becomes

$$\frac{1 + |t|}{1 - |t|} \le \frac{1+b}{1-b} \frac{1+a}{1-a}, \qquad t = \frac{be^{i\beta} - a}{1 - abe^{i\beta}}. \qquad (4)$$

The left side of (4) is a monotonic increasing function of $|t|$, so we prove (3) by keeping a and b fixed and finding the maximum of $|t|$ for $0 \le \beta \le 2\pi$. The mapping $t = (w - a)/(1 - aw)$ takes $|w| = b$ into a euclidean circle with center on the real axis, carrying $-b$ into $-(b + a)/(1 + ab)$, which is the point on the image of $|w| = b$ farthest from the origin. For this point, $|t| = (b + a)/(1 + ab)$, and

$$\frac{1 + |t|}{1 - |t|} = \frac{1 + ab + a + b}{1 + ab - a - b} = \frac{(1 + b)(1 + a)}{(1 - b)(1 - a)},$$

and the three points lie on a N.E. line, proving the triangle inequality.

Now fix a point w_0 in the N.E. plane G, and let Σ be the set of points equivalent to w_0 with respect to Γ. Since Γ is discontinuous, any N.E. circle with N.E. center at $w' \in G$ contains only a finite number of points in Σ. Therefore there are a finite number of points, such as $w_j \in \Sigma$, which have the property that $d(w', w_j) \leq d(w', w_k)$ for all $w_k \in \Sigma$. In this case, we say that w' is *nearest* w_j and define the *normal set N_j with center w_j* to be the set of all points $w \in G$ which are nearest w_j. Let N_0 be the normal set with center w_0.

THEOREM 9-9. *The normal set has a nonempty interior.*

If $d(w', w_0) < d(w', w_k)$ for all $w_k \in \Sigma$, $w_k \neq w_0$, we say that w' is *strictly nearer* w_0. Then for some $\epsilon > 0$, a whole N.E. disk $d(w, w') < \epsilon$ is strictly nearer w_0. In fact, let $\epsilon = \frac{1}{2} \min [d(w', w_k) - d(w', w_0)]$, $w_k \in \Sigma$, $w_k \neq w_0$. Then if there is a w'' with $d(w', w'') < \epsilon$ and

$$d(w'', w_k) \leq d(w'', w_0),$$

we know that

$$d(w', w_k) \leq d(w', w'') + d(w'', w_k) \leq 2d(w', w'') + d(w', w_0)$$

$$< 2\epsilon + d(w', w_0),$$

or

$$\tfrac{1}{2}[d(w', w_k) - d(w', w_0)] < \epsilon,$$

which is a contradiction.

THEOREM 9-10. *No pair of points interior to N_0 can be equivalent.*

For if w' and w'' are interior to N_0 and are equivalent, the rigid motion in Γ taking w' into w'' carries w_0 into a point $w_k \in \Sigma$, $w_k \neq w_0$. Then $d(w', w_0) = d(w'', w_k) > d(w'', w_0)$. The rigid motion in Γ taking w'' into w' takes w_0 into w_n, $w_n \in \Sigma$, $w_n \neq w_0$. Then $d(w'', w_0) = d(w', w_n) > d(w', w_0)$. Combining these inequalities yields $d(w', w_0) < d(w', w_0)$, clearly a contradiction.

The rigid motion in Γ which carries w_0 into w_j also takes N_0 into N_j, since all distances are preserved; thus all the normal sets N_j with centers $w_j \in \Sigma$ are congruent. Any point $w \in G$ belongs to at least one normal set (say N_j) and every normal set N_k contains at least one point equivalent to w. For the rigid motion in Γ taking w_j into w_k takes w into an equivalent point in N_k. Thus the union of all normal sets covers the N.E. plane, and each pair of normal sets has disjoint interiors. Since each normal set has an interior, we may select a point in each interior which has rational real and imaginary parts, so that the normal sets can be put into one-to-one correspondence with a subset of a countable set. Thus *the number of normal sets and hence of centers is countable and* Σ *is a countable set.*

THEOREM 9-11. *Each normal set is a convex polygon in the N.E. plane.*

The locus of points whose N.E. distances from two fixed points w_1 and w_2 are equal is an N.E. line orthogonal to the N.E. line joining w_1 and w_2 (the perpendicular bisector of the segment from w_1 to w_2). Indeed, a rigid motion can be used to take w_1 and w_2 into the two points $-a$ and $a, a > 0$, on the real axis. Then the locus of points w equidistant from $-a$ and a is given by

$$\left| \frac{w + a}{1 + aw} \right| = \left| \frac{w - a}{1 - aw} \right|,$$

using (2). Expressed in terms of u and v, where $w = u + iv$, this becomes $4au(1 - a^2)(1 - u^2 - v^2) = 0$; which is the locus $u = 0$ or $|w| = 1$. The latter locus consists of points having infinite distance from a and $-a$, so the problem is solved by the imaginary axis which is the N.E. line orthogonal to the segment from a to $-a$. The boundary of the normal set consists of points which are equally distant from two or more (but always a finite number of) equivalent points. Let b be a boundary point of N_0. For any $R > 0$, there are only a finite number of points in Σ which have the same distance from points in the N.E. disk $d(b, w) < R$ as does w_0, for those points must lie in $d(b, w) < 2R$. Thus only a finite number of segments of N.E. lines (perpendicular bisectors) which are equidistant from w_0 and some point equivalent to w_0 penetrate $d(b, w) < R$. The boundary of N_0 then consists of segments of N.E. lines such that any N.E. disk meets only a finite number of these segments. N_0 is an N.E. polygon having either a finite or an infinite number of sides whose vertices have no finite limit point.

To show that N_0 is a convex polygon, we must establish that if a and b are in N_0, then the N.E. line segment joining them is completely in N_0. We observe first that two N.E. lines intersect in at most one point inside G; if two N.E. lines have more than one point in common in G, they are identical. Assume that c is a point on the N.E. line l_1 joining a and b, with c outside of N_0, so that $d(c, w_k) < d(c, w_0)$ for some $w_k \in \Sigma$, $w_k \neq w_0$. Consider the perpendicular bisector l_2 of the segment from w_0 to w_k. Since $d(a_1, w_0) \leq d(a, w_k)$ and $d(b, w_0) \leq d(b, w_k)$, we know that c is on the w_k side of l_2, while a and b are either on the w_0 side of l_2 or on l_2. Thus

l_2 must cut l_1 in at least two points, so that l_1 and l_2 are identical. Then $d(c, w_0) = d(c, w_k)$, which is a contradiction, proving the convexity of N_0. From now on we shall refer to N_0 as a *normal polygon*.

The normal polygon N_0 contains at least one representative of each class of equivalent points with respect to Γ. Thus N_0 contains in it a fundamental domain. This fundamental domain consists of the interior of N_0 and certain of its boundary points. The sides of N_0 are of two types, (i) those that lie entirely on $|w| = 1$, which we call *free sides*, and (ii) those one or both of whose end points are on $|w| = 1$ or lie entirely in $|w| < 1$, which we call *inner sides*.

THEOREM 9–12. *The inner sides of N_0 are pairwise equivalent; that is, to each inner side s corresponds one and only one side s' and a rigid motion $L \in \Gamma$ such that $L(s) = s'$.*

Indeed, let s be the side of N_0 consisting of points equally distant from w_0 and w_k. The unique rigid motion L in Γ taking w_k into w_0 carries N_k into N_0, and their common side s goes into another side s' of N_0 which is equivalent to s. Furthermore, any rigid motion in Γ which takes s into another side of N_0 must move w_0 out of N_0 and w_k into N_0, and hence w_k into w_0. But this is just the rigid motion that took s into s', so s is equivalent only to s'. We can also state that s and s' are not adjacent sides of N_0. Indeed, if w were the common vertex of s and s', the rigid motion taking s into s' would leave w invariant, for the side of s in N_0 must map into the side of s' outside of N_0.

THEOREM 9–13. *An interior point w of a free side of N_0 has no equivalent point in N_0.*

To prove this, assume that the point w' in N_0 is equivalent to w by a rigid motion $L \in \Gamma$. Then L maps $|w| = 1$ onto itself, taking the free side about w into a free side about w'. We can take a neighborhood U of w relative to $|w| \le 1$ which lies in N_0, and $L(U)$ is then a neighborhood of w' which must also lie in N_0. But this means that interior points of N_0 are equivalent, which is a contradiction.

THEOREM 9–14. *The rigid motions $\{M_1, M_2, \ldots\} = \Theta \subset \Gamma$, which take an inner edge of N_0 into an equivalent edge of N_0, generate the whole group Γ.*

We begin the proof with the remark that if L is a rigid motion in Γ taking N_0 into N, the rigid motion taking a side of N into an equivalent side of N can be written in the form $L \circ M_i \circ L^{-1}$, where $M_i \in \Theta$. Let M be an arbitrary motion in Γ, and let $M(w_0) = w_k$. We can join w_0 to w_k by a N.E. polygonal path π composed of a finite number of segments of N.E. lines in $|w| < 1$. This path is compact and meets only a finite number of the normal polygons. Otherwise there would be a point w' on π which is the limit of a sequence of points $w_1', w_2', \ldots$ each in a different normal polygon. But w' itself either is interior to a normal polygon or belongs to the boundary of a finite number of them, which form a complete neighborhood of w'. Since the vertices of the finite number of normal polygons meeting π do not have a finite limit point, we can choose π so that it does not pass through any vertices of normal polygons. Starting at N_0, let $N_1, N_2, \ldots, N_k$ be the normal polygons with centers $w_1, w_2, \ldots, w_k$ crossed by π in succession (with possible repetitions) in going from w_0 to w_k. Then N_0 and N_1 have a common side and the rigid motion in Γ taking w_0 into w_1 is in Θ; call it M_i. Then N_1 and N_2 have a common side and the rigid motion in Γ taking w_1 into w_2 carries an edge of N_1 into an equivalent edge of N_1, so the motion may be written $L_1 = M_i \circ M_j \circ M_i^{-1}$ for some $M_j \in \Theta$. The motion $L_1 \circ M_i$ takes N_0 into N_2. The rigid motion taking w_2 into w_3 carries a side of N_2 into an equivalent side of N_2, so that it may be written $L_2 = (L_1 \circ M_i) \circ M_l \circ (L_1 \circ M_i)^{-1}$, $M_l \in \Theta$, and the rigid motion in Γ taking N_0 into N_3 can be written $L_2 \circ L_1 \circ M_i$. Continuing in this way, we express M in terms of the rigid motions in Θ, proving our assertion.

A vertex v of N_0 belongs to $n \geq 3$ normal polygons; and v is equally distant from the centers of these n polygons. The rigid motions in Γ taking the centers of these normal polygons into w_0 take v into n different vertices of N_0 (the identity included), and these vertices are equivalent points. The n angles coming together at v move into n different angles interior to N_0 at the vertices equivalent to v, so that the sum of the angles of N_0 at each set of equivalent vertices is 2π.

There are two possibilities for N_0: (1) N_0 is bounded in the N.E. plane (there is an $R < \infty$ such that N_0 is contained in the N.E. circle $d(w_0, w) \geq R$), or (2) N_0 is unbounded (points of N_0 are arbitrarily close to $|w| = 1$).

THEOREM 9–15. *The normal polygon is bounded if and only if the Riemann surface S is compact.*

The inverse of the mapping $\hat{S} \to G$ combined with the projection $\hat{S} \to S$ maps G continuously on S, with the image of N_0 covering S. When N_0 is bounded, N_0 is also compact, since N_0 is a closed bounded set in a metric space. The inverse image of any open covering of S is an open covering of G. Since N_0 is compact, a finite number of these sets suffice to cover N_0 and their images in S form a finite subcovering of the original covering of S. Thus S is also compact.

On the other hand, assume that S is compact. The mapping $G \to S$ is locally one-to-one so that each point $w' \in G$ is, for some sufficiently small ϵ, the center of a disk $d(w, w') < \epsilon$, which is homeomorphic to an open set on S. Each finite point of N_0 can be made the center of such a disk, and hence their images on S form an open covering of S. The interior of N_0 is mapped one-to-one onto a part of S, so that the inverse image of these finite number of disks still covers the interior of N_0. The set composed of a finite number of disks is bounded and hence the interior of N_0 is bounded, but then, so is all of N_0. *When N_0 is bounded, it has a finite number of sides*, since its vertices cannot have a finite limit point.

9–3 Triangulation of a Riemann surface

THEOREM 9–16. *Every Riemann surface can be triangulated, and in such a way that the edges of the triangles are analytic arcs.*

Let S be an arbitrary Riemann surface and let its universal covering surface $\hat{S}$ be mapped onto a canonical region G on the w-sphere.

(1) If G is the whole sphere, S is conformally equivalent to the sphere and the sphere may be triangulated using the equator and two orthogonal meridian circles.
(2) If G is the whole finite plane, there are three cases:
   (a) S is conformally equivalent to G, in which case G may be paved with rectangles and drawing the diagonals provides a triangulation.
   (b) The fundamental region is an infinite strip containing only one of its edges, in which a triangulation is illustrated in Fig. 9–4. One must be careful that the vertices on the edges of the strip fall on equivalent points so that when the two edges are identified we get a triangulation of S.

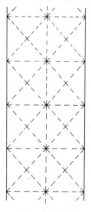

FIGURE 9–4.

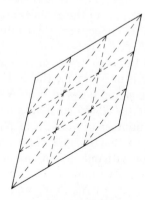

FIGURE 9–5.

(c) The fundamental region is a parallelogram containing one of its vertices and the two edges meeting at this vertex. Figure 9–5 shows a triangulation of this parallelogram with vertices on its edges occurring in identified pairs. This gives us a triangulation of S.

(3) When G is the unit circle, there are two cases:
    (a) The normal polygon N_0 is bounded.
    (b) It is not bounded.

In case (3a), N_0 has a finite number of edges which are pairwise equivalent. We draw the N.E. lines from the center w_0 of N_0 to each of the vertices dividing N_0 into triangles. But this does not give us a triangulation of S yet, for the triangles having the identified pair of edges s and s' of N_0 as their outer edges also have w_0 in common, but we required that two triangles have at most one edge in common. We get around this by further subdividing each triangle T. We trisect (N.E.) the edge of N_0 and bisect (N.E.) each of the other two edges of T. Let w' be the point in T equidistant from the three vertices of T. Then draw the five N.E. lines from w' to the two trisection points, the two bisection points, and w_0. Then join the bisector to the trisector on the same side with two more lines. Figure 9–6 shows this subdivision for a euclidean triangle T. Since rigid motions of Γ are distance-preserving, the new vertices on the outer edges fall on equivalent pairs of points and we now get a valid triangulation of S when we identify edges of N_0. Thus we have triangulated the compact Riemann surfaces. Incidentally, applying all of the motions in Γ to N_0 gives us a triangulation of the N.E. plane using N.E. triangles.

In case (3b), N_0 extends out to the boundary of the unit circle. We first take an arbitrary triangulation of the interior of the unit circle by N.E. triangles. One such was displayed in part (a) from the triangulation of N_0 for a compact surface and then applying Γ. Since N_0 and each triangle T_i, $i = 1, 2, \ldots,$ of the given triangulation of G are convex, their intersection $N_0 \cap T_i$ is also a convex set (in the N.E. geometry); for if p and q are both in $N_0 \cap T_i$, the N.E. line joining p and q lies in both N_0 and T_i. Since T_i is compact, only a finite number of vertices of N_0 are in T_i, so that $N_0 \cap T_i$ is a convex polygon with only a finite number of vertices. We now select any point P_i interior to $N_0 \cap T_i$ and draw N.E. lines from P_i to each vertex

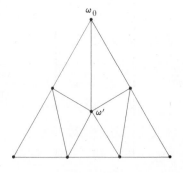

FIGURE 9–6.

of $N_0 \cap T_i$. This gives us a triangulation of N_0 but not of G_Γ (or S); for when we identify equivalent edges of N_0, a vertex may be equivalent to a point that is not a vertex. To remedy this, we add new vertices to our triangulation by looking at each pair of equivalent sides s and s' of N_0. Only a finite number of vertices of the triangulation of N_0 lie on s and s'. We add to s' the points equivalent to vertices on s and add to s the points equivalent to vertices on s'. Each new vertex lies on certain of the $N_0 \cap T_i$, and we join it to the corresponding P_i with a N.E. line. This gives us the triangulation of G_Γ and hence of S when equivalent points of N_0 are identified. *Thus every Riemann surface can be triangulated using geodesic arcs in the geometry of the uniformizing plane.*

In the case of a compact surface of genus $g > 1$, we can get a relationship between the number of edges of the normal polygon N_0 and the genus g. Assume that N_0 has $2e$ edges, and v different sets of equivalent vertices. We triangulate N_0 as before by drawing N.E. lines from w_0 to the vertices and then subdividing each such triangle as in Fig. 9–6. In this triangulation of N_0, there are $8e + 1$ vertices, $24e$ edges, and $14e$ triangles. We next identify the equivalent edges of N_0 to get a triangulation of S. Assuming that there are F triangles, E edges, and V vertices in this triangulation of S, we have, according to Section 5–9,

$$2 - 2g = F - E + V.$$

However, $F = 14e$ and $E = 21e$, since the outer edges of N_0 are identified in pairs, and $V = 1 + v + 6e$, giving us $2 - 2g = 1 + v - e$ or

$$2g = 1 - v + e.$$

Thus the genus of the compact Riemann surface can be computed if we know the group of N.E. rigid motions Γ (or the normal polygon with the proper identification of edges).

We can also get an upper limit on e in terms of g. N_0 has $2e$ vertices, and each vertex is nearest at least three points of Σ, so that each equivalence class of vertices of N_0 contains at least 3 vertices. Thus $3v \leq 2e$, or $-v \geq \frac{2}{3}e$ and $e - v \geq \frac{1}{3}e$. We have

$$\tfrac{1}{3}e + 1 \leq e - v + 1 = 2g,$$

or simply $2e \leq 12g - 6$. Since $v \geq 1$, we also have $2e \geq 4g$, so we have as bounds for the number of edges of the normal polygon corresponding to a surface of genus g

$$4g \leq 2e \leq 12g - 6.$$

9–4 Mappings of a Riemann surface onto itself. Let Γ be a group of linear fractional transformations of $|w| < 1$ onto itself. The identity mapping in Γ will be denoted by I. We say that Γ *contains infinitesimal transformations* if there exists a sequence $\{T_n\}$, $T_n \in \Gamma$, $T_n \neq I$, for which $\lim_{n \to \infty} T_n(w) = w$ for each w in $|w| < 1$. In what follows, $T_n \to T$ means that for each w in $|w| < 1$, $\lim_{n \to \infty} T_n(w) = T(w)$. According to the Vitali convergence theorem, the pointwise convergence of this uniformly bounded sequence of mappings implies uniform convergence on every compact subset of $|w| < 1$. The group Γ thus contains infinitesimal transformations if there is a sequence $T_n \in \Gamma$, $T_n \neq I$, with $T_n \to I$.

Each $T_n \in \Gamma$ can be written as

$$T_n(w) = e^{i\alpha_n} \frac{w - a_n}{1 - \bar{a}_n w}, \qquad 0 \leq \alpha_n \leq 2\pi, \quad |a_n| < 1.$$

This mapping depends continuously upon its parameters $e^{i\alpha_n}$ and a_n, which means that a necessary and sufficient condition for $T_n \to T$,

$$T(w) = e^{i\alpha} \frac{w - a}{1 - \bar{a}w},$$

is that $e^{i\alpha} = \lim_{n \to \infty} e^{i\alpha_n}$ and $a = \lim_{n \to \infty} a_n$. Since

$$T_n^{-1}(w) = e^{-i\alpha_n} \frac{w + a_n e^{i\alpha_n}}{1 + \bar{a}_n e^{-i\alpha_n} w}$$

and

$$T^{-1}(w) = e^{-i\alpha} \frac{w + a e^{i\alpha}}{1 + \bar{a} e^{-i\alpha} w},$$

the convergence $T_n \to T$ implies $T_n^{-1} \to T^{-1}$. Similarly, if $M_n \to M$, where

$$M_n(w) = e^{i\beta_n} \frac{w - b_n}{1 - \bar{b}_n w}, \qquad M(w) = e^{i\beta} \frac{w - b}{1 - \bar{b}w},$$

we have $M_n \circ T_n \to M \circ T$, since

$$M_n \circ T_n = e^{i\beta_n} \frac{w(e^{i\alpha_n} + b_n \bar{a}_n) - (e^{i\alpha_n} a_n + b_n)}{(1 + a_n \bar{b}_n e^{i\alpha_n}) - w(\bar{a}_n + \bar{b}_n e^{i\alpha_n})}$$

and

$$M \circ T = e^{i\beta} \frac{w(e^{i\alpha} + b\bar{a}) - (e^{i\alpha} a + b)}{(1 + a\bar{b}e^{i\alpha}) - w(\bar{a} + \bar{b}e^{i\alpha})},$$

and the parameters in $M_n \circ T_n$ converge to those in $M \circ T$.

After these preliminary observations, we are in a position to compare the notions of a group Γ as discontinuous and having infinitesimal transformations.

THEOREM 9–17. *Γ is discontinuous if and only if Γ does not contain infinitesimal transformations.*

First, if Γ does contain infinitesimal mappings, $T_n \to I$, $T_n \neq I$, each T_n has at most one fixed point in $|w| < 1$, so that the fixed points of all T_n's form at most a countable set. Thus we may select some point a in $|w| < 1$ which is not a fixed point of any T_n. Then the points $\{T_n(a)\}$ are all equivalent to a and $\lim_{n\to\infty} T_n(a) = a$. Thus Γ is not discontinuous.

Assume, conversely, that Γ is not discontinuous. Then there is a sequence of distinct equivalent points $\{a_n\}$ with respect to Γ which converge to a point a in $|w| < 1$, $a_n \neq a$. Then the mapping $T_n \in \Gamma$ which takes a_n into a_{n+1} is given explicitly by

$$T_n: \frac{w' - a_{n+1}}{1 - \bar{a}_{n+1}w'} = e^{i\alpha_n} \frac{w - a_n}{1 - \bar{a}_n w}, \qquad 0 \leq \alpha_n \leq 2\pi.$$

We may select a subsequence in which the α_n's converge to some limit α, and for convenience we shall use the same notation $\{T_n\}$ for this subsequence. Since $a_n \to a$ and $\alpha_n \to \alpha$, we see that $T_n \to R_\alpha$, where

$$R_\alpha: \frac{w' - a}{1 - \bar{a}w'} = e^{i\alpha} \frac{w - a}{1 - \bar{a}w},$$

is a N.E. rotation through an angle α about a. If $\alpha = 0$ or $\alpha = 2\pi$, $R_\alpha = I$ and Γ contains infinitesimal mappings. Otherwise $T_n^{-1} \to R_\alpha^{-1}$, so that $T_{n+1}^{-1} \circ T_n \neq I$, $T_{n+1}^{-1} \circ T_n \in \Gamma$, and $T_{n+1}^{-1} \circ T_n \to R_\alpha^{-1} R_\alpha = I$, completing the proof.

The one-to-one conformal mappings of a Riemann surface S onto itself form a group which we shall denote by Λ. A set of points Σ on S is called an equivalent set of points with respect to Λ if (1) $P \in \Sigma$ implies that $f(P) \in \Sigma$ for all $f \in \Lambda$, and (2) $P \in \Sigma$, $Q \in \Sigma$ implies that $Q = f(P)$ for some $f \in \Lambda$. We again say that the group Λ is discontinuous if no equivalent set of points with respect to Λ has a point of accumulation on S.

Certain surfaces that we have encountered have groups of self-mappings which are not discontinuous. In particular, the surfaces whose universal covering surfaces are elliptic or parabolic are of this type. This comprises four classes of conformally equivalent surfaces which we enumerate now by giving a representative of each:

(1) *a sphere* (compact surface of genus zero),
(2) *a once-punctured sphere* (sphere with one point removed),

(3) *a twice-punctured sphere* (sphere with two points removed),

(4) *a torus* (compact surface of genus 1).

In addition to these, there are three very simple surfaces with hyperbolic universal covering surfaces which do not have discontinuous groups Λ. These are

(5) *a disk*,

(6) *a once-punctured disk* (disk with one point removed),

(7) *an annulus*.

The "torus" and the "annulus" each represent an infinite class of distinct conformal types (problem 3, Chapter 9).

THEOREM 9–18. *The seven surfaces enumerated above are the only Riemann surfaces which do not have discontinuous groups of one-to-one conformal self-transformations.*

In proving this theorem, we may assume that S has a hyperbolic universal covering surface $\hat{S}$. Let $P' = f(P)$ be a one-to-one conformal mapping of S onto itself. Then f induces a one-to-one conformal mapping F of $\hat{S}$ onto itself. For if $P = \varphi(\hat{P})$ is the projection mapping of $\hat{S}$ onto S, then $f \circ \varphi$ is a projection mapping from $\hat{S}$ to $f(S)$. With this new projection mapping $f \circ \varphi$, $\hat{S}$ becomes a new unlimited unbranched covering surface of $f(S) = S$, which we shall denote by $F(\hat{S})$. All the points of $\hat{S}$ lying over $P \in S$ now lie over $f(P) \in S$. Since $F(\hat{S})$ is simply connected, it is the universal covering surface of S. We have thus obtained a one-to-one conformal mapping F of the universal covering surface $\hat{S}$ of S onto the universal covering surface $f(S) = S$ (hence onto $\hat{S}$ itself) such that each point $\hat{P} \in \hat{S}$ lying over $P \in S$ maps into a point $F(\hat{P})$ lying over the point $f(P) \in S$. This mapping is determined only up to a covering transformation of $F(\hat{S})$ and is uniquely specified if we ask that a given point $\hat{P}_0$ of $\hat{S}$ lying over $P \in S$ map into some given point lying over $f(P)$.

When $\hat{S}$ is mapped onto the unit disk, the mapping F of $\hat{S}$ onto itself defines a mapping T of the unit disk onto itself. The fact that points having the same projection on S map into another set of points projecting into one point expresses itself in the unit disk as T carries each set of points equivalent with respect to the group Γ (covering transformations of $\hat{S}$) into another set of points equivalent with respect to Γ. If M is any rigid motion in Γ, $T^{-1} \circ M \circ T$ is also a rigid motion which corresponds to a covering transformation of $\hat{S}$ and hence is in Γ. Thus T has the property that $T^{-1}\Gamma T = \Gamma$ or $\Gamma T = T\Gamma$, and T commutes with the group Γ. Conversely, any rigid motion that commutes with Γ must map each set of equivalent points with respect to Γ into another such set, so T corresponds to a mapping of G_Γ onto itself and hence of S onto itself.

Let Γ_c represent the group of rigid motions of the N.E. plane which commute with Γ. Γ_c contains Γ as a normal subgroup, with each transformation in Γ corresponding to the identity mapping of S onto itself. The group which we wish to study is therefore isomorphic to Γ_c/Γ. If Λ were not discontinuous, equivalent points P_1, P_2, ... on S would have a cluster point P_0. But then the corresponding points in G_Γ would have a cluster point and Γ_c would not be discontinuous. Thus in order to show that Λ is discontinuous, we need only show that Γ_c is discontinuous. But this will be accomplished if we demonstrate that Γ_c contains no infinitesimal transformations.

To obtain the exceptional cases, let us assume that Γ_c does have infinitesimal mappings, say T_1, T_2, ..., with $T_n \neq I$ and $T_n \to I$. If Γ consists only of the identity I, then G_Γ is just the interior of the unit circle and S must be conformally equivalent to a disk, which is exception (5). Thus we may assume that $M \in \Gamma$ and $M \neq I$. The rigid motion $T_n^{-1} \circ M \circ T_n \in \Gamma$, so that $M^{-1}(T_n^{-1}MT_n)$ is also in Γ. Since $T_n \to I$, we have

$$M^{-1}T_n^{-1}MT_n \to I.$$

But Γ contains no infinitesimal transformations, so this could be possible only if $M^{-1}T_n^{-1}MT_n = I$ for all sufficiently large n, or simply

$$MT_n = T_nM \text{ for } n > n_0.$$

We must now determine when the N.E. translation or limit rotation M can commute with the rigid motion T_n. Since $T_n^{-1}MT_n = M$, M and $T_n^{-1}MT_n$ have the same fixed points. This means that if $M(w_0) = w_0$ and $T_n(w_0) = w_1$, while $M(w_1) = w_2$, then $T_n^{-1}(w_2) = w_0$. But $T_n^{-1}(w_1) = w_0$, so that $w_1 = w_2$, and $M(w_1) = w_1$. Hence T_n maps a fixed point of M into a fixed point of M.

(a) If M is a limit rotation with a single fixed point w_0, then w_0 must also be a fixed point for all T_n, $n > n_0$. If T_n had another fixed point $w_1 \neq w_0$, $M^{-1} \circ T_n \circ M = T_n$ for $n > n_0$ and $M(w_1) = w_2$, $w_2 \neq w_1$ or w_0. Also $T_n(w_2) = w_3$ and $M^{-1}(w_3) = w_1$. But $M^{-1}(w_2) = w_1$ so $w_2 = w_3$ and w_2 is also a fixed point of T_n, which is impossible since T_n has at most two fixed points. Thus T_n has only one fixed point w_0 for all $n > n_0$. But now, since any $M \in \Gamma$ commutes with T_n, the same argument shows that all $M \in \Gamma$ are limit rotations with the same fixed point w_0 on $|w| = 1$. The mapping $\sigma = (2iw_0)/(w - w_0) - i$ takes $|w| < 1$ into the half-plane Im $\sigma > 0$, with the limit rotations in Γ going into the group of translations parallel to the real axis. The discontinuous group of mappings Γ now consists of the translations

$$\sigma' = \sigma + kb, \quad k = 0, \pm 1, \pm 2, \ldots, \quad b = \text{positive constant.}$$

The mapping $\zeta = e^{2\pi i\sigma/b}$ takes this half-plane into $0 < |\zeta| < 1$ in such a way that each set of equivalent points $\sigma + kb$, $k = 0$, ± 1, ± 2, $\ldots$, maps into the same point ζ. Thus G_Γ is mapped conformally onto a punctured disk, which is exception (6).

(b) We may now assume that Γ contains no limit rotations. If $M \in \Gamma$ is a N.E. translation with fixed points w_1 and w_2 on $|w| = 1$, either T_n has the same two fixed points and is also a N.E. translation, or T_n interchanges the fixed points of M. Referring to the definitions of the three kinds of N.E. rigid motions, we see that the only rigid motion that interchanges two boundary points of $|w| = 1$ is a N.E. rotation through an angle π. But the N.E. rotation through an angle π has one fixed point w_2 inside of $|w| < 1$. In order for $M^{-1}T_nM = T_n$ to hold, w_2 would have to be a fixed point of M; for $M(w_2) = w_3$, $T_n(w_3) = w_4$, and $M^{-1}(w_4) = w_2$. But $M^{-1}(w_3) = w_2$, so $w_3 = w_4$ and $T_n(w_3) = w_3$. This finally implies that $w_3 = w_2$ or $M(w_2) = w_2$, which is impossible. Thus T_n has exactly the same fixed points as M for $n > n_0$. Since M is arbitrary in Γ, M consists only of N.E. translations with the same two fixed points w_1 and w_2. In this case,

$$\sigma = s + it = \sqrt{\frac{w_2}{w_1}} \frac{w - w_1}{w_2 - w_1},$$

$\arg w_2 > \arg w_1$, maps $|w| < 1$ onto the half-plane $t > 0$. The N.E. translations in Γ now appear as magnifications $\sigma' = e^{kc}\sigma$, $c = $ real constant, $k = 0$, ± 1, ± 2, $\ldots$. The mapping $\zeta = \log \sigma$ maps the upper half-plane into a strip $-\infty < \xi < \infty$, $0 < \eta < \pi$, of the $(\zeta = \xi + i\eta)$-plane. The N.E. translations now correspond to translations of this strip parallel to the ξ-axis:

$$\zeta' = \zeta + kc, \qquad k = 0, \pm 1, \pm 2, \ldots.$$

Finally, the mapping $\omega = e^{-2\pi i\zeta/c}$ takes the strip into the annulus $1 < |\omega| < e^{2\pi^2/c}$ so that each set of equivalent points $\zeta + kc$ maps into the same point ω. Thus G_Γ is mapped conformally onto an annulus, which is exception (7). This exhausts all possibilities and completes the proof of the theorem.

A corollary of the previous theorem is obtained when we apply it to compact surfaces. On a compact Riemann surface S, a group of self-mappings of S is discontinuous if and only if it consists of a finite number of mappings. For a set of equivalent points has no cluster point on a compact surface if and only if it is a finite set of points. Thus we obtain the theorem of H. A. Schwarz.

THEOREM 9–19. *A compact Riemann surface of genus $g > 1$ has only a finite number of one-to-one conformal mappings onto itself.*

Problems

1. Show that any doubly connected plane region is conformally equivalent to one of the following three canonical domains: (a) a twice-punctured sphere, (b) a punctured disk, or (c) an annulus.† Show that these are the only surfaces whose covering group Γ is a free cyclic group with one generator.

2. For the annulus $r_1 < z < r_2$ show that each number $m = |\log (r_2/r_1)|$ determines a different conformal class of doubly connected regions.

3. Let ρ be the number of real parameters in the group of conformal self-transformations of a Riemann surface into itself. Determine ρ in the seven cases in which the groups are not discontinuous. For compact surfaces, show that when $g = 0$, $\rho = 6$; $g = 1$, $\rho = 2$; and $g > 1$, $\rho = 0$.

4. S is a compact Riemann surface of genus $g \geq 2$. Let Γ represent the group of N.E. rigid motions of $G: |w| < 1$ corresponding to the covering transformations of S. Prove that there exists a $\delta > 0$ such that any N.E. disk $d(w, w_0) < \delta$ contains no pair of points equivalent with respect to Γ.

5. By differentiating equation (1) of Section 9–2 and making use of the invariance of the distance under rigid motions, show that the element of N.E. arc length is

$$ds = \frac{|dw|}{1 - |w^2|}.$$

6. If the unit circle is mapped onto the upper half-plane, what are the images of the N.E. straight lines and rigid motions? Show that the element of N.E. arc length expressed in terms of $w = u + iv$ in $v > 0$ is

$$ds = \frac{|dw|}{v}.$$

7. Any N.E. limit rotation can be represented as a euclidean translation $w' = w + b$, b real, of the upper half-plane, so that w_0 and $w_0 + b$ are always equivalent points. From problems 4 and 6 conclude that the group Γ for a compact surface of genus $g \geq 2$ contains no N.E. limit rotations.

8. Prove that the universal covering surface $\tilde{S}$ of the z-sphere with three points a_1, a_2, a_3 removed is hyperbolic. This may be done by first mapping a_1, a_2, a_3 into 0, 1, ∞ with a linear fractional transformation. Then construct the elliptic modular function $w = \lambda(z; 0, 1, \infty)$ which maps the upper half-plane into the region in the $(w = u + iv)$-plane defined by $0 < u < 1$, $(u - \frac{1}{2})^2 + v^2 > \frac{1}{4}$, $v > 0$, in such a way that $0 \to 0$, $1 \to 1$, and $\infty \to \infty$. The existence of such a mapping follows from the Riemann mapping theorem and the ability to prescribe three boundary points arbitrarily. Then continuing λ analytically over

---

†In general, a region is said to have connectivity n when its fundamental group has $n - 1$ independent generators. Thus for a doubly connected region the fundamental group is a free group with one generator.

the three segments of the real axis (Schwarz reflection principle) yields a mapping of $\tilde{S}$ onto the upper half-plane, which in turn can be mapped onto the unit circle. We shall denote this composite mapping of S onto the unit circle by $\lambda(z; a_1, a_2, a_3)$.

9. Prove the *Picard theorem* that if there are three values a_1, a_2, a_3 not assumed by a meromorphic function $z = f(t)$ defined in the complex t-plane, then f is a constant. [Observe that $\lambda(f(t), a_1, a_2, a_3)$ is a bounded single-valued regular analytic function in the whole t-plane.]

10. Prove that the universal covering surface of the sphere with n points removed ($n \geq 3$) is hyperbolic by assuming that it is parabolic and applying the Picard theorem.

CHAPTER 10

COMPACT RIEMANN SURFACES

10–1 Regular harmonic differentials. We shall now restrict our attention to the study of harmonic and analytic functions on compact Riemann surfaces. The basic problems we pose are to determine whether there exist analytic functions (exact analytic differentials) with prescribed singularities, how many "different" such functions there are, and the relations between these functions. These will lead us to the connection between compact Riemann surfaces and algebraic functions. Our point of departure will be the study of the everywhere regular harmonic differentials on such surfaces.

A finite collection of nonzero differentials $\omega_1, \omega_2, \ldots, \omega_n$ on the Riemann surface S is called *linearly dependent* over a number field F if there exist numbers $c_1, c_2, \ldots, c_n$ in F, not all equal to zero, such that $c_1\omega_1 + c_2\omega_2 + \cdots + c_n\omega_n \equiv 0$ on S. If no such constants exist, we say the differentials $\omega_1, \omega_2, \ldots, \omega_n$ are *linearly independent* over the field F. We shall take for the field F either the real numbers or the complex numbers.

Let us assume that S is of genus g and study the Hilbert space H of harmonic differentials on S. The normal form of S is a polygon Π with $4g$ sides having the symbol $\mathbf{a}_1 \mathbf{b}_1 \mathbf{a}_1^{-1} \mathbf{b}_1^{-1} \ldots \mathbf{a}_g \mathbf{b}_g \mathbf{a}_g^{-1} \mathbf{b}_g^{-1}$. The closed curves $\mathbf{a}_i$ and $\mathbf{b}_i$ can be taken to be piecewise analytic curves on S, since we have seen that S may be triangulated in such a way that the edges of triangles are analytic curves. Furthermore, the $\mathbf{a}_i$ and $\mathbf{b}_i$ form a homology basis for S and any cycle $\mathbf{c}$ on S is homologous to an integral linear combination of the $\mathbf{a}_i$ and $\mathbf{b}_i$. If $\omega \in H$, ω is closed and the period of ω on any cycle $\mathbf{c}$ is equal to the period of ω on any cycle homologous to $\mathbf{c}$. Since $\mathbf{c} \sim \sum_{i=1}^{g} \lambda_i \mathbf{a}_i + \mu_i \mathbf{b}_i$, we have

$$\int_{\mathbf{c}} \omega = \int_{\Sigma \lambda_i \mathbf{a}_i + \mu_i \mathbf{b}_i} \omega = \sum_{i=1}^{g} \lambda_i \int_{\mathbf{a}_i} \omega + \mu_i \int_{\mathbf{b}_i} \omega.$$

Thus the periods of ω on any cycle can be expressed as a linear combination of its periods on the basic cycles $\mathbf{a}_i$ and $\mathbf{b}_i$, $i = 1, 2, \ldots, g$. Let us denote by A_i and B_i the periods of ω over $\mathbf{a}_i$ and $\mathbf{b}_i$, respectively, so that

$$A_i = \int_{\mathbf{a}_i} \omega, \qquad B_i = \int_{\mathbf{b}_i} \omega.$$

If $A_i = 0$ and $B_i = 0$ for $i = 1, 2, \ldots, g$, then ω is exact, but on a compact surface an exact harmonic differential must be identically zero.

The fact that the period of ω on any cycle is completely determined by the periods A_i and B_i will allow us to prove that H is a complex vector space of dimension at most $2g$. Let $\omega_1, \ldots, \omega_n$ be harmonic differentials in H, and let

$$A_{i,j} = \int_{\mathbf{a}_j} \omega_i, \qquad B_{i,j} = \int_{\mathbf{b}_j} \omega_i.$$

Then consider the following system of homogeneous equations for the unknowns $\lambda_1, \lambda_2, \ldots, \lambda_n$:

$$\lambda_1 A_{1,1} + \lambda_2 A_{2,1} + \cdots + \lambda_n A_{n,1} = 0,$$
$$\lambda_1 A_{1,2} + \lambda_2 A_{2,2} + \cdots + \lambda_n A_{n,2} = 0,$$
$$\vdots$$
$$\lambda_1 A_{1,g} + \lambda_2 A_{2,g} + \cdots + \lambda_n A_{n,g} = 0,$$
$$\lambda_1 B_{1,1} + \lambda_2 B_{2,1} + \cdots + \lambda_n B_{n,1} = 0,$$
$$\vdots$$
$$\lambda_1 B_{1,g} + \lambda_2 B_{2,g} + \cdots + \lambda_n B_{n,g} = 0.$$

If $n > 2g$, this system of $2g$ equations for the n unknowns $\lambda_1, \ldots, \lambda_n$ has a nontrivial solution; one for which not all λ_i's are zero. Then all periods of the differential

$$\omega = \lambda_1 \omega_1 + \lambda_2 \omega_2 + \cdots + \lambda_n \omega_n$$

are zero, so that $\omega \equiv 0$. Thus if $n > 2g$, any system of n harmonic differentials on S is linearly dependent over the complex numbers, so that H is just a vector space of dimension at most $2g$ over the complex number field. In particular, if $g = 0$, $\dim H = 0$, which says that there are no everywhere regular everywhere harmonic differentials on a Riemann surface of genus zero.

To show that there actually are $2g$ linearly independent harmonic differentials in H, we construct real harmonic differentials ω_i, $i = 1, 2, \ldots, 2g$, in H such that each ω_i, $i = 1, \ldots, g$, has period 1 on $\mathbf{a}_i$ and period 0 on $\mathbf{a}_j$, $j \neq i$, and on all $\mathbf{b}_j$, while ω_{g+i}, $i = 1, 2, \ldots, g$, has period 1 on $\mathbf{b}_i$ and period 0 on all $\mathbf{b}_j$, $j \neq i$, and on all $\mathbf{a}_j$. The construction of ω_1 will be typical and will suffice to show how to construct the others.

In the normal form corresponding to S, we select the points P, Q, R consecutively interior to the curve $\mathbf{a}_1$ and denote by P', Q', R' the points on $\mathbf{a}_1^{-1}$ which are identified with P, Q, R, respectively. We then draw the line segments $\overline{PP'}$, $\overline{QQ'}$, and $\overline{RR'}$. Carrying these back to S, we construct a function f on S as follows:

(a) $f \equiv 0$ in the part of S outside the quadrilateral $PP'R'RP$ (the ruled area in Fig. 10–1);

(b) $f \equiv 1$ in the quadrilateral $QQ'R'RQ$ (the dotted area in Fig. 10–1);

(c) f is defined in the quadrilateral $PP'Q'QP$ (unshaded in Fig. 10–1) so as to have continuous second derivatives there and on the lines $\overline{PP'}$ and $\overline{QQ'}$.

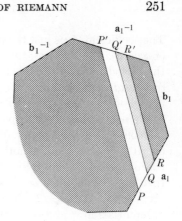

We notice that f has a jump of 1 across the line $\overline{RR'}$ but that f is constant on each side of $\overline{RR'}$. Thus we may set $\pi_1 = df$ on all of S except on $\overline{RR'}$ and there set $\pi_1 = 0$. The differential π_1 is closed, for $\pi_1 \equiv 0$ outside the quadrilateral $PP'Q'QP$

FIGURE 10–1.

and inside $\pi_1 = df$ and $d\pi_1 = ddf = 0$. The period of π_1 on $\mathbf{a}_1$ is given by

$$\int_{\mathbf{a}_1} \pi_1 = \int_P^Q df = f(Q) - f(P) = 1 - 0 = 1,$$

since $\pi_1 = 0$ on the part of $\mathbf{a}_1$ outside $\overline{PQ}$. Furthermore, $\pi_1 = 0$ on all $\mathbf{a}_i$, $i = 2, 3, \ldots, g$, and on all $\mathbf{b}_i$, $i = 1, 2, \ldots, g$, so that the periods of π_1 on these cycles are zero. Now we use the decomposition theorem (lemma 8–1) to find a real harmonic differential ω_1 having the same periods as the closed differential π_1. This is just the ω_1 for which we were searching.

It is clear that these $2g$ differentials $\omega_1, \omega_2, \ldots, \omega_{2g}$ are linearly independent; for if

$$\omega = \lambda_1 \omega_1 + \lambda_2 \omega_2 + \cdots + \lambda_{2g} \omega_{2g} \equiv 0,$$

the period of ω over $\mathbf{a}_i$, $i \leq g$, is just λ_i, so $\lambda_i = 0$; and the period of ω over $\mathbf{b}_i$, $i \leq g$, is λ_{g+i}, so $\lambda_{g+i} = 0$, and all λ_i, $i = 1, \ldots, 2g$, are zero. We have proved

THEOREM 10–1. *On a compact Riemann surface of genus g, the vector space of regular harmonic differentials over the complex number field has dimension $2g$.*

10–2 The bilinear relations of Riemann. Any harmonic differential $\omega \in H$ can be represented as a linear combination of the $2g$ differentials $\omega_1, \omega_2, \ldots, \omega_{2g}$ constructed above as

$$\omega = A_1 \omega_1 + \cdots + A_g \omega_g + B_1 \omega_{g+1} + \cdots + B_g \omega_{2g}.$$

The coefficient A_i is just the period of ω on the cycle $\mathbf{a}_i$, and B_i is the period of ω on $\mathbf{b}_i$. We shall call the periods of ω on the $\mathbf{a}_i$'s the *A-periods* of ω, and the periods of ω on the $\mathbf{b}_i$'s the *B-periods* of ω. The set $\{\omega_i\}_{i=1}^{2g}$ is called the *canonical basis* for harmonic differentials on S. A harmonic differential ω is uniquely determined by its $2g$ periods, $A_1, B_1, A_2, B_2, \ldots, A_g, B_g$.

We next study the subspace $\mathcal{C}$ of H consisting of holomorphic differentials on S. Each harmonic differential ω gives rise to a holomorphic differential $\varphi = \omega + i*\omega$. Another subspace of H is the space $\bar{\mathcal{C}}$ of complex conjugates of holomorphic differentials; if $\varphi \in \mathcal{C}$, then $\bar{\varphi} \in \bar{\mathcal{C}}$. If $\omega \in H$, then $\bar{\omega} \in H$ and $\varphi' = \bar{\omega} + i*\bar{\omega} \in \mathcal{C}$. Then $\bar{\varphi}' = \omega - i*\omega \in \bar{\mathcal{C}}$ and adding gives $\omega = \varphi/2 + \bar{\varphi}'/2$. Therefore every differential in H is the sum of differentials in $\mathcal{C}$ and $\bar{\mathcal{C}}$, so that $\mathcal{C}$ and $\bar{\mathcal{C}}$ span H.

THEOREM 10–2. *$\mathcal{C}$ and $\bar{\mathcal{C}}$ are orthogonal subspaces in H, and $H = \mathcal{C} \oplus \bar{\mathcal{C}}$.*

Let $\varphi \in \mathcal{C}$ and $\bar{\varphi}' \in \bar{\mathcal{C}}$. Then $*\varphi = -i\varphi$ and $*\varphi' = -i\varphi'$ or $*\bar{\varphi}' = i\bar{\varphi}'$. We have

$$(\varphi, \bar{\varphi}') = (*\varphi, *\bar{\varphi}') = (-i\varphi, i\bar{\varphi}') = (-i)(-i)(\varphi, \bar{\varphi}') = -(\varphi, \bar{\varphi}'),$$

so that $(\varphi, \bar{\varphi}') = 0$ and $\mathcal{C} \perp \bar{\mathcal{C}}$.

The complex conjugation operator $^-$ defines an isomorphism of $\mathcal{C}$ onto $\bar{\mathcal{C}}$, so that $\dim \mathcal{C} = \dim \bar{\mathcal{C}}$. Also $\dim \mathcal{C} + \dim \bar{\mathcal{C}} = 2g$, so that $\dim \mathcal{C} = g$. Therefore,

THEOREM 10–3. *The space of holomorphic differentials on a compact Riemann surface has dimension equal to its genus g.*

The holomorphic differentials on S are called *abelian differentials of the first kind*.

We next study the periods of holomorphic differentials. Let ω be a closed differential on S and let η be a differential which is regular ($\eta \in C^1$) in a neighborhood of each point on the cycles $\mathbf{a}_i$ and $\mathbf{b}_i$, $i = 1, 2, \ldots, g$. Let $\int_{\mathbf{a}_i} \omega = A_i$, $\int_{\mathbf{b}_i} \omega = B_i$, $\int_{\mathbf{a}_i} \eta = A_i'$, and $\int_{\mathbf{b}_i} \eta = B_i'$. The interior of the normal form Π is simply connected and corresponds to a region on S which we shall again denote by Π. In Π the closed differential ω is exact, for Π is simply connected and each cycle in Π is homotopic to a point, so that all periods of ω in Π are zero. Thus $\omega = df$, where the function f has continuous second derivatives in Π and may even be extended to have continuous second derivatives on $\partial\Pi$ in such a way that $\omega = df$, but now f is not single-valued on S.

Each point Q on $\mathbf{a}_i$ is identified with a point Q' on $\mathbf{a}_i^{-1}$ in $\partial\Pi$. Let $\overline{QQ'}$ be the line segment joining Q to Q' in Π; then $\overline{QQ'}$ corresponds to a cycle on S and $\int_{\overline{QQ'}} \omega$ is defined and can be evaluated as

$$\int_{\overline{QQ'}} \omega = \int_{\overline{QQ'}} df = f(Q') - f(Q).$$

But the cycle $\overline{QQ'}$ is homologous to the cycle $(\overline{QP}) + (\overline{PP'}) + \cdot(\overline{P'Q'})$, where $\overline{PP'} = \mathbf{b}_i$ (see Fig. 10–2); so $f(Q') - f(Q) = \int_{\overline{QP}} \omega + \int_{\mathbf{b}_i} \omega + \int_{\overline{P'Q'}} \omega$. Recalling that $\overline{QP}$ and $\overline{Q'P'}$ are the same arc on S, we see that $\int_{\overline{QP}} \omega = -\int_{\overline{P'Q'}} \omega$, and $\int_{\mathbf{b}_i} \omega = B_i$. Therefore $f(Q') - f(Q) = B_i$. Similarly, the point R on $\mathbf{b}_i$ is identified with R' on $\mathbf{b}_i^{-1}$, and $f(R') - f(R) = -A_i$. We now compute the integral $\int_{\partial\Pi} f\eta$. First,

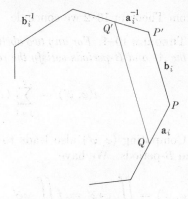

FIGURE 10–2.

$$\int_{\mathbf{a}_i+\mathbf{b}_i+\mathbf{a}_i^{-1}+\mathbf{b}_i^{-1}} f\eta = \int_{\mathbf{a}_i} f\eta + \int_{\mathbf{b}_i} f\eta - \int_{\mathbf{a}_i} (f + B_i)\eta - \int_{\mathbf{b}_i} (f - A_i)\eta$$

$$= -B_i \int_{\mathbf{a}_i} \eta + A_i \int_{\mathbf{b}_i} \eta = A_i B'_i - B_i A'_i.$$

Therefore,

$$\int_{\partial\Pi} f\eta = \sum_{i=1}^{g} (A_i B'_i - B_i A'_i), \tag{1}$$

which is an important relationship upon which we shall draw heavily in the following discussion.

If φ and φ' are both abelian differentials of the first kind on S, φ and $\bar{\varphi}'$ are orthogonal. We may evaluate $(\varphi, \bar{\varphi}')$ in terms of the periods $A_j, B_j,$ $j = 1, \ldots, g,$ of φ and $A'_j, B'_j, j = 1, \ldots, g,$ of φ':

$$(\varphi, \bar{\varphi}') = \iint_S \varphi * \varphi' = -i \iint_S \varphi\varphi' = -i \iint_\Pi \varphi\varphi'.$$

But φ is closed on S, so that in Π, $\varphi = df$ while $d\varphi' = 0$ on S. Even though the $\mathbf{a}_j$ and $\mathbf{b}_j$ are piecewise analytic and $\bar{\Pi}$ is compact on S, Π is not a regular region for Stokes' theorem; for Π lies on both sides of each $\mathbf{a}_j$ and $\mathbf{b}_j$. But we may divide Π into a finite number $(4g)$ of regular regions by connecting an interior point with each vertex of Π, and the fact that Stokes' theorem holds for each implies that it holds in their union. Therefore,

$$(\varphi, \bar{\varphi}') = -i \int_{\partial\Pi} f\varphi' = -i \sum_{j=1}^{g} (A_j B'_j - B_j A'_j).$$

From Theorem 10–2 we conclude

THEOREM 10–4. *For any two abelian differentials of the first kind φ and φ', the A- and B-periods satisfy the relationship*

$$i(\varphi, \bar{\varphi}') = \sum_{j=1}^{g} (A_j B'_j - B_j A'_j) = 0. \qquad (2)$$

Computing (φ, φ') also leads to an interesting relationship for the A- and B-periods. We have

$$(\varphi, \varphi') = \iint_S \varphi {*} \bar{\varphi}' = i \iint_S \varphi \bar{\varphi}' = i \int_{\partial \Pi} f \bar{\varphi}' = i \sum_{j=1}^{g} (A_j \bar{B}'_j - B_j \bar{A}'_j).$$

Applying this to $\|\varphi\|^2 = (\varphi, \varphi)$, we obtain

THEOREM 10–5. *The A- and B-periods of any abelian differential of the first kind φ satisfy*

$$\|\varphi\|^2 = i \sum_{j=1}^{g} (A_j \bar{B}_j - B_j \bar{A}_j) \geq 0. \qquad (3)$$

The relations (2) and (3) are called the *bilinear relations of Riemann* for abelian differentials of the first kind.

We conclude immediately from (3) that

COROLLARY 10–1. *An everywhere holomorphic differential all of whose A-periods (or B-periods) vanish is identically zero.*

Thus a differential of the first kind on S is completely determined by its A-periods (or B-periods). Moreover, from (3) we conclude that

COROLLARY 10–2. *Any abelian differential of the first kind all of whose periods are real must vanish identically.*

Let $\psi_1, \psi_2, \ldots, \psi_g$ be a basis for the abelian differentials of the first kind. Denote the period of ψ_i over $\mathbf{a}_j$ by $A_{i,j}$. The determinant $|(A_{i,j})| \neq 0$; for if it were zero, then the system of homogeneous equations

$$\sum_{i=1}^{g} \lambda_i A_{i,j} = 0, \quad j = 1, \ldots, g,$$

would have a nontrivial solution for $\lambda_1, \ldots, \lambda_g$. But then the holomorphic differential $\lambda_1 \psi_1 + \cdots + \lambda_g \psi_g$ would have zero A-periods and would vanish identically, contradicting the linear independence of the ψ_i's. Thus we can solve the system of equations

$$\sum_{i=1}^{g} \lambda_{i,k} A_{i,j} = \delta_{j,k}, \quad j = 1, 2, \ldots, g,$$

where $\delta_{j,k} = 0$ if $j \neq k$ and $\delta_{k,k} = 1$, for each $k = 1, 2, \ldots, g$, and define $\varphi_k = \sum_{i=1}^{g} \lambda_{i,k} \psi_i$, $k = 1, \ldots, g$. The φ_k's again form a basis for the abelian differentials of the first kind and φ_k has period 1 over $\mathbf{a}_k$ and period 0 over $\mathbf{a}_j$, $j \neq k$. If we write $B_{k,j}$ for the period of φ_k over the cycle $\mathbf{b}_j$, we get the following period diagram for the basis $\varphi_1, \varphi_2, \ldots, \varphi_g$:

	$\mathbf{a}_1$	$\mathbf{a}_2$	$\ldots$	$\mathbf{a}_g$	$\mathbf{b}_1$	$\mathbf{b}_2$	$\ldots$	$\mathbf{b}_g$	
φ_1	1	0	$\ldots$	0	$B_{1,1}$	$B_{1,2}$	$\ldots$	$B_{1,g}$	
φ_2	0	1	$\ldots$	0	$B_{2,1}$	$B_{2,2}$	$\ldots$	$B_{2,g}$	(4)
$\vdots$	$\vdots$	$\vdots$		$\vdots$	$\vdots$	$\vdots$		$\vdots$	
φ_g	0	0	$\ldots$	1	$B_{g,1}$	$B_{g,2}$	$\ldots$	$B_{g,g}$	

We call this basis the *canonical basis for the abelian differentials of the first kind*.

The matrix of B-periods of the canonical basis

$$(B_{i,j}) = \begin{bmatrix} B_{1,1} & B_{1,2} & \ldots & B_{1,g} \\ \vdots & \vdots & & \vdots \\ B_{g,1} & B_{g,2} & \ldots & B_{g,g} \end{bmatrix}$$

is a symmetric matrix, for if we apply (2) with $\varphi = \varphi_i$ and $\varphi' = \varphi_j$, we get $\sum_{k=1}^{g} (A_{i,k} B_{j,k} - B_{i,k} A_{j,k}) = 0$. The periods $A_{i,j} = \delta_{i,j}$, so this simply reduces to $B_{j,i} - B_{i,j} = 0$, proving the symmetry. In addition, the matrix

$$(\operatorname{Im} B_{i,j}) = \begin{bmatrix} \operatorname{Im} B_{1,1} & \operatorname{Im} B_{1,2} & \ldots & \operatorname{Im} B_{1,g} \\ \vdots & \vdots & & \vdots \\ \operatorname{Im} B_{g,1} & \operatorname{Im} B_{g,2} & \ldots & \operatorname{Im} B_{g,g} \end{bmatrix}$$

is positive definite. To see this, we need only apply (3) to the analytic differential $\varphi = x_1 \varphi_1 + \cdots + x_g \varphi_g$, where the x_i are real numbers not all zero. Then $\|\varphi\|^2 > 0$ and $A_k = x_k$,

$$B_k = x_1 B_{1,k} + x_2 B_{2,k} + \cdots + x_g B_{g,k}.$$

We have

$$0 < i \sum_{j=1}^{g} x_j \overline{(x_1 B_{1,j} + \cdots + x_g B_{g,j})} - \bar{x}_j(x_1 B_{1,j} + \cdots + x_g B_{g,j}),$$

or, simply,

$$0 < \sum_{j=1}^{g} \sum_{k=1}^{g} x_j x_k \, \mathrm{Im} \, B_{j,k},$$

proving that $(\mathrm{Im} \, B_{j,k})$ is positive definite.

10–3 Bilinear relations for differentials with singularities. Having determined the number of holomorphic differentials on a compact Riemann surface S and some information about the nature of their periods, we now turn to the study of analytic differentials with singularities. In the previous work, the case $g = 0$ was always excluded as trivial, for there were no everywhere holomorphic differentials on the sphere. With singularities, however, this case must also be studied. We take into consideration only meromorphic differentials whose only singularities are then of the form

$$\left(\frac{a_n}{z^n} + \frac{a_{n-1}}{z^{n-1}} + \cdots + \frac{a_1}{z^1} \right) dz$$

expressed in the local coordinate $z = x + iy$. On a compact surface S, a meromorphic differential can have only a finite number of singularities of this type. For locally $\omega = f(z) \, dz$, where $f(z)$ is an analytic function of z. If there were an infinite number of singular points, there would have to be a point of accumulation of singular points, at which f must have an essential singularity and not one of the prescribed type. We shall, in general, call a holomorphic or meromorphic differential on S an *abelian differential*.

In Chapter 8 we established the existence of abelian differentials having the singularity

$$\left(\frac{a_n}{z^n} + \cdots + \frac{a_2}{z^2} \right) dz, \quad n \geq 2,$$

at a single point of S, and differentials having the singularities $(a_1/z) \, dz$ at P and $(-a_1/z) \, dz$ at Q, where P and Q are two distinct points of S.

Let ω_1 and ω_2 be analytic differentials which have exactly the same singularities on S. Then $\varphi = \omega_1 - \omega_2$ is a holomorphic differential. If φ has A-periods $A_1, A_2, \ldots, A_g$, then $\varphi - A_1\varphi_1 - A_2\varphi_2 - \cdots - A_g\varphi_g$ has zero A-periods and must vanish identically. Then $\omega_1 = \omega_2 + A_1\varphi_1 + A_2\varphi_2 + \cdots + A_g\varphi_g$, and we see that the abelian differential ω_1 is completely determined by its singularities and its A-periods.

A meromorphic differential all of whose singularities are poles of order ≥ 2 will be called an abelian differential of the *second kind*. In other words, *a meromorphic differential all of whose residues are zero is called an abelian differential of the second kind*. The abelian differentials of the *third kind* are taken to be all abelian differentials on S. We observe that differentials of the second kind include those of the first kind and that those of the third kind include those of the first and second kind.

If ω is an abelian differential having A-periods $A_1, A_2, \ldots, A_g$, the differential

$$\omega' = \omega - A_1\varphi_1 - A_2\varphi_2 - \cdots - A_g\varphi_g$$

is an abelian differential having the same singularities as ω and with all its A-periods zero. We call such a differential with zero A-periods a *normalized* abelian differential. In particular, given any two points P_1 and P_2 on S, we can construct a normalized differential $\omega_{1,2}$ having the singularity $(1/z)\,dz$ at P_1 and $(-1/z)\,dz$ at P_2. This will be called a *normal differential of the third kind*.

An arbitrary abelian differential ω can be decomposed into a normalized differential of the second kind, a finite sum of normal differentials of the third kind, and a finite sum of differentials of the first kind, as follows. If ω has residues $c_1, c_2, \ldots, c_n$ at the points $P_1, P_2, \ldots, P_n$, we select a point P_0 on S, $P_0 \neq P_j, j = 1, \ldots, n$, and construct the normal differentials of the third kind $\omega_{1,0}, \omega_{2,0}, \ldots, \omega_{n,0}$. Since $\sum_{j=1}^n c_j = 0$, the differential $\sum_{j=1}^n c_j\omega_{j,0}$ is regular at P_0 and has residue c_j at P_j. If $\omega - \sum_{j=1}^n c_j\omega_{j,0}$ has A-periods $A_1, A_2, \ldots, A_g$, then

$$\omega_2 = \omega - \sum_{j=1}^n c_j\omega_{j,0} - \sum_{k=1}^g A_k\varphi_k$$

is a differential of the second kind with zero A-periods. Therefore

$$\omega = \omega_2 + \sum_{j=1}^n c_j\omega_{j,0} + \sum_{k=1}^g A_k\varphi_k$$

is the desired representation of an arbitrary abelian differential.

THEOREM 10–6. *Let ω_3 be a differential of the third kind whose only singularities are simple poles (poles of order 1) with residues c_i at P_i, $i = 1, 2, \ldots, m$, and let ω_1 be an arbitrary differential of the first kind. Select the canonical cycles $\mathbf{a}_1, \mathbf{b}_1, \ldots, \mathbf{a}_g, \mathbf{b}_g$ in such a way that no pole of ω_3 lies on any of the $\mathbf{a}_i$'s or $\mathbf{b}_i$'s. Then set $A_i = \int_{\mathbf{a}_i} \omega_1$, $B_i = \int_{\mathbf{b}_i} \omega_1$, $A'_i = \int_{\mathbf{a}_i} \omega_3$, and $B'_i = \int_{\mathbf{b}_i} \omega_3$, for $i = 1, 2, \ldots, g$. Fix a point P_0 in the normal polygon Π, and let L_i be a fixed path in Π from P_0 to P_i. Then*

$$\sum_{i=1}^g (A_iB'_i - B_iA'_i) = 2\pi i \sum_{k=1}^m c_k \int_{L_k} \omega_1. \qquad (1)$$

This is the *bilinear relation for abelian differentials of the first and third kinds*.

We remark first that the canonical cycles not passing through the poles of ω_3 can be found, since there are only a finite number of these poles. Let f be the holomorphic function defined in the simply connected region Π such that $\omega_1 = df$ in Π and, for the fixed point P_0 of Π, $f(P_0) = 0$. Then (1) of Section 10–2 tells us that

$$\sum_{i=1}^{g} (A_iB'_i - B_iA'_i) = \int_{\partial\Pi} f\omega_3 = 2\pi i \sum_{k=1}^{m} \mathrm{res}_{P_k}(f\omega_3),$$

where $\mathrm{res}_{P_k}(f\omega_3)$ denotes the residue of $f\omega_3$ at P_k. The residue of $f\omega_3$ at P_i is given by $f(P_i)c_i$, where $f(P_i) = \int_{L_i} \omega_1$, so that we have proved Theorem 10–6.

COROLLARY 10–3. *If ω_3 is a normalized differential of the third kind (all $A'_i = 0$) and $\omega_1 = \varphi_k$ is the differential of the first kind with period 1 on $\mathbf{a}_k$ and all other A-periods 0, then*

$$\int_{\mathbf{b}_k} \omega_3 = B'_k = 2\pi i \sum_{j=1}^{m} c_j \int_{L_j} \varphi_k,$$

where $c_j = \mathrm{res}_{P_j} \omega_3$.

COROLLARY 10–4. *If ω_3 is a normal differential of the third kind which has residue 1 at P and -1 at Q and no other poles, and if L_P and L_Q are paths lying in Π from P_0 to P and from P_0 to Q respectively, then*

$$\int_{\mathbf{b}_k} \omega_3 = B'_k = 2\pi i \left(\int_{L_P} \varphi_k - \int_{L_Q} \varphi_k \right) = -2\pi i \int_{P}^{Q} \varphi_k,$$

where the integral on the right is taken over a path from P to Q which does not cross any of the cycles $\mathbf{a}_i$, $\mathbf{b}_i$, $i = 1, \ldots, g$, and which therefore lies in Π.

If ω_3 once again represents an arbitrary differential of the third kind, we make one further remark about its periods. We triangulate Π so that the poles of ω_3 lie interior to the triangles with no more than one pole interior to each triangle. If γ^1 is a simplicial 1-cycle in this triangulation Δ, γ^1 is homologous to a linear combination over the integers of the $\mathbf{a}_i$ and $\mathbf{b}_i$. We have then

$$\gamma^1 = \sum_{i=1}^{g} k_i\mathbf{a}_i + k_{g+i}\mathbf{b}_i + \gamma_0^1,$$

where γ_0^1 is homologous to zero; that is, $\gamma_0^1 = \partial \sum_{j=1}^{N} m_j s_j^2$, for integers m_j and $s_j^2 \in \Delta$. Now

$$\int_{\gamma_0^1} \omega_3 = \sum_{j=1}^{N} m_j \int_{\partial s_j^2} \omega_3 = 2\pi i \sum_{j=1}^{N} m_j (\text{res } \omega_3 \text{ in } s_j^2).$$

If the 2-simplex s_j^2 contains the point P_l at which ω_3 has the residue c_l, we shall set $m_j = m'_l$, otherwise set $m_j = 0$. Then

$$\int_{\gamma_0^1} \omega_3 = 2\pi i \sum_{l=1}^{m} m'_l c_l.$$

Furthermore,

$$\int_{\sum_{i=1}^{g} k_i \mathbf{a}_i + k_{g+i} \mathbf{b}_i} \omega_3 = \sum_{i=1}^{g} k_i A'_i + k_{g+i} B'_i.$$

The period of ω_3 over γ^1 is then

$$\int_{\gamma^1} \omega_3 = \sum_{l=1}^{g} (k_l A'_l + k_{g+l} B'_l) + 2\pi i \sum_{j=1}^{m} m'_j c_j.$$

The A-periods and B-periods of ω_3 are referred to as the *cyclic periods* of ω_3, and the $2\pi i c_j$ which appear as periods of ω_3 over cycles homologous to zero are called *polar periods of ω_3*.

Let C be an arbitrary closed curve on the surface $S' = S - \{P_j\}_{j=1}^{m}$, so that on S, C does not pass through any of the poles of ω_3. We can put a parametric disk D_j about each of the points P_j such that $\overline{D}_j$ does not contain any points of C. We barycentrically subdivide the triangulation Δ of S (and hence of Π) so that all triangles of the subdivision Δ' which contain points of C do not meet any $\overline{D}_j$. By a slight modification of the edges of triangles in D_j, we can fix Δ' so that P_j is not on an edge or a vertex of Δ'. The homotopic deformation of C into a simplicial 1-cycle γ^1 in Δ' which we have defined does not move any point of C through any D_j, $j = 1, 2, \ldots, m$. Since ω_3 is a regular closed differential on S', we have

$$\int_C \omega_3 = \int_{\gamma^1} \omega_3 = \sum_{l=1}^{g} (k_l A'_l + k_{g+l} B'_l) + 2\pi i \sum_{j=1}^{m} m'_j c_j.$$

Therefore we have proved the following theorem.

THEOREM 10–7. *All periods of ω_3 are integral linear combinations of the cyclic periods and polar periods of ω_3.*

We next apply a similar argument to the differentials ω_1 of the first kind and ω_2 of the second kind. Let us assume that ω_2 has a single pole at

P_0 with principal part $(1/z^n)\, dz$ in a fixed local parameter $\Phi(P) = z$, $\Phi(P_0) = 0$. In this same local coordinate system, ω_1 has the representation

$$\omega_1 = (c_0 + c_1 z + c_2 z^2 + \cdots)\, dz.$$

Once again we shall set $A_i = \int_{\mathbf{a}_i} \omega_1$, $B_i = \int_{\mathbf{b}_i} \omega_1$, $A_i' = \int_{\mathbf{a}_i} \omega_2$, and $B_i' = \int_{\mathbf{b}_i} \omega_2$, and let $\omega_1 = df$ in Π. Then (1) of Section 10–2 yields

$$\Sigma(A_i B_i' - B_i A_i') = \int_{\partial\Pi} f\omega_2 = 2\pi i \operatorname{res}_{P_0} (f\omega_2).$$

Since

$$f(z) = c + c_0 z + \frac{c_1}{2} z^2 + \frac{c_2}{3} z^3 + \cdots + \frac{c_n}{n+1} z^{n+1} + \cdots$$

about P_0, the residue of $f\omega_2$ at P_0 is equal to $c_{n-2}/(n-1)$. Thus we have proved

THEOREM 10–8 (*Bilinear relations for differentials of the first and second kinds*). *Let ω_2 be a differential of the second kind whose only pole is at P_0 with principal part $(1/z^n)\, dz$. Let ω_1 be a differential of the first kind which has the representation $\omega_1 = (c_0 + c_1 z + c_2 z^2 + \cdots)\, dz$ about P_0. Let $A_i = \int_{\mathbf{a}_i} \omega_1$, $B_i = \int_{\mathbf{b}_i} \omega_1$, $A_i' = \int_{\mathbf{a}_i} \omega_2$, and $B_i' = \int_{\mathbf{b}_i} \omega_2$ for $i = 1, 2, \ldots, g$. Then*

$$\sum_{i=1}^{g} (A_j B_j' - B_j A_j') = 2\pi i \frac{c_{n-2}}{n-1}. \tag{2}$$

COROLLARY 10–5. *If ω_2 is a normalized differential of the second kind (all $A_i' = 0$) and if $\omega_1 = \varphi_k$ is the differential of the first kind which has period 1 on $\mathbf{a}_k$ and all other A-periods zero, then*

$$\int_{\mathbf{b}_k} \omega_2 = 2\pi i \frac{c_{n-2}^{(k)}}{n-1}, \tag{3}$$

where $\varphi_k = \left(\sum_{n=0}^{\infty} c_n^{(k)} z^n\right) dz$ and $\omega_2 = (1/z^n)\, dz$ about P_0.

If we take $n = 2$, so that ω_2 has the singularity $(1/z^2)\, dz$ at P_0, then $c_0^{(k)} = (df/dz)_{z=0} = (\varphi_k/dz)_{P_0}$, and we obtain

COROLLARY 10–6. *If ω_2 is a normalized differential of the second kind whose only pole is at P_0, at which $\omega_2 = (1/z^2)\, dz$, and if φ_k is a canonical differential of the first kind with period 1 on $\mathbf{a}_k$ and other A-periods zero, then*

$$\int_{\mathbf{b}_k} \omega_2 = 2\pi i \left(\frac{\varphi_k}{dz}\right)_{P_0} \tag{4}$$

Thus we have found expressions for the B-periods of normalized differentials of the second and third kinds in terms of the differentials of the first kind.

10–4 Divisors. The differentials of the second kind which we have discussed above have nonvanishing periods and are not exact. It is possible to find exact differentials of the second kind; for the ratio of any two abelian differentials is a meromorphic function f on S whose differential df is of the second kind. The difficulty with this construction is that we cannot specify the location of the singularities of f. We shall next study what freedom we enjoy in specifying the poles of a meromorphic function (exact differential of the second kind). That we are not completely free is demonstrated by the fact that there must be at least one pole, for we have shown that everywhere regular (nonconstant) analytic functions do not exist on compact Riemann surfaces.

To simplify the discussion, we shall introduce several new notations. If about a point P on S, the analytic function f has a series expansion $f(z) = a_n z^n + a_{n+1} z^{n+1} + \cdots$, $a_n \neq 0$, we say that n is the *order of f* at P and write $v_P(f) = n$. This notation comes from the term *valuation* of f at P commonly used in algebraic geometry. It is convenient to say that for $f \equiv 0$ on S, $v_P(f) = +\infty$. We have already seen that if coordinates are changed, $v_P(f)$ remains invariant. If f_1 and f_2 are analytic functions on S, then for the product $f_1(P)f_2(P)$ we immediately verify that $v_P(f_1 f_2) = v_P(f_1) + v_P(f_2)$ by multiplying the power series. Similarly, $v_P(f_1 + f_2) \geq$ min $\{v_P(f_1), v_P(f_2)\}$. For an analytic differential ω which locally appears as $\omega = (a_n z^n + a_{n+1} z^{n+1} + \cdots) \, dz$, $a_n \neq 0$, we say that the *order of ω* at P is equal to n and write $v_P(\omega) = n$.

We shall be interested in specifying the location and orders of the poles of the functions on S. This means that we want to designate several points $P_1, P_2, \ldots, P_n$ and associate orders $\alpha_1, \alpha_2, \ldots, \alpha_n$ to these points. We shall use the symbol

$$P_1^{\alpha_1} P_2^{\alpha_2} \ldots P_n^{\alpha_n}$$

to denote the points $P_1, P_2, \ldots, P_n$ with the associated integers $\alpha_1, \alpha_2, \ldots, \alpha_n$. The symbol $P_1^{\alpha_1} P_2^{\alpha_2} \ldots P_n^{\alpha_n}$ is called a *divisor* and will be denoted by lower-case German letters $\mathfrak{a} = P_1^{\alpha_1} P_2^{\alpha_2} \ldots P_n^{\alpha_n}$. The integer α_k is called the *order* of the divisor $\mathfrak{a}$ at P_k and will also be denoted by $v_{P_k}(\mathfrak{a}) = \alpha_k$. By the *degree* $d[\mathfrak{a}]$ of a divisor $\mathfrak{a}$, we mean the sum of the orders of $\mathfrak{a}$ or simply

$$d[\mathfrak{a}] = \sum_{k=1}^{n} \alpha_k.$$

The product of two divisors $\mathfrak{a} = P_1^{\alpha_1} P_2^{\alpha_2} \ldots P_n^{\alpha_n}$ and $\mathfrak{b} = Q_1^{\beta_1} Q_2^{\beta_2} \ldots Q_m^{\beta_m}$ is defined to be

$$\mathfrak{a}\mathfrak{b} = P_1^{\alpha_1} P_2^{\alpha_2} \ldots P_n^{\alpha_n} Q_1^{\beta_1} Q_2^{\beta_2} \ldots Q_m^{\beta_m},$$

where we further ask that multiplication be commutative ($P_i^{\alpha_i} Q_j^{\beta_j} = Q_j^{\beta_j} P_i^{\alpha_i}$) and that it satisfy $P_1^{\alpha} P_1^{\beta} = P_1^{\alpha+\beta}$. Similarly, we define

$$\mathfrak{a}^{-1} = \frac{1}{\mathfrak{a}} = P_1^{-\alpha_1} P_2^{-\alpha_2} \ldots P_n^{-\alpha_n}$$

and take as the quotient of the two divisors $\mathfrak{a}$ and $\mathfrak{b}$ the divisor $\mathfrak{a}/\mathfrak{b} = \mathfrak{a}\mathfrak{b}^{-1}$. It follows immediately from these definitions that $d[\mathfrak{a} \cdot \mathfrak{b}] = d[\mathfrak{a}] + d[\mathfrak{b}]$ and $d[\mathfrak{a}/\mathfrak{b}] = d[\mathfrak{a}] - d[\mathfrak{b}]$. For completeness, we shall denote by 1 the divisor that has order 0 at each point, so that $\mathfrak{a}/\mathfrak{a} = 1$.

We shall call a divisor $\mathfrak{a} = P_1^{\alpha_1} P_2^{\alpha_2} \ldots P_n^{\alpha_n}$ *integral* if $\alpha_k \geq 0$ for $k = 1, 2, \ldots, n$. If the divisor $\mathfrak{a}/\mathfrak{b}$ is integral, we say that $\mathfrak{b}$ *divides* $\mathfrak{a}$ and write $\mathfrak{b}|\mathfrak{a}$, or that $\mathfrak{a}$ is a *multiple* of $\mathfrak{b}$. Two integral divisors are *relatively prime* if there is no integral divisor which divides both of them.

If f is a meromorphic function not identically zero on S and ω is an abelian differential ($\omega \not\equiv 0$) on S, we define the divisor (f) of f to be

$$(f) = \prod_{P \in S} P^{v_P(f)}$$

and the divisor (ω) of ω to be

$$(\omega) = \prod_{P \in S} P^{v_P(\omega)}.$$

For two meromorphic functions f_1 and f_2, the fact that $v_P(f_1 f_2) = v_P(f_1) + v_P(f_2)$ implies that $(f_1)(f_2) = (f_1 f_2)$, and similarly $(f\omega) = (f)(\omega)$. If $f \equiv c = $ constant, $c \neq 0$, we have $(f) = 1$. We shall say that f is a multiple of the divisor $\mathfrak{a}$ if $\mathfrak{a} | (f)$ so that $v_{P_i}(f) \geq v_{P_i}(\mathfrak{a})$ for each P_i in $\mathfrak{a}$.

At the end of Chapter 6 we showed that for a meromorphic function on a compact Riemann surface, the sum of the orders of its zeros is equal to the sum of the orders of its poles. Thus $d[(f)] = 0$ *for any meromorphic function* f. We see that not all divisors are divisors of meromorphic functions. We shall call the divisors of meromorphic functions (not $\equiv 0$) the *principal divisors*.

The set of all divisors forms a commutative group with the multiplication, identity, and inverses we have defined. If $\mathfrak{a} = (f)$ and $\mathfrak{b} = (g)$, then $\mathfrak{a}^{-1} = (1/f)$ and $\mathfrak{a}\mathfrak{b} = (fg)$, so that the principal divisors form a subgroup of the group of all divisors and we may form the quotient group of the group of all divisors over the subgroup of principal divisors. Each element of the quotient group is a coset of divisors such that $\mathfrak{a}$ and $\mathfrak{b}$ are in the same coset ($\mathfrak{a} \sim \mathfrak{b}$) if and only if $\mathfrak{a}/\mathfrak{b} = (f)$ for some meromorphic function f on S. We call each such coset of divisors a *divisor class*. Clearly if $\mathfrak{a} \sim \mathfrak{b}$, then $d[\mathfrak{a}/\mathfrak{b}] = d[(f)] = 0$ or $d[\mathfrak{a}] = d[\mathfrak{b}]$. If $\mathfrak{a} \sim \mathfrak{b}$, we say that $\mathfrak{a}$ is *equivalent* to $\mathfrak{b}$.

If ω_1 and ω_2 are any two abelian differentials on S, ω_1/ω_2 is a meromorphic function and hence $(\omega_1) \sim (\omega_2)$. Thus the divisors of all differentials are in the same divisor class. The degree of the divisor (ω) of an abelian differential therefore does not depend upon ω but rather upon the surface S alone. We shall prove later that $d[(\omega)] = 2g - 2$.

Our interest will now be directed toward specifying a divisor $\mathfrak{a}$ and determining whether there are any meromorphic functions on S which are multiples of $\mathfrak{a}$. In particular, *we shall denote by $L(\mathfrak{a})$ the set of meromorphic functions on S which are multiples of the divisor* $\mathfrak{a}$. Thus if $v_P(\mathfrak{a}) = n$, then about P, $f(z) = a_k z^k + a_{k+1} z^{k+1} + \cdots$, $k \geq n$. For any complex constant λ, $\lambda f \in L(\mathfrak{a})$ whenever $f \in L(\mathfrak{a})$, and since

$$v_P(f_1 + f_2) \geq \min \{v_P(f_1), v_P(f_2)\},$$

$f_1 + f_2 \in L(\mathfrak{a})$ whenever f_1 and f_2 are in $L(\mathfrak{a})$. Thus $L(\mathfrak{a})$ *is a complex vector space. We denote by $r[\mathfrak{a}]$ the dimension of $L(\mathfrak{a})$*, that is, the number of linearly independent functions in $L(\mathfrak{a})$ over the complex numbers. If $\mathfrak{a} | \mathfrak{b}$, then $v_P(\mathfrak{a}) \leq v_P(\mathfrak{b})$, so that $L(\mathfrak{b}) \subseteq L(\mathfrak{a})$ and $r[\mathfrak{a}] \geq r[\mathfrak{b}]$. If $\mathfrak{a} = 1$, $v_P(1) = 0$ for all P and the only functions f satisfying $v_P(f) \geq 0$ for all P are the constant functions. Thus $L(1)$ is the 1-dimensional vector space of complex numbers and $r[1] = 1$. If $d[\mathfrak{a}] > 0$, then $d[(f)] > 0$ would have to hold for any $f \in L(\mathfrak{a})$; but we know that $d[(f)] = 0$, so $L(\mathfrak{a}) = 0$ if $d[\mathfrak{a}] > 0$. Knowing $r[\mathfrak{a}]$ will enable us to know not only whether any functions exist which are multiples of $\mathfrak{a}$ but also how many linearly independent such functions there are.

Another vector space which will play an important role is the space $\Omega(\mathfrak{a})$ consisting of those abelian differentials ω whose divisors (ω) are multiples of $\mathfrak{a}$. *We shall denote by $i[\mathfrak{a}]$ the dimension of the space $\Omega(\mathfrak{a})$*. We shall now prove that $i[\mathfrak{a}]$ and $r[\mathfrak{a}]$ depend only upon the divisor class of $\mathfrak{a}$. Indeed, if $\mathfrak{a} \sim \mathfrak{b}$, then $\mathfrak{a}/\mathfrak{b} = (h)$ for some meromorphic function h. For each $g \in L(\mathfrak{b})$, we know that $(g)/\mathfrak{b}$ is an integral divisor and hence $(gh) = ((g)/\mathfrak{b})\mathfrak{a}$ is a multiple of $\mathfrak{a}$, so $gh \in L(\mathfrak{a})$. The mapping $g \to gh$ gives us a linear mapping of $L(\mathfrak{b})$ into $L(\mathfrak{a})$. This mapping is *onto*, for each $f \in L(\mathfrak{a})$ is the image of $f/h \in L(\mathfrak{b})$; and it is one-to-one, since $gh \equiv 0$ implies $g \equiv 0$. Thus $r[\mathfrak{a}] = r[\mathfrak{b}]$ if $\mathfrak{a} \sim \mathfrak{b}$. Similarly, if $\omega \in \Omega(\mathfrak{b})$, $h\omega \in \Omega(\mathfrak{a})$, so that $\omega \to h\omega$ is a linear mapping of $\Omega(\mathfrak{b}) \to \Omega(\mathfrak{a})$, which is also one-to-one and onto, proving that $i[\mathfrak{a}] = i[\mathfrak{b}]$ if $\mathfrak{a} \sim \mathfrak{b}$.

We summarize the results of the preceding paragraphs in the following lemma.

LEMMA 10–1. *$d[\mathfrak{a}]$, $r[\mathfrak{a}]$, and $i[\mathfrak{a}]$ depend only upon the divisor class of $\mathfrak{a}$.*

THEOREM 10–9. *If ω is any abelian differential, $\omega \not\equiv 0$, then*

$$i[\mathfrak{a}] = r\left[\frac{\mathfrak{a}}{(\omega)}\right] \tag{1}$$

for any divisor $\mathfrak{a}$.

For let $\pi \in \Omega(\mathfrak{a})$. Then $(\pi)/\mathfrak{a}$ is integral and

$$\left(\frac{\pi}{\omega}\right) = \frac{(\pi)}{\mathfrak{a}} \frac{\mathfrak{a}}{(\omega)}$$

is a multiple of $\mathfrak{a}/(\omega)$. The function $\pi/\omega \in L(\mathfrak{a}/(\omega))$, so that $\pi \to \pi/\omega$ is a linear mapping of $\Omega(\mathfrak{a}) \to L(\mathfrak{a}/(\omega))$, which is clearly one-to-one and onto, proving our statement.

10–5 The Riemann-Roch theorem

THEOREM 10–10 (*Riemann-Roch theorem*). *Let S be a compact Riemann surface of genus g. Given a divisor $\mathfrak{a}$ of degree $d[\mathfrak{a}]$, we shall denote by $r[\mathfrak{a}^{-1}]$ the dimension of the vector space $L(\mathfrak{a}^{-1})$ of meromorphic functions which are multiples of $\mathfrak{a}^{-1}$, and we shall denote by $i[\mathfrak{a}]$ the dimension of the vector space of abelian differentials which are multiples of $\mathfrak{a}$. Then*

$$r[\mathfrak{a}^{-1}] = d[\mathfrak{a}] + i[\mathfrak{a}] - g + 1. \tag{1}$$

We shall first prove this theorem for the case in which $\mathfrak{a}$ is an integral divisor and later remove this restriction. Then $\mathfrak{a} = P_1^{n_1} P_2^{n_2} \ldots P_m^{n_m}$, $n_k > 0$, $k = 1, 2, \ldots, m$. Let $\omega_k^{(n)}$ be the normalized differential of the second kind which has principal part $1/z^n$ at P_k and is otherwise regular. If $f \in L(\mathfrak{a}^{-1})$, then df is a differential of the second kind, and at P_k, using the same local parameter as we did to express $\omega_k^{(n)}$, we have

$$df = \left(\sum_{j=-n_k-1}^{\infty} c_j^{(k)} z^j\right) dz, \quad c_{-1}^{(k)} = 0.$$

The differential

$$\omega_k = c_{-n_k-1}^{(k)} \omega_k^{(n_k+1)} + c_{-n_k}^{(k)} \omega_k^{(n_k)} + \cdots + c_{-2}^{(k)} \omega_k^{(2)}$$

has the same principal part at P_k as does df, so

$$\varphi = df - \sum_{k=1}^{m} \omega_k = df - \sum_{k=1}^{m} \sum_{j=2}^{n_k+1} c_{-j}^{(k)}\omega_k^{(j)} \qquad (2)$$

is a differential of the first kind. Furthermore, if the set of numbers $\{c_{-j}^{(k)}\}$, $k = 1, 2, \ldots, m$, $j = 2, \ldots, n_k + 1$, is given, and if we can find a differential of the first kind φ such that

$$\omega = \varphi + \sum_{k=1}^{m} \sum_{j=2}^{n_k+1} c_{-j}^{(k)}\omega_k^{(j)}$$

is exact, then $\omega = df$ and $f \in L(\mathfrak{a}^{-1})$.

The set of complex numbers $\{c_{-j}^{(k)}\}$, $k = 1, \ldots, m$, $j = 2, \ldots, n_k + 1$, may be viewed as elements in a complex vector space V; for if $\{c_{-j}^{(k)}\}$ and $\{d_{-j}^{(k)}\}$ are two sets corresponding to differentials of functions in $L(\mathfrak{a}^{-1})$, then $\{\lambda c_{-j}^{(k)} + \mu d_{-j}^{(k)}\}$ is also a set corresponding to the differential of a function in $L(\mathfrak{a}^{-1})$. To each function $f \in L(\mathfrak{a}^{-1})$ corresponds a set of complex numbers $\{c_{-j}^{(k)}\}$, $k = 1, \ldots, m$, $j = 2, \ldots, n_k + 1$, and if two functions f_1 and f_2 in $L(\mathfrak{a}^{-1})$ correspond to the same set $\{c_{-j}^{(k)}\}$, then f_1 and f_2 differ by a constant. Thus we have a linear mapping of $L(\mathfrak{a}^{-1})$ onto V whose kernel consists of the constant functions on S (a space of dimension 1). Thus

$$r\left[\frac{1}{\mathfrak{a}}\right] = \dim L\left(\frac{1}{\mathfrak{a}}\right) = \dim V + 1.$$

Our job now is to compute $\dim V$.

If $\{c_{-j}^{(k)}\}$, $k = 1, \ldots, m$, $j = 2, \ldots, n_k + 1$, is an element of V, then according to (2), $\sigma = \sum_{k=1}^{m} \sum_{j=2}^{n_k+1} c_{-j}^{(k)}\omega_k^{(j)}$ has the same periods as a differential φ of the first kind. Conversely, if σ has the same periods as a differential of the first kind, then $\{c_{-j}^{(k)}\} \in V$. If the period of $\omega_k^{(j)}$ on $\mathbf{b}_l$ is $B_{k,l}^{(j)}$, the period of σ on $\mathbf{b}_l$ is given by $B_l = \sum_{k=1}^{m} \sum_{j=2}^{n_k+1} c_{-j}^{(k)} B_{k,l}^{(j)}$. If σ has the same periods as a differential of the first kind φ, the vanishing of all its A-periods implies that $\varphi \equiv 0$. Then $B_l = 0$, $l = 1, \ldots, g$, or

$$\sum_{k=1}^{m} \sum_{j=2}^{n_k+1} c_{-j}^{(k)} B_{k,l}^{(j)} = 0, \quad l = 1, 2, \ldots, g. \qquad (3)$$

Conversely, if the $\{c_{-j}^{(k)}\}$ satisfy such a system of linear equations, the σ constructed with the $c_{-j}^{(k)}$'s has vanishing periods and is exact; so $\{c_{-j}^{(k)}\} \in V$. This gives us as a necessary and sufficient condition for $\{c_{-j}^{(k)}\}$ to belong to V that the $\{c_{-j}^{(k)}\}$ satisfy the system of equations (3).

The problem now is to find the number of linearly independent $\{c^{(k)}_{-j}\}$ satisfying (3). There are g equations for the $d[\mathfrak{a}]$ unknowns $\{c^{(k)}_{-j}\}$. Thus there are at least $d[\mathfrak{a}] - g$ linearly independent solutions, and dim $V \geq d[\mathfrak{a}] - g$ or

$$r\left[\frac{1}{\mathfrak{a}}\right] \geq d[\mathfrak{a}] - g + 1. \tag{4}$$

This is the *Riemann inequality*, which tells us that the number of linearly independent meromorphic functions having poles of order at most n_k at the m distinct points P_k, $k = 1, 2, \ldots, m$, is at least $\sum_{k=1}^{m} n_k - g + 1$. Thus we are assured of at least one nonconstant meromorphic function on S which has poles of order at most 1 at $g + 1$ distinct points of S.

To get the correction term in (4) to give us an exact expression for $r[\mathfrak{a}^{-1}]$, we observe that the system of equations (3) has as its matrix

$$\begin{bmatrix} B^{(2)}_{1,1} & B^{(3)}_{1,1} & \cdots & B^{n_1+1}_{1,1} & B^{(2)}_{2,1} & \cdots & B^{n_m+1}_{m,1} \\ B^{(2)}_{1,2} & B^{(3)}_{1,2} & \cdots & B^{n_1+1}_{1,2} & B^{(2)}_{2,2} & \cdots & B^{n_m+1}_{m,2} \\ \vdots & \vdots & & \vdots & \vdots & & \vdots \\ B^{(2)}_{1,g} & B^{(3)}_{1,g} & \cdots & B^{n_1+1}_{1,g} & B^{(2)}_{2,g} & \cdots & B^{n_m+1}_{m,g} \end{bmatrix} = (B^{(j)}_{k,l}). \tag{5}$$

If $(B^{(j)}_{k,l})$ has row rank ρ (that is, ρ linearly independent rows, which implies also ρ linearly independent columns) then only ρ of the equations (3) are linearly independent and we can find exactly $d[\mathfrak{a}] - \rho$ linearly independent solutions for the $\{c^{(k)}_{-j}\}$. Thus

$$r\left[\frac{1}{\mathfrak{a}}\right] = d[\mathfrak{a}] - \rho + 1.$$

We next give ρ an interpretation in terms of the differentials of the first kind. Let φ_l be the differential of the first kind in the canonical basis which has period 1 on $\mathbf{a}_l$ and all other A-periods zero, and let the series expansion of φ_l at P_k be

$$\varphi_l = (\alpha^{(k)}_{l,0} + \alpha^{(k)}_{l,1}z + \alpha^{(k)}_{l,2}z^2 + \cdots)\, dz$$

in terms of the same local parameter in which $\omega^{(n)}_k$ has the expansion $(1/z^n)\, dz$. Then, according to (3) of Section 10–3,

$$B^{(j)}_{k,l} = 2\pi i\, \frac{\alpha^{(k)}_{l,j-2}}{j - 1}.$$

We then know that the matrix

$$
\begin{bmatrix}
\alpha_{1,0}^{(1)} & \frac{1}{2}\alpha_{1,1}^{(1)} & \cdots & \frac{1}{n_1}\alpha_{1,n_1-1}^{(1)} & \alpha_{1,0}^{(2)} & \cdots & \frac{1}{n_m}\alpha_{1,n_m-1}^{(m)} \\
\alpha_{2,0}^{(1)} & \frac{1}{2}\alpha_{2,1}^{(1)} & \cdots & \frac{1}{n_1}\alpha_{2,n_1-1}^{(1)} & \alpha_{2,0}^{(2)} & \cdots & \frac{1}{n_m}\alpha_{2,n_m-1}^{(m)} \\
\vdots & \vdots & & \vdots & \vdots & & \vdots \\
\alpha_{g,0}^{(1)} & \frac{1}{2}\alpha_{g,1}^{(1)} & \cdots & \frac{1}{n_1}\alpha_{g,n_1-1}^{(1)} & \alpha_{g,0}^{(2)} & \cdots & \frac{1}{n_m}\alpha_{g,n_m-1}^{(m)}
\end{bmatrix}
= (B_{k,l}^{(j)})
$$

also has column rank ρ, so that there are $g - \rho$ linearly independent vectors $(e_1, e_2, \ldots, e_g)$ such that $\sum_{l=1}^{g} e_l \alpha_{l,j}^{(k)} = 0$, for $j = 0, 1, \ldots, n_k - 1$, $k = 1, \ldots, m$. But there is a one-to-one correspondence between such vectors $(e_1, e_2, \ldots, e_g)$ and differentials of the first kind $\varphi = \sum_{l=1}^{g} e_l \varphi_l$, which have order $\geq n_k$ at P_k, so that $\mathfrak{a}|(\varphi)$. Thus there are exactly $g - \rho$ linearly independent differentials of the first kind which are multiples of the divisor $\mathfrak{a}$, so that $g - \rho = i[\mathfrak{a}]$, and we have proved the Riemann-Roch theorem for integral divisors $\mathfrak{a}$.

We shall use the following important fact in order to complete the proof of the Riemann-Roch theorem for arbitrary divisors.

THEOREM 10–11. *For any abelian differential ω*

$$
d[(\omega)] = 2g - 2. \tag{6}
$$

If $g > 0$, let $\varphi_1, \varphi_2, \ldots, \varphi_g$ be a basis for the differentials of the first kind. The divisor (φ_1) is an integral divisor, so (1) holds and

$$
r\left[\frac{1}{(\varphi_1)}\right] = d[(\varphi_1)] - g + 1 + i[(\varphi_1)].
$$

If ω_1 is any other abelian differential which is a multiple of (φ_1), ω_1/φ_1 is a function with no singularities on the compact surface S and is hence a constant. Thus $\omega_1 = c\varphi_1$ and $i[(\varphi_1)] = 1$. Furthermore, $r[(\varphi_1)^{-1}] = g$, for

$$
\frac{\varphi_1}{\varphi_1}, \frac{\varphi_2}{\varphi_1}, \ldots, \frac{\varphi_g}{\varphi_1}
$$

are g linearly independent functions which are multiples of $1/(\varphi_1)$. If f is a multiple of $1/(\varphi_1)$, then $f\varphi_1$ is a differential of the first kind and $f\varphi_1 = c_1\varphi_1 + c_2\varphi_2 + \cdots + c_g\varphi_g$, or

$$
f = c_1 \frac{\varphi_1}{\varphi_1} + c_2 \frac{\varphi_2}{\varphi_1} + \cdots + c_g \frac{\varphi_g}{\varphi_1}.
$$

Thus $g = d[(\varphi_1)] - g + 1 + 1$ or $d[(\varphi_1)] = 2g - 2$. Since, according to lemma 10–1, the degree of any abelian differential ω on S is the same, we conclude that $d[(\omega)] = 2g - 2$.

There still remains the case of genus zero. Here every differential of the second kind is exact, since its only periods would be polar periods and all residues are zero. Thus we may construct a differential ω of the second kind with only one pole $d(1/z)$ at P_0. Then $\omega = df$ and f has only a simple pole $1/z$ at P_0. Since f takes on every complex value the same number of times as it does infinity, f gives us a one-to-one conformal mapping of S onto the w-sphere, with $P_0 \to w = \infty$. We may therefore use $w = f(P)$ as a uniformizing parameter at all points of S except at P_0. Then dw has no zeros and has a pole of order 2 at P_0, so that $d[(\omega)] = -2$, which is (6) for $g = 0$.

Let us return to the Riemann-Roch theorem for an arbitrary divisor $\mathfrak{a}$. If (ω) is the divisor of an abelian differential ω, then $i[\mathfrak{a}] = r[\mathfrak{a}/(\omega)]$ for any divisor $\mathfrak{a}$, according to (1) of Section 10–4. Also, $d[\mathfrak{a}^{-1}] = -d[\mathfrak{a}]$, $d[\mathfrak{a}/(\omega)] = d[\mathfrak{a}] - d[(\omega)]$, and $d[(\omega)] = 2g - 2$, so that (1) may be rewritten to read

$$r\left[\frac{1}{\mathfrak{a}}\right] + \frac{1}{2}d\left[\frac{1}{\mathfrak{a}}\right] = r\left[\frac{\mathfrak{a}}{(\omega)}\right] + \frac{1}{2}d\left[\frac{\mathfrak{a}}{(\omega)}\right]. \tag{7}$$

The statement (7) is unchanged if $\mathfrak{a}$ is replaced by $(\omega)/\mathfrak{a}$, so (7) has been proved true for any divisor $\mathfrak{a}$ such that either $\mathfrak{a}$ or $(\omega)/\mathfrak{a}$ is an integral divisor. Furthermore, i, r, and d each depend only upon the divisor class of a divisor; therefore the Riemann-Roch theorem holds for any divisor which is equivalent to a divisor $\mathfrak{a}$ such that $\mathfrak{a}$ or $(\omega)/\mathfrak{a}$ is integral.

If neither $\mathfrak{a}$ nor $(\omega)/\mathfrak{a}$ is integral, then $r[\mathfrak{a}^{-1}] = 0$ and $i[\mathfrak{a}] = r[\mathfrak{a}/(\omega)] = 0$. For in general, if $r[\mathfrak{b}] \neq 0$ for a divisor $\mathfrak{b}$, there is a meromorphic function $f \in L(\mathfrak{b})$, and $\mathfrak{c} = (f)/\mathfrak{b}$ is an integral divisor. Then $\mathfrak{c}/\mathfrak{b}^{-1} = (f)$, or $1/\mathfrak{b} \sim \mathfrak{c}$. We see that if $r[\mathfrak{b}] \neq 0$, then $1/\mathfrak{b}$ is equivalent to an integral divisor. As a consequence, the Riemann-Roch theorem for a divisor $\mathfrak{a}$ such that neither $\mathfrak{a}$ nor $(\omega)/\mathfrak{a}$ is integral reads $d[\mathfrak{a}] = g - 1$, which is all that remains to be proved.

We may now assume that $r[\mathfrak{a}^{-1}] = 0$ and $r[\mathfrak{a}/(\omega)] = i[\mathfrak{a}] = 0$, and prove $d[\mathfrak{a}] = g - 1$. Let $\mathfrak{a} = \mathfrak{b}/\mathfrak{c}$, where $\mathfrak{b}$ and $\mathfrak{c}$ are integral and relatively prime. Then $d[\mathfrak{a}] = d[\mathfrak{b}] - d[\mathfrak{c}]$ and

$$r\left[\frac{1}{\mathfrak{b}}\right] \geq d[\mathfrak{b}] - g + 1 = d[\mathfrak{c}] + d[\mathfrak{a}] - g + 1.$$

Therefore, if $d[\mathfrak{a}] \geq g$, we would also have

$$r\left[\frac{1}{\mathfrak{b}}\right] \geq d[\mathfrak{c}] + 1.$$

Assume that $c = Q_1^{n_1} \ldots Q_k^{n_k}$; then the condition that a meromorphic function f have zeros of order n_j at each Q_j gives rise to $d[c]$ linear relations. Since there are at least $d[c] + 1$ linearly independent functions in $L(\mathfrak{b}^{-1})$, each regular at the points Q_j, $j = 1, 2, \ldots, k$, there is one such $f \in L(\mathfrak{b}^{-1})$ which does satisfy $v_{P_j}(f) \geq n_j$, $j = 1, \ldots, k$. Consequently, $f \in L(c/\mathfrak{b}) = L(\mathfrak{a}^{-1})$. But, by hypothesis, $r[\mathfrak{a}^{-1}] = 0$, which is a contradiction proving that for any divisor $\mathfrak{a}$ with $r[\mathfrak{a}^{-1}] = 0$, $d[\mathfrak{a}] < g$. Then $r[\mathfrak{a}/(\omega)] = 0$ implies that $d[(\omega)/\mathfrak{a}] < g$, or $d[(\omega)] - d[\mathfrak{a}] < g$. Since $d[(\omega)] = 2g - 2$, we have $d[\mathfrak{a}] > g - 2$. Therefore $d[\mathfrak{a}] = g - 1$, completing the proof of the Riemann-Roch theorem.

The Riemann-Roch theorem tells us something about the existence of meromorphic functions with prescribed singularities on a compact Riemann surface. A word should be said here about the problem for open (non-compact) Riemann surfaces. For the finite plane (once-punctured sphere) the Mittag-Leffler theorem says that we may prescribe the principal parts of the poles at an arbitrary sequence of points with no finite cluster point and there will always exist a meromorphic function with precisely the prescribed singularities. Behnke and Stein (Ref. 7) have proved the analogous theorem on an arbitrary noncompact Riemann surface S; that is, if one arbitrarily prescribes the principal parts of poles on any sequence of points with no cluster point on S, there exists a meromorphic function on S with precisely these singularities. For an easily accessible proof of this theorem, the reader is referred to the book by Behnke and Sommer (Ref. 6, pp. 555–567).

10–6 Weierstrass points. We shall now draw some immediate consequences from the Riemann-Roch theorem.

If $g = 1$, the surface S is topologically a torus. In this case, for any abelian differential ω, $d[(\omega)] = 2g - 2 = 0$, and any differential must have as many zeros as poles. In particular, a differential of the first kind has no poles and hence no zeros. If we specify the divisor $\mathfrak{a} = P$ for an arbitrary point P, the Riemann-Roch theorem says that $r[P^{-1}] = 1$, since $d[P] = 1$ and $i[P] = 0$. Since the constant functions are in $L(P^{-1})$ and themselves form a 1-dimensional subspace, we see that $L(P^{-1})$ consists only of constant functions. Therefore, we have proved

THEOREM 10–12. *A function cannot have a single simple pole on a surface of genus one (a torus).*

If $d[\mathfrak{a}] > 2g - 2$, then $i[\mathfrak{a}] = 0$, for we know that for any differential ω, $d[(\omega)] = 2g - 2$, whereas for ω to belong to $\Omega(\mathfrak{a})$, we would have to have $d[(\omega)] > 2g - 2$. Thus for $d[\mathfrak{a}] > 2g - 2$, the Riemann-Roch theorem reads $r[\mathfrak{a}] = d[\mathfrak{a}] - g + 1$, giving us equality in the Riemann inequality.

THEOREM 10–13. *If $g > 0$, there is no point P on S at which all differentials of the first kind vanish, so that $i[P] < g$.*

For if, on the contrary, $v_P(\omega) > 0$ for all $\omega \neq 0$, we have $i[P] = g$ and $r[P^{-1}] = d[P] + 1 = 2$. This means that there is a nonconstant meromorphic function f with a simple pole at P. Thus f assumes every complex number as a value exactly once and gives us a one-to-one conformal mapping of S onto the sphere. Since this mapping is topological, the genus of S must be the same as that of the sphere, that is, $g = 0$, which is a contradiction proving that if $g > 0$, $i[P] \leq g - 1$. Now if $\mathfrak{a}$ is an integral divisor and $\mathfrak{a} \neq 1$, then there is some P such that $P|\mathfrak{a}$ and hence $\Omega(\mathfrak{a}) \subseteq \Omega(P)$. We then have $i[\mathfrak{a}] < g$ if $g > 0$ and since there are no differentials of the first kind for $q = 0$, $i[\mathfrak{a}] = 0$ if $g = 0$. Consequently,

THEOREM 10–14. *If $\mathfrak{a}$ is an integral divisor, then*

$$r\left[\frac{1}{\mathfrak{a}}\right] \leq d[\mathfrak{a}] + 1$$

with equality holding if and only if $g = 0$, the only case when $i[\mathfrak{a}] = g$.

Let us investigate more closely the conditions under which $i[\mathfrak{a}] = 0$ so that

$$r\left[\frac{1}{\mathfrak{a}}\right] = d[\mathfrak{a}] - g + 1.$$

We have for any integral divisor $r[\mathfrak{a}^{-1}] \geq 1$, so that $d[\mathfrak{a}] + i[\mathfrak{a}] - g \geq 0$. If $\mathfrak{a} = P_1 P_2 \dots P_n$ for the n distinct points $P_1, P_2, \dots, P_n$, then $d[\mathfrak{a}] = n$ and we conclude that $i[\mathfrak{a}] \geq g - n$. This relationship is interesting only when $n \leq g$ since $i[\mathfrak{a}] \geq 0$ for all $\mathfrak{a}$. With the assumption that $n \leq g$, look at $i[P_1]$. We have seen above that $i[P_1] \leq g - 1$, which together with our present inequality gives $i[P_1] = g - 1$ for any point P_1 on S, $g \geq 1$. Next, we know that $\Omega(P_1 P_2) \subseteq \Omega(P_1)$, and if $i[P_1 P_2] = g - 1$, then $g - 1$ linearly independent differentials in $\Omega(P_1)$ vanish at P_2. But these form a basis for $\Omega(P_1)$, so that each differential in $\Omega(P_1)$ would vanish at P_2. If $g \geq 2$, there is at least one differential φ in $\Omega(P_1)$ which is not identically zero. Let P_2 be taken as a point where φ is not zero. Then $i[P_1 P_2] \leq g - 2$, which actually means that $i[P_1 P_2] = g - 2$. Repeating this argument n times gives the result that if $g \geq n$, there exist n distinct points $P_1 P_2 \dots P_n$ on S such that $i[P_1 P_2 \dots P_n] = g - n$. In particular, there exist g distinct points on S such that $i[P_1 P_2 \dots P_g] = 0$ and consequently

$$r\left[\frac{1}{P_1 P_2 \dots P_g}\right] = 1.$$

Therefore,

THEOREM 10–15. *It is possible to find g distinct points on a surface of genus g such that there does not exist any nonconstant meromorphic function whose only singularities are poles of order at most 1 at the points $P_1, P_2, \ldots, P_g$.*

On the other hand, if $d[\mathfrak{a}] > g$, we have $r[\mathfrak{a}^{-1}] \geq 2$. Consequently,

THEOREM 10–16. *When $d[\mathfrak{a}] > g$, there do exist nonconstant meromorphic functions in $L(\mathfrak{a}^{-1})$.*

Let Ω_2 represent the vector space over the complex number field of the differentials of the second kind on S, and let Ω_e represent the subspace of Ω_2 consisting of exact differentials of the second kind. Then the quotient group Ω_2/Ω_e is also a vector space, and we now prove

THEOREM 10–17. *If S is of genus g, the dimension of Ω_2/Ω_e is equal to $2g$.*

Any differential in Ω_2 with zero A- and B-periods is in Ω_e. To each coset of $\Omega_2 \pmod{\Omega_e}$ corresponds a $2g$-tuple of numbers $(A_1, A_2, \ldots, A_g, B_1, B_2, \ldots, B_g)$ consisting of the A- and B-periods of a representative of the coset. The A-periods (B-periods) are linear functions of the cosets of $\Omega_2 \pmod{\Omega_e}$ so that Ω_2/Ω_e is isomorphic to a subspace of the $2g$-dimensional space of $2g$-tuples, and $\dim \Omega_2/\Omega_e \leq 2g$. To show equality, we select g points $P_1, P_2, \ldots, P_g$ on S such that $i[P_1 P_2 \ldots P_g] = 0$. There is, then, no nonconstant meromorphic function on S having as its only singularities poles of order at most 1 at $P_1, P_2, \ldots, P_g$. We can construct differentials $\omega_1, \omega_2, \ldots, \omega_g \in \Omega_2$ such that the only singularity of ω_j is a pole of order 2 at P_j. Also let $\varphi_1, \varphi_2, \ldots, \varphi_g$ be a canonical basis for the differentials of the first kind. Then $\omega_1, \ldots, \omega_g, \varphi_1, \ldots, \varphi_g$ are $2g$ linearly independent differentials in Ω_2/Ω_e; for if

$$\omega = c_1\omega_1 + \cdots + c_g\omega_g + c_{g+1}\varphi_1 + \cdots + c_{2g}\varphi_g$$

is exact, ω is the differential of a meromorphic function having simple poles at each of the points $P_1, P_2, \ldots, P_g$, at which $c_k \neq 0$, $k = 1, \ldots, g$. But this is impossible, so $c_1 = c_2 = \cdots = c_g = 0$. But the rest of the c_k's are then zero too, for no linear combination of the φ_k's can be exact. Thus $\dim \Omega_2/\Omega_e \geq 2g$ and we have proved $\dim \Omega_2/\Omega_e = 2g$.

Let P be an arbitrary point on the Riemann surface S. For the unit divisor 1, we have $i[1] = g$, $d[1] = 0$, so that $r[1] = 1$ and the constant functions are the only ones in $L(1)$. This merely restates the fact that there are no everywhere regular analytic functions on a compact surface. For $\mathfrak{a} = P$, $d[P] = 1$, so that

$$r\left[\frac{1}{P}\right] = 2 - g + i[P].$$

If $i[P] = i[1] = g$, then there is a function which has a simple pole at P and is otherwise regular. If $i[P] = i[1] - 1 = g - 1$, then $r[P^{-1}] = 1$ and there is no meromorphic function regular except for a simple pole at P. Now consider the transition from $\mathfrak{a} = P^{n-1}$ to $\mathfrak{a} = P^n$. We have $r[P^{-(n-1)}] = n - g + i[P^{n-1}]$, while $r[P^{-n}] = n + 1 - g + i[P^n]$. If $i[P^n] = i[P^{n-1}]$, then $r[P^{-n}] = r[P^{-(n-1)}] + 1$ and there is a function having a pole of order n at P and otherwise regular. If $i[P^n] = i[P^{n-1}] - 1$, then $r[P^{-n}] = r[P^{-(n-1)}]$ and no function exists whose only singularity is a pole of order n at P. Thus, if $i[P^n]$ remains the same while n increases by 1, a new linearly independent function is added in going from $L(1/P^n)$ to $L(1/P^{n+1})$. The number of times that $i[P^n]$ does not remain the same must be g times, since $i[1] = g$, $i[P^{2g-1}] = 0$, and at each change it decreases by 1. Thus we have proved the following theorem.

THEOREM 10–18   (*Weierstrass gap theorem*).   *There are exactly g orders $n_i, 0 < n_1 < n_2 < \cdots < n_g < 2g$, that can be specified at each point P such that no meromorphic function exists having as its only singularity a pole of order n_i at P.*

Since $d[P^n] = n$, we have seen that if $n > g$, $r[P^{-n}] \geq 2$ and we can find a nonconstant meromorphic function whose only singularity is a pole of order at most n at P. If, however, $n = g$, there are nonconstant functions in $L(P^{-g})$ only when $i[P^g] > 0$. We shall now prove

THEOREM 10–19.   *There are only a finite number of points P on S at which $i[P^g] > 0$.*

Assume that there are an infinite number of points $\{P_n\}$ at which $i[P_n^g] > 0$, $n = 1, 2, 3, \ldots$. These points have a cluster point P_0 on S. In terms of $z = \Phi(P)$, $\Phi(P_0) = 0$, a local parameter z about P_0, each of the g basis differentials of the first kind $\varphi_j, j = 1, 2, \ldots, g$, can be represented as $\varphi_j = f_j(z) \, dz$, where the $f_j, j = 1, 2, \ldots, g$, are linearly independent functions about P_0. We may assume that the points P_n lie in the parametric neighborhood of P_0 and that $\Phi(P_n) = z_n$. Since $i[P_n^g] > 0$, for each z_n there is a $\varphi = c_1\varphi_1 + c_2\varphi_2 + \cdots + c_g\varphi_g \in \Omega(P_n^g)$ with $\sum_{i=1}^{g} |c_i|^2 \neq 0$ and

$$
\begin{aligned}
c_1 f_1(z_n) &+ c_2 f_2(z_n) + \cdots + c_g f_g(z_n) &= 0, \\
c_1 f_1'(z_n) &+ c_2 f_2'(z_n) + \cdots + c_g f_g'(z_n) &= 0, \\
c_1 f_1''(z_n) &+ c_2 f_2''(z_n) + \cdots + c_g f_g''(z_n) &= 0, \\
&\qquad\qquad\qquad\qquad\qquad\qquad\qquad\vdots \\
c_1 f_1^{(g-1)}(z_n) &+ c_2 f_2^{(g-1)}(z_n) + \cdots + c_g f_g^{(g-1)}(z_n) &= 0,
\end{aligned}
$$

where $f^{(m)}$ denotes the mth derivative of f.

Thus the determinant

$$W_g(z) = \begin{vmatrix} f_1(z) & f_2(z) & \cdots & f_g(z) \\ f_1'(z) & f_2'(z) & \cdots & f_g'(z) \\ f_1''(z) & f_2''(z) & \cdots & f_g''(z) \\ \vdots & \vdots & & \vdots \\ f_1^{(g-1)}(z) & f_2^{(g-1)}(z) & \cdots & f_g^{(g-1)}(z) \end{vmatrix}$$

must vanish at the points z_n. Since $W_g(z)$ is an analytic function of z, $W_g(z) \equiv 0$ in the entire neighborhood of P_0. But $W_g(z)$ is the Wronskian determinant of the functions $f_1, f_2, \ldots, f_g$, and its vanishing identically implies that the $f_1, f_2, \ldots, f_g$ are linearly dependent, which has brought us to a contradiction.

To show that $W_g(z) \equiv 0$ implies that $f_1, f_2, \ldots, f_g$ are linearly dependent, we note that for some k, $1 \le k < g$, $W_k(z)$ is not identically zero; for if $k = 1$, $W_k(z) = f_1(z)$. Let us select k so that $W_k(z) \not\equiv 0$ but $W_{k+1}(z) \equiv 0$. Then if $u_1, u_2, \ldots, u_{k+1}$ are the minors of the elements in the last row of the determinant

$$\begin{vmatrix} f_1 & f_2 & \cdots & f_{k+1} \\ f_1' & f_2' & \cdots & f_{k+1}' \\ \vdots & \vdots & & \vdots \\ f_1^{(k)} & f_2^{(k)} & \cdots & f_{k+1}^{(k)} \end{vmatrix},$$

we have

$$u_1 f_1^{(r)} + u_2 f_2^{(r)} + \cdots + u_{k+1} f_{k+1}^{(r)} \equiv 0, \quad r = 0, 1, \ldots, k.$$

Each of the u_j, $j = 1, 2, \ldots, k + 1$, is an analytic function of z in a neighborhood of $z = 0$ and $u_{k+1} = W_k \not\equiv 0$. We may divide this identity by u_{k+1} to get

$$v_1 f_1^{(r)} + v_2 f_2^{(r)} + \cdots + v_k f_k^{(r)} + f_{k+1}^{(r)} \equiv 0, \quad r = 0, 1, \ldots, k, \quad (1)$$

where $v_j = u_j/u_{k+1}$ is an analytic function of z having at most a finite number of poles in a neighborhood of $z = 0$. Therefore, there is some point z' such that all v_j's are regular in a neighborhood of z', and we may differentiate (1) with respect to z, and use the identity for $r + 1$ to get

$$v_1' f_1^{(r)} + v_2' f_2^{(r)} + \cdots + v_k' f_k^{(r)} \equiv 0, \quad r = 0, 1, \ldots, k - 1.$$

$W_k(z)$ is the determinant of this system of equations, and since $W_k(z) \not\equiv 0$

in a neighborhood of z', we have $v_j' \equiv 0, j = 1, 2, \ldots, k$. Thus $v_j = c_j =$ constant, and we have

$$c_1 f_1(z) + c_2 f_2(z) + \cdots + c_k f_k(z) + f_{k+1}(z) \equiv 0,$$

showing the linear dependence of the $f_1, f_2, \ldots, f_g$.

We have now shown that there are only a finite number of points P on S at which $i[P^g] > 0$. It is only at these points that we can specify a pole of order g or less as the only singularity of a nonconstant meromorphic function on S. These points are called the *Weierstrass points* of S. If $g = 0$ or $g = 1$, there are no Weierstrass points on S. It can be shown that if $g \geq 2$, such points do actually exist. In fact, it is shown by Hurwitz (Ref. 24, pp. 409–442) that there are at least $2g + 2$ Weierstrass points on a surface of genus $g \geq 2$, with equality only for hyperelliptic surfaces. An upper bound for the number of Weierstrass points is $(g - 1)g(g + 1)$.

If $n \geq g + 1$, we can specify an integral divisor $\mathfrak{a}$ of degree n such that there is a nonconstant meromorphic function in $L(\mathfrak{a}^{-1})$. Let $z(P)$ be a nonconstant meromorphic function in $L(\mathfrak{a}^{-1})$. Then $z(P)$ takes on every complex number as a value exactly the same number of times on S, and if it assumes the value $z = \infty$ exactly n times, it assumes every value $z = a$ exactly n times. Thus $z(P)$ gives us a conformal mapping of the surface S onto the complex number sphere S_0, such that each point of S_0 is covered exactly n times. We have then shown that $z(P)$ gives us a one-to-one conformal mapping of S onto an n-sheeted covering surface of S_0.

If we say that the point P, at which $z(P) = a$, lies over the point a of S_0, we may picture S as an n-sheeted covering surface of S_0. The n points at which $z(P) = a$ need not be distinct. If at P_0, $z(P)$ assumes the value a r times, in terms of a local parameter t about P_0, we have $z(t) - a = c_r t^r + c_{r+1} t^{r+1} + \cdots$. We see that $\sqrt[r]{z - a}$ can be taken as a local parameter about P_0, and the point P_0 lying over a is an $(r - 1)$th-order branch point of the covering surface S of S_0. If the value $z = \infty$ is assumed s times at the point P_0, then $z(t) = c_{-s} t^{-s} + c_{-s+1} t^{-s+1} + \cdots$, or we may take as local parameter $\sqrt[s]{1/z}$, and we say that $z = \infty$ is a branch point of order $s - 1$. Let V denote $\Sigma(r - 1) + \Sigma(s - 1)$, where the first sum is taken over all finite multiple points and the second over all poles of $z(P)$. V is called the *ramification index* of the covering S of S_0.

The branch points of S as a covering of S_0 will occur only at points where $z(P)$ has a multiple point. These are just the points where the differential of the second kind dz has its zeros or poles of order >3. For each multiple point where a value a is assumed r times, dz has a zero of order $r - 1$; for each multiple point where the value ∞ is assumed s times, dz has a pole of order $s + 1$. Since the degree of (dz) is $2g - 2$, we have

$$\Sigma(r - 1) - \Sigma(s + 1) = 2g - 2,$$

or
$$\Sigma(r - 1) + \Sigma(s - 1) - 2\Sigma s = 2g - 2.$$

But $\Sigma s = n$, so that
$$V - 2n = 2g - 2,$$
or
$$V = 2(n + g - 1). \tag{2}$$
Thus

THEOREM 10–20. *For any Riemann surface S considered as an n-sheeted covering surface of the sphere S_0, the genus g can be computed according to (2) in terms of the number of sheets n and the ramification index V.*

If we now pick a point P_0 on S which is not a Weierstrass point, we can prescribe a pole of order $g + 1$ at P_0 as the only singularity of the meromorphic function $z(P)$. Thus

THEOREM 10–21. *Every compact Riemann surface of genus g is conformally equivalent to a $(g + 1)$-sheeted covering surface of the sphere.*

In the beginning of our study, the abstract notion of a Riemann surface seemed to embrace more surfaces than those which are branched coverings of the sphere. We now have shown that each compact Riemann surface is conformally equivalent to a branched covering surface of the sphere with a finite number of sheets. When we keep in mind that from a function-theoretic point of view conformally equivalent surfaces may be considered the same, we can say that in the compact case, the abstract concept gave us nothing more than the branched coverings of the sphere with a finite number of sheets.

A particular case of interest is that of genus $g = 0$. Then S is conformally equivalent to the sphere itself and we conclude again that the sphere is the only compact Riemann surface of genus zero. For $g = 1$, there are no meromorphic functions with only one simple pole, but one does exist with a pole of order 2 at a single point as its only singularity. Thus any surface of genus 1 can be mapped on a two-sheeted covering surface of the sphere. In cases $g \geq 2$, the number $g + 1$ of sheets in the covering surface of the sphere can be reduced to $\leq g$ by using a mapping function whose only pole is at a Weierstrass point.

10–7 Abel's theorem. Let S be a compact Riemann surface and let $z(P)$ be a fixed (nonconstant) meromorphic function on S which maps S conformally onto an n-sheeted branched covering surface of the sphere S_0. Thus S itself may be considered as this branched covering of S_0 such that each point z of S_0 is the projection of the n points $P_1, P_2, \ldots, P_n$ (not necessarily distinct) on S. If f is any meromorphic function on S, we define the *trace of* f to be the function on S_0 given by

$$\text{Tr } f(z) = f(P_1) + f(P_2) + \cdots + f(P_n).$$

Similarly, if ω is an abelian differential on S, at each point P_k,

$$\omega = h_k(t_k)\, dt_k,$$

where t_k is a local parameter about P_k, $k = 1, 2, \ldots, n$. We define the *trace of* ω to be the differential on S_0 given by

$$\text{Tr } \omega = h_1(t_1)\, dt_1 + h_2(t_2)\, dt_2 + \cdots + h_n(t_n)\, dt_n.$$

To see that $\text{Tr } \omega$ is an analytic differential on S_0, we recall that locally about P_k, $z = c_{s_k} t_k^{s_k} + c_{s_k+1} t_k^{s_k+1} + \cdots$, so that we may take z^{1/s_k} as local parameter about P_k instead of t_k. Then $s_k t_k^{s_k-1}\, dt_k = dz$ and we can write

$$\text{Tr } \omega = \left(\frac{h_1(t_1)}{s_1 t_1^{s_1-1}} + \frac{h_2(t_2)}{s_2 t_2^{s_2-1}} + \cdots + \frac{h_n(t_n)}{s_n t_n^{s_n-1}} \right) dz = H(z)\, dz,$$

where $H(z)$ is locally an analytic function of z, since $t_k = g_k(z^{1/s_k})$, and g_k is analytic about $z = 0$.

We prove next that if ω is a differential of the first kind, $\text{Tr } \omega$ is a differential of the first kind on S_0 and is consequently identically zero. First, if n distinct points $P_1, P_2, \ldots, P_n$ correspond to z, then we can take $t_k = z$, $k = 1, 2, \ldots, n$, as local parameter, and we have $\text{Tr } \omega = [h_1(z) + \cdots + h_n(z)]\, dz$, where $h_k(z)$ is locally a regular function, making $\text{Tr } \omega$ regular about this point. If s points $P_1, P_2, \ldots, P_s$ coincide, then $z = c_s t^s + c_{s+1} t^{s+1} + \cdots$, $c_s \neq 0$, while $\omega = h(t)\, dt = \sum_{j=0}^{\infty} a_j t^j\, dt$. We change parameter to $t = \epsilon_k z^{1/s}$, where $\epsilon_k = e^{2\pi i k/s}$, $k = 1, 2, \ldots, s$, and the s different values of k correspond to the s points which map into z, and a branch of $z^{1/s}$ is selected which is real for real z. Then

$$\omega = \sum_{j=0}^{\infty} a_j \epsilon_k^j z^{j/s} \left(\frac{1}{s} \epsilon_k z^{(1/s)-1} \right) dz = \frac{1}{s} \sum_{j=0}^{\infty} a_j \epsilon_k^{j+1} z^{(j+1-s)/s}\, dz.$$

In forming $\text{Tr } \omega$, we add these series for $k = 1, 2, \ldots, s$ (as well as those corresponding to the other $n - s$ points mapping into z), getting

$$\frac{1}{s} \sum_{j=0}^{\infty} a_j \left(\sum_{k=1}^{s} \epsilon_k^{j+1} \right) z^{(j+1-s)/s}\, dz.$$

But $\sum_{k=1}^{s} \epsilon_k^{j+1} = \sum_{k=1}^{s} e^{2\pi i(j+1)k/s} = 0$ if $j + 1$ is *not* a multiple of s, and is equal to s otherwise. If $j + 1 = ms$, then we have as the contribution of $P_1, P_2, \ldots, P_s$ in Tr ω the series

$$\sum_{m=1}^{\infty} a_{ms-1} z^{m-1} \, dz,$$

so that the points $P_1, P_2, \ldots, P_s$ contribute a regular analytic term to Tr ω. Thus even at the branch points of the covering of S_0 by S, Tr ω is regular, so Tr $\omega \equiv 0$ for any ω of the first kind.

Let γ^1 be a singular 1-chain on S. Its boundary is a singular 0-chain which we write as $\partial \gamma^1 = \sum_{j=1}^{N} \alpha_j \langle P_j \rangle$, where the α_j are integers. Thus $\partial \gamma^1$ may be considered as a divisor $P_1^{\alpha_1} P_2^{\alpha_2} \ldots P_N^{\alpha_N}$. If $\gamma^1 = \sum_{n=1}^{m} c_n \sigma_n^1$, each σ_n^1 has $\partial \sigma_n^1 = \langle Q \rangle - \langle P \rangle$, and so the degree of the divisor $\partial \sigma_n^1$ is zero $(d[\partial \sigma_n^1] = 0)$. Furthermore,

$$d[\partial \gamma^1] = d\left[\partial \sum_{n=1}^{m} c_n \sigma_n^1\right] = \sum_{n=1}^{m} c_n d[\partial \sigma_n^1] = 0,$$

so the boundary of any singular 1-chain considered as a divisor has degree zero.

It was pointed out earlier that not every divisor is the divisor of a meromorphic function on S. We now seek conditions that must be imposed on a divisor in order that it be a principal divisor. The answer is embodied in *Abel's theorem*:

THEOREM 10–22 (*Abel's theorem*). *A necessary and sufficient condition for a divisor $\mathfrak{a}$ to be the divisor of a meromorphic function is that there exist a singular 1-chain γ^1 such that*

$$\partial \gamma^1 = \mathfrak{a} \tag{1}$$

and

$$\int_{\gamma^1} \varphi = 0 \tag{2}$$

for each differential of the first kind φ on S.

For $g = 0$, there are no differentials of the first kind, so this condition merely states that $\mathfrak{a} = \partial \gamma^1$. Since S is connected, the condition that $\mathfrak{a} = \partial \gamma^1$ is the same as $d[\mathfrak{a}] = 0$. But on the sphere, this is just the well-known condition that any points may be specified as the zeros and poles of a rational function so long as the sum of the orders of the poles is equal to the sum of the orders of the zeros. This proves Abel's theorem for $g = 0$.

We shall assume, hereafter, that $g \geq 1$. We first prove the *necessity*. Let f be a meromorphic function on S with divisor $\mathfrak{a} = (f)$. Then f gives us a conformal mapping of S onto the sphere S_0. To each point z on S_0 correspond n points $P_1(z)$, $P_2(z)$, $\ldots$, $P_n(z)$ on S (not all necessarily distinct). If φ is a differential of the first kind, we may take its trace using the mapping by f and recalling that $\mathrm{Tr}\, \varphi \equiv 0$ on S_0.

Now let $\tilde{\gamma}$ be any meridian on S_0 oriented from the north pole to the south pole. Then $\tilde{\gamma}$ is the image of n curves γ_1, γ_2, $\ldots$, γ_n on S which join the poles of f to the zeros of f. If we set $\gamma^1 = \gamma_1 + \gamma_2 + \cdots + \gamma_n$, we have $(f) = \partial \gamma^1$. Now we integrate φ over γ^1 and get

$$\int_{\gamma^1} \varphi = \int_{\gamma_1 + \gamma_2 + \cdots + \gamma_n} \varphi = \int_{\gamma_1} \varphi + \int_{\gamma_2} \varphi + \cdots + \int_{\gamma_n} \varphi$$

$$= \int_{\tilde{\gamma}} \mathrm{Tr}\, \varphi = 0,$$

proving the necessity of Abel's conditions.

To prove the *sufficiency* in Abel's theorem, we let φ_1, φ_2, $\ldots$, φ_g be a canonical basis for differentials of the first kind with a period diagram like (4) of Section 10–2. Let $\mathfrak{a} = P_1^{\alpha_1} P_2^{\alpha_2} \ldots P_s^{\alpha_s}$. Since $\mathfrak{a} = \partial \gamma^1$, we know that $d[\mathfrak{a}] = 0$ or $\sum_{i=1}^{s} \alpha_i = 0$. Thus there exists a differential of the third kind η having simple poles at P_1, P_2, $\ldots$, P_s, and no others, and with residues α_i at P_i. Furthermore, we can normalize η so that all its A-periods are zero.

We now apply the bilinear relation for differentials of the first and third kinds [see (1) of Section 10–3]. This gives

$$\int_{\mathfrak{b}_j} \eta = 2\pi i \sum_{k=1}^{s} \alpha_k \int_{L_k} \varphi_j = 2\pi i \int_{\gamma_0^1} \varphi_j, \quad j = 1, 2, \ldots, g, \qquad (3)$$

where L_k is a fixed path in the normal polygon Π joining a fixed point P_0 of Π to the point P_k, $k = 1, 2, \ldots, s$, and γ_0^1 is the singular 1-chain $\gamma_0^1 = \alpha_1 L_1 + \alpha_2 L_2 + \cdots + \alpha_s L_s$, with each L_k oriented from P_0 to P_k. Then $\partial \gamma_0^1 = \alpha_1 \langle P_1 \rangle + \cdots + \alpha_s \langle P_s \rangle = \mathfrak{a} = \partial \gamma^1$, since $\sum_{i=1}^{s} \alpha_i = 0$. Consequently, $\gamma_0^1 - \gamma^1$ is a 1-cycle which is homologous to an integral linear combination of the $\mathbf{a}_i$ and $\mathbf{b}_i$, $i = 1, \ldots, g$, forming the edges of the normal polygon Π:

$$\gamma_0^1 - \gamma^1 \sim k_1 \mathbf{a}_1 + k_2 \mathbf{a}_2 + \cdots + k_g \mathbf{a}_g + k_{g+1} \mathbf{b}_1 + \cdots + k_{2g} \mathbf{b}_g,$$

where the k_i are integers.

We may now rewrite (3) as

$$\int_{b_j} \eta = 2\pi i \int_{\gamma^1} \varphi_j + 2\pi i \int_{\gamma_0^1 - \gamma^1} \varphi_j$$

$$= 2\pi i (k_j + k_{g+1} B_{j,1} + k_{g+2} B_{j,2} + \cdots + k_{2g} B_{j,g}).$$

Let us define a differential of the third kind θ as

$$\theta = \eta - 2\pi i (k_{g+1}\varphi_1 + k_{g+2}\varphi_2 + \cdots + k_{2g}\varphi_g).$$

Then

$$\int_{a_j} \theta = -2\pi i k_{g+j}, \quad \int_{b_j} \theta = 2\pi i k_j, \quad j = 1, 2, \ldots, g.$$

Finally, if we place a small circle c_j around each point P_j in some parametric disk about P_j, we get

$$\int_{c_j} \theta = 2\pi i \alpha_j, \quad j = 1, 2, \ldots, s.$$

Thus all the cyclic and polar periods of θ are integral multiples of $2\pi i$.

Let C be an arbitrary closed curve on S not passing through any P_j, $j = 1, 2, \ldots, s$. Then the period of θ on C is an integral multiple of $2\pi i$, so that if we take a fixed point P_0 on S, $P_0 \neq P_j$, $j = 1, 2, \ldots, s$, the integral $\int_{P_0}^{P} \theta$ is determined up to an additive constant which is an integral multiple of $2\pi i$, depending upon the curve joining P_0 to P. The function

$$f(P) = \exp\left[\int_{P_0}^{P} \theta\right]$$

is therefore single-valued on S, and we proceed to show that f is meromorphic and $(f) = \mathfrak{a}$.

If $t = \Phi(P)$ is a local parameter about P, then

$$\theta = \left[\frac{\operatorname{res}_P \theta}{t} + h(t)\right] dt,$$

where $h(t)$ is a locally regular analytic function about $t = 0$ and $\operatorname{res}_P \theta$ represents the residue of θ at P. For any points Q and R in the neighborhood of P, we have

$$f(Q) = \exp\left[\int_{P_0}^{R} \theta + \int_{R}^{Q} \theta\right] = K \exp\left[\int_{R}^{Q} \theta\right],$$

where

$$K = \exp\left[\int\!\!\int_{P_0}^{R} \theta\right].$$

If $\Phi(Q) = t_2$ and $\Phi(R) = t_1$, then

$$\int_{R}^{Q} \theta = [(\text{res}_P \theta) \log t_2 + H(t_2)]$$

where

$$H(t_2) = \int_{t_1}^{t_2} h(t)\, dt - \text{res}_P \theta \log t_1$$

is a regular analytic function of t_2 in a neighborhood of $t_2 = 0$. Thus

$$f(Q) = Ke^{(\text{res}_P \theta) \log t_2} e^{H(t_2)} = t_2^{\text{res}_P \theta} Ke^{H(t_2)}.$$

If $P \neq P_i$, $i = 1, \ldots, s$, we have defined θ so that $\text{res}_P \theta = 0$ and $f(Q)$ is regular in a neighborhood of P. On the other hand, if $P = P_i$, $\text{res}_{P_i} \theta = \alpha_i$ and

$$f(Q) = t_2^{\alpha_i} Ke^{H(t_2)},$$

so that f is a meromorphic function having $\mathfrak{a}$ as its divisor. This completes the proof of Abel's theorem.

If we express the divisor $\mathfrak{a}$ as

$$\mathfrak{a} = \frac{P_1 P_2 \ldots P_n}{Q_1 Q_2 \ldots Q_n},$$

Abel's theorem tells us that *the necessary and sufficient condition that the P_j's be the only zeros and the Q_j's be the only poles of a meromorphic function on S (that is, that $P_1 P_2 \ldots P_n \sim Q_1 Q_2 \ldots Q_n$) is that we can join each Q_j to P_j, $j = 1, \ldots, n$, by an arc γ_j such that $\sum_{j=1}^{n} \int_{\gamma_j} \varphi = 0$ for each differential of the first kind φ on S.*

Let $\varphi_1, \varphi_2, \ldots, \varphi_g$, $g \geq 1$, be a basis for the differentials of the first kind on S and let P_0 be a fixed point on S. Then

$$u_i = u_i(P) = \int_{P_0}^{P} \varphi_i, \quad i = 1, 2, \ldots, g,$$

is an everywhere regular multiple-valued function on S, its value depending upon the path of integration γ from P_0 to P. If γ' is another path from P_0

to P, and $\int_\gamma \varphi_i = c_i$, $\int_{\gamma'} \varphi_i = c'_i$, then $c_i - c'_i = \int_{\gamma - \gamma'} \varphi_i$, where $\gamma - \gamma'$ is a 1-cycle. Thus $c_i - c'_i$ is a period of φ_i and, in short, we shall say that $c_i - c'_i$ is congruent to zero modulo periods and write $c_i - c'_i \equiv 0$ (mod periods), these periods naturally taken over the same cycle for all $i = 1, 2, \ldots, g$. We shall say that $(c_1, c_2, \ldots, c_g) \equiv (c'_1, c'_2, \ldots, c'_g)$ (mod periods) when $c_i - c'_i \equiv 0$ (mod periods) for $i = 1, 2, \ldots, g$.

Given the integral divisor $P_1 P_2 \ldots P_n$, we define the corresponding vector $(c_1, c_2, \ldots, c_g)$ modulo periods in which

$$c_i = \sum_{j=1}^n u_i(P_j) = \sum_{j=1}^n \int_{P_0}^{P_j} \varphi_i = \sum_{j=1}^n \int_{\gamma_j} \varphi_i = \int_\gamma \varphi_i,$$

where $\gamma = \sum_{j=1}^n \gamma_j$. Two integral divisors are in the same equivalence class of divisors if and only if the corresponding vectors are congruent modulo periods.

10–8 Jacobi inversion problem. We next pose the following question: given arbitrary complex numbers c_i, $i = 1, \ldots, g$, can we find n points $Q_1, Q_2, \ldots, Q_n$ on S such that $\sum_{j=1}^n u_i(Q_j) \equiv c_i$ (mod periods), $i = 1, 2, \ldots, g$? We have asked whether the g-tuples $(c_1, c_2, \ldots, c_g)$ of abelian sums fill out the space of g complex variables. Since the c_i corresponding to an integral divisor is of the form $c_i = \int_\gamma \varphi_i$ for some singular 1-chain γ, we first wish to know what part of the space of g complex variables is filled out by the g-tuples

$$\left(\int_\gamma \varphi_1, \int_\gamma \varphi_2, \int_\gamma \varphi_3, \ldots, \int_\gamma \varphi_g \right),$$

as γ varies through all singular 1-chains. We observe that

$$h(\gamma) = \left(\int_\gamma \varphi_1, \int_\gamma \varphi_2, \ldots, \int_\gamma \varphi_g \right)$$

is a homomorphism of the group of singular 1-chains on S into K^g, the space of g complex variables. We shall prove that h is an *onto* homomorphism, so that the image of the group of singular 1-chains by h fills out all of K^g.

Let $P_1, P_2, \ldots, P_g$ be distinct points on S such that $i[P_1 P_2 \ldots P_g] = 0$. Let z_j be a local parameter in the disk D_j about P_j, with $z_j = \Phi_j(P)$, $\Phi_j(P_j) = 0$. Select a point Q_j in the neighborhood of P_j and let $\Phi_j(Q_j) = t_j$. The straight line segment in D_j joining P_j to Q_j will be denoted by γ_j.

Then we may define a mapping

$$h_1(t_1, t_2, \ldots, t_g) = h\left(\sum_{j=1}^{g} \gamma_j\right) = \left(\int_\gamma \varphi_1, \int_\gamma \varphi_2, \ldots, \int_\gamma \varphi_g\right),$$

where $\gamma = \sum_{j=1}^{g} \gamma_j$, which takes the topological product of the parametric disks $D_1 \times D_2 \times \cdots \times D_g$ into the space of g complex variables K^g. The Jacobian (functional determinant) of this mapping is

$$\begin{vmatrix} \dfrac{\partial}{\partial t_1} \int_\gamma \varphi_1 & \cdots & \dfrac{\partial}{\partial t_g} \int_\gamma \varphi_1 \\ \vdots & & \vdots \\ \dfrac{\partial}{\partial t_1} \int_\gamma \varphi_g & \cdots & \dfrac{\partial}{\partial t_g} \int_\gamma \varphi_g \end{vmatrix}.$$

But $\int_\gamma \varphi_i = \sum_{\nu=1}^{g} \int_{\gamma_\nu} \varphi_i$, and only the one integral $\int_{\gamma_j} \varphi_i$ depends upon t_j. In D_j, $\varphi_i = v_{i,j}(z_j)\, dz_j$, where $v_{i,j}$ is regular in D_j, and

$$\frac{\partial}{\partial t_j} \int_0^{t_j} v_{i,j}(z_j)\, dz_j = v_{i,j}(t_j).$$

Thus the Jacobian determinant is equal to

$$\begin{vmatrix} v_{1,1}(t_1) & v_{1,2}(t_2) & \ldots & v_{1,g}(t_g) \\ \vdots & \vdots & & \vdots \\ v_{g,1}(t_1) & v_{g,2}(t_2) & \ldots & v_{g,g}(t_g) \end{vmatrix}.$$

If this determinant were zero at $(0, 0, \ldots, 0)$, we could find numbers $e_1, e_2, \ldots, e_g$, not all zero, such that

$$\sum_{i=1}^{g} e_i v_{i,j}(t_j) = 0, \quad j = 1, 2, \ldots, g.$$

This says that the differential of the first kind $\varphi = \sum_{i=1}^{g} e_i \varphi_i$ has zeros at $P_1, P_2, \ldots, P_g$. But since $i[P_1 P_2 \ldots P_g] = 0$, no such differential of the first kind can exist, telling us that the Jacobian is not zero at $(0, 0, \ldots, 0)$ and that the mapping h_1 is locally one-to-one from a neighborhood of $(0, 0, \ldots, 0)$ in $D_1 \times D_2 \times \cdots \times D_g$ to a complete neighborhood of $(0, 0, \ldots, 0)$ in K^g. Therefore for a sufficiently small neighborhood U about $(0, 0, \ldots, 0)$ in K^g, each point $(c_1, c_2, \ldots, c_g)$ is the image of a singular 1-chain γ under the homomorphism h. Now given any vector $(c_1, c_2, \ldots, c_g)$ in K^g, there exists an integer N such that

$$(c_1/N, c_2/N, \ldots, c_g/N)$$

is in U. Then $(c_1/N, c_2/N, \ldots, c_g/N) = h(\gamma)$ and $(c_1, c_2, \ldots, c_g) = h(N\gamma)$ and the mapping h carries the group of singular 1-chains onto K^g.

Let $P_1, P_2, \ldots, P_g$ be any points on S, $g > 0$, and let $(c_1, c_2, \ldots, c_g)$ be any points in K^g. Then there is a singular 1-chain γ_0 such that $h(\gamma_0) = (c_1, c_2, \ldots, c_g)$. Let us set $\partial\gamma_0 = \mathfrak{a}$. Then $d[\mathfrak{a}] = 0$ and

$$d[\mathfrak{a}P_1P_2 \ldots P_g] = g.$$

By the Riemann-Roch theorem,

$$r\left[\frac{1}{\mathfrak{a}P_1P_2 \ldots P_g}\right] = i[\mathfrak{a}P_1P_2 \ldots P_g] + 1 \geq 1,$$

so that there is a meromorphic function f which is a multiple of the divisor $1/(\mathfrak{a}P_1P_2 \ldots P_g)$. Hence $(f)\mathfrak{a}P_1P_2 \ldots P_g$ is an integral divisor with $d[(f)\mathfrak{a}P_1P_2 \ldots P_g] = g$ (since $d[(f)] = 0$). Consequently, there are g points $Q_1, Q_2, \ldots, Q_g$ (not necessarily distinct) on S such that

$$Q_1Q_2 \ldots Q_g = (f)\mathfrak{a}P_1P_2 \ldots P_g$$

or

$$Q_1Q_2 \ldots Q_g \sim \mathfrak{a}P_1P_2 \ldots P_g.$$

By Abel's theorem, there exists a singular 1-chain γ_1 such that

$$\partial\gamma_1 = \frac{Q_1Q_2 \ldots Q_g}{\mathfrak{a}P_1P_2 \ldots P_g}$$

and $h(\gamma_1) = (0, 0, \ldots, 0)$. Therefore, $h(\gamma_0 + \gamma_1) = (c_1, c_2, \ldots, c_g)$ and $\partial(\gamma_0 + \gamma_1) = Q_1Q_2 \ldots Q_g P_1^{-1}P_2^{-1} \ldots P_g^{-1}$. We can select from $\gamma_0 + \gamma_1$ certain paths l_j from P_j to Q_j so that $\sum_{j=1}^{g} l_j - (\gamma_0 + \gamma_1)$ is a cycle. Then

$$\sum_{j=1}^{g} \int_{l_j} \varphi_i \equiv c_i \quad (\text{mod periods}), \quad i = 1, 2, \ldots, g.$$

By adding cycles to the l_j, we obtain paths L_j from P_j to Q_j such that

$$\sum_{j=1}^{g} \int_{L_j} \varphi_i = c_i, \quad i = 1, 2, \ldots, g.$$

This solves the Jacobi inversion problem as formulated at the beginning of this section. For take $P_1 P_2 \ldots P_g = P_0^g$; then there are g points $Q_1, Q_2, \ldots, Q_g$ such that

$$\sum_{j=1}^{g} \int_{l_j} \varphi_i = \sum_{j=1}^{g} \int_{P_0}^{Q_j} \varphi_i \equiv c_i \quad \text{(mod periods)}, \quad i = 1, \ldots, g.$$

But $\int_{l_j} \varphi_i = u_i(Q_j)$, so we have found g points, $Q_1, Q_2, \ldots, Q_g$, such that

$$\sum_{j=1}^{g} u_i(Q_j) \equiv c_i \quad \text{(mod periods)}.$$

If $n > g$, we can find n points $Q_1, Q_2, \ldots, Q_n$ solving the inversion problem by arbitrarily specifying $n - g$ of the points and then solving a revised problem for the remaining g points. The problem cannot be solved for $n < g$, for then the vectors $(c_1, c_1, \ldots, c_g)$, $c_i = \sum_{j=1}^{n} u_i(P_j)$, depend upon n parameters $P_1, P_2, \ldots, P_n$ and could not fill out the space of g complex variables.

Let us again consider the set J of equivalence classes of vectors in K^g obtained by setting

$$(c_1, c_2, \ldots, c_g) \equiv (c_1', c_2', \ldots, c_g') \quad \text{(mod periods)}$$

if and only if $c_i \equiv c_i$ (mod periods), $i = 1, 2, \ldots, g$. (J is a compact commutative complex Lie group of complex dimension g, which is called the *Jacobian variety* of the surface S.) To each divisor $\mathfrak{a}$ of degree zero, say

$$\mathfrak{a} = \frac{P_1^{\alpha_1} P_2^{\alpha_2} \ldots P_n^{\alpha_n}}{Q_1^{\beta_1} Q_2^{\beta_2} \ldots Q_m^{\beta_m}}, \qquad \alpha_i \geq 0, \quad \beta_i \geq 0, \quad \sum_{i=1}^{n} \alpha_i = \sum_{i=1}^{m} \beta_i,$$

corresponds a singular 1-chain γ such that $\partial \gamma = \mathfrak{a}$, for we need only select an arbitrary point P_0 on S and take paths γ_i from P_0 to P_i and δ_i from P_0 to Q_i. Then $\sum_{i=1}^{n} \alpha_i \gamma_i - \sum_{i=1}^{m} \beta_i \delta_i = \gamma$. Two such 1-chains γ and γ', with $\partial \gamma = \partial \gamma' = \mathfrak{a}$, differ by a cycle, so that

$$h(\gamma) - h(\gamma') \equiv 0 \quad \text{(mod periods)},$$

or $h(\gamma)$, considered as a point of J, depends only upon $\mathfrak{a}$ and not on the 1-chain γ with $\partial \gamma = \mathfrak{a}$. We may define the mapping $\tilde{h}$ from the divisors of degree zero to J as $\tilde{h}(\mathfrak{a}) = h(\gamma)$, where $\partial \gamma = \mathfrak{a}$. The divisors of degree zero form a multiplicative group D_0, and if $\mathfrak{a} \in D_0$, $\mathfrak{b} \in D_0$ and if $\mathfrak{a} = \partial \gamma_1$ and $\mathfrak{b} = \partial \gamma_2$, then $\partial(\gamma_1 + \gamma_2) = \mathfrak{a}\mathfrak{b}$. Thus $\tilde{h}(\mathfrak{a}\mathfrak{b}) = h(\gamma_1) + h(\gamma_2) = \tilde{h}(\mathfrak{a}) + \tilde{h}(\mathfrak{b})$, and $\tilde{h}$ is a homomorphism of D_0 onto J.

According to Abel's theorem, $\tilde{h}(\mathfrak{a}) = (0, 0, \ldots, 0)$ if and only if $\mathfrak{a}$ is the divisor of a meromorphic function. Thus the kernel of $\tilde{h}$ is just the class of principal divisors, and we conclude that *there is an isomorphism $\tilde{h}$ of the divisor classes of degree zero onto J.*

Finally, if we fix a point P_0 on S and map P_0 arbitrarily into J [say $k(P_0) = (0, 0, \ldots, 0)$], we may define a mapping k of S into J as follows: For each point $P \in S$, we may find a singular 1-chain γ such that $\partial\gamma = P - P_0$. Then we define

$$k(P) = \tilde{h}\left(\frac{P}{P_0}\right) = h(\gamma) = \left(\int_{P_0}^{P} \varphi_1, \int_{P_0}^{P} \varphi_2, \ldots, \int_{P_0}^{P} \varphi_g\right),$$

which is independent of γ, depending only upon the point P. Given an arbitrary point $(c_1, c_2, \ldots, c_g)$ of J, there are g points $Q_1, Q_2, \ldots, Q_g$ (not necessarily distinct) such that

$$(c_1, c_2, \ldots, c_g) = k(Q_1) + k(Q_2) + \cdots + k(Q_g).$$

If $P_1, P_2, \ldots, P_g$ is another set of points mapping into the same

$$(c_1, c_2, \ldots, c_g),$$

then

$$\tilde{h}\left[\frac{P_1 P_2 \ldots P_g}{Q_1 Q_2 \ldots Q_g}\right] = (0, 0, \ldots, 0),$$

and by Abel's theorem, there is a meromorphic function which has

$$\frac{P_1 P_2 \ldots P_g}{Q_1 Q_2 \ldots Q_g}$$

as its divisor. Therefore

$$r\left[\frac{1}{Q_1 Q_2 \ldots Q_g}\right] > 1$$

for at least one P_i is different from the Q_j's, so the meromorphic function is not a constant but must vanish at P_i. Then by the Riemann-Roch theorem, $i[Q_1 Q_2 \ldots Q_g] \neq 0$.

Conversely, if $i[Q_1 Q_2 \ldots Q_g] \neq 0$, there is a nonconstant meromorphic function f on S which is a multiple of $1/(Q_1 Q_2 \ldots Q_g)$, so that

$$P_1 P_2 \ldots P_g = (f) Q_1 Q_2 \ldots Q_g$$

leads to another set of g points mapping into the same $(c_1, c_2, \ldots, c_g)$ as $Q_1 Q_2 \ldots Q_g$. We conclude that each point of J corresponds to an integral divisor $\mathfrak{a}$ of degree g on S. The correspondence is unique if and only if $i[\mathfrak{a}] = 0$.

In the case $g = 1$, S is topologically a torus and there is only one independent differential of the first kind φ. Then $h(\gamma) = \int_\gamma \varphi$ maps the group of singular 1-chains on S *onto* the complex plane K^1. Since $\mathbf{a}_1$ and $\mathbf{b}_1$ form a homology basis for S, any period of φ is a linear combination over the integers of the A-period A and the B-period B. We may normalize φ so that $A = 1$. Then $\operatorname{Im} B > 0$, since the imaginary part of the B-matrix is positive definite. To form J, we identify with each point c in K^1 all points $c + nA + mB$, $n,m = 0, \pm 1, \pm 2, \ldots$. We get one representative of each point in J if we draw the parallelogram with one vertex at the origin O and the vectors A and B as adjacent sides. The interior of this parallelogram, augmented by the interiors of the segments $\overline{OA}$ and $\overline{OB}$ and the point O, gives us one representative for each point of J. Then $k(P) = \int_{P_0}^P \varphi$ maps S conformally onto J in a one-to-one fashion, since $i[P] = 0$ for all $P \in S$. This shows us, moreover, that the universal covering surface $\hat{S}$ of the torus is parabolic, for $k(P) = \int_{P_0}^P \varphi$ gives us a complex uniformizing parameter which ranges through the whole finite complex plane and which has the parallelogram as its fundamental domain.

10–9 The field of algebraic functions

THEOREM 10–23. *On the compact Riemann surface S let $z = z(P)$ be a meromorphic function which assumes each value n times. Let $f = f(P)$ be any other meromorphic function on S. Then f satisfies an algebraic equation of degree n*

$$f^n + r_1(z)f^{n-1} + \cdots + r_{n-1}(z)f + r_n(z) = 0,$$

where the $r_k(z)$, $k = 1, 2, \ldots, n$, are rational functions of z.

To establish this theorem, we consider the mapping $z = z(P)$ of S onto an n-sheeted branched covering surface of the z-sphere. Let us delete from the z-sphere the finite set of points consisting of the point $z = \infty$, the branch points of the covering surface, and those points whose inverse images on S are poles of f. Then there are n points $P_1, P_2, \ldots, P_n$ on S "lying over" each point of z and we may define the *symmetric functions*

$$r_1(z) = -f(P_1) - f(P_2) - \cdots - f(P_n),$$

$$r_2(z) = f(P_1)f(P_2) + f(P_1)f(P_3) + \cdots = \sum_{\substack{i,j=1 \\ i<j}}^n f(P_i)f(P_j),$$

$$r_\nu(z) = (-1)^\nu \sum_{\substack{\{n_k\}=1 \\ n_1 < n_2 < \cdots < n_\nu}}^{n} f(P_{n_1}) f(P_{n_2}) \ldots f(P_{n_\nu}),$$

$$\vdots$$

$$r_n(z) = (-1)^n f(P_1) f(P_2) \ldots f(P_n).$$

If the order of the points $P_1, P_2, \ldots, P_n$ is changed, the symmetric functions remain unaltered. Thus continuation of $r_\nu(z)$ over the punctured sphere yields a single-valued function. At the point P_i^0 on S, $i = 1, 2, \ldots, n$, for which $z_0 = z(P_i^0)$, the function $z - z_0$ serves as a local uniformizing parameter and hence $f(P_i)$ expressed in this local parameter is a regular power series in $z - z_0$. Thus $r_\nu(z)$ is a single-valued regular analytic function on the punctured z-sphere.

At any one of the finite deleted points, the uniformizing parameter is $\sqrt[k]{z - z_0}$, so that $r_\nu(z)$ may be expressed as a Laurent series in fractional powers of $z - z_0$. But since $r_\nu(z)$ is single-valued in a neighborhood of each deleted point, only integral powers of $z - z_0$ appear in the series for $r_\nu(z)$. Finally, since each $f(P_i)$ has, at most, a pole as its singularity, the Laurent series has only a finite number of terms with negative powers, and hence $r_\nu(z)$ has, at most, poles as its singularities at any finite z. At $z = \infty$, $\sqrt[k]{1/z}$ for some k, $1 \leq k \leq n$, serves as local parameter at the poles of $z(P)$ and the same argument shows that $r_\nu(z)$ has, at most, a pole at infinity. Thus $r_\nu(z)$ is a rational function of z.

Since the symmetric function $r_\nu(z)$ is just the coefficient of $u^{n-\nu}$ in $(u - f(P_1))(u - f(P_2)) \ldots (u - f(P_n))$, we see that f satisfies the algebraic equation

$$F_z(u) = (u - f(P_1))(u - f(P_2)) \ldots (u - f(P_n))$$

$$= u^n + r_1(z)u^{n-1} + \cdots + r_n(z) = 0,$$

where the $r_\nu(z)$ are rational functions of z.

THEOREM 10–24. *If z is a given meromorphic function on S taking on each value n times, we can find a second meromorphic function f on S such that the nth-degree algebraic equation satisfied by f in terms of z is irreducible.*

By this we mean that the polynomial $F_z(u)$ cannot be factored into the product of two polynomials $F_z^{(1)}(u) \cdot F_z^{(2)}(u)$, each being of degree > 0 in u and the coefficients of each being rational functions of z.

First we note that if z takes on the value z_0 at the n distinct points $P_1^{(0)} P_2^{(0)}, \ldots, P_n^{(0)}$ on S, we can find a function f which takes on different values at each of these n points. For let ω_ν, $\nu = 1, 2, \ldots, n$, be a differential of the second kind on S which has as its only pole on S a pole of order 2 at $P_\nu^{(0)}$ with principal part

$$\frac{-dz}{(z - z_0)^2}$$

in terms of the local parameter $z - z_0$. Then let $c_1, c_2, \ldots, c_n$ be a set of mutually different constants. We set

$$f = (z - z_0)^2 \left(c_1 \frac{\omega_1}{dz} + c_2 \frac{\omega_2}{dz} + \cdots + c_n \frac{\omega_n}{dz} \right).$$

Each $(z - z_0)^2 \, \omega_\nu / dz$ is a meromorphic function on S which takes on the value zero at each $P_\mu^{(0)}$, $\mu \neq \nu$, and the value 1 at $P_\nu^{(0)}$. Thus f is rational and assumes the value c_ν at P_ν, $\nu = 1, \ldots, n$.

Now assume that the algebraic equation $F_z(u) = 0$ satisfied by f is reducible: $F_z(u) = F_z^{(1)}(u) F_z^{(2)}(u)$. About the point $P_1^{(0)}$, f can be expanded in a power series in the local parameter $z - z_0$. This series must satisfy either $F_z^{(1)}(u) = 0$ or $F_z^{(2)}(u) = 0$ when substituted for z; assume that it satisfies the first one. We can join $P_1^{(0)}$ to any $P_\nu^{(0)}$ with a curve γ_ν on S which does not pass through any of the multiple points of z. Then as we continue the function elements (z, f) along γ_ν, each must satisfy $F_z^{(1)}(u) = 0$ according to the permanence of a functional equation. Thus $F_z^{(1)}(u)$ has n distinct roots and must itself be of degree n, leaving $F_z^{(2)}(u)$ to be of degree zero. Thus $F_z(u)$ is irreducible.

At each point P on S, where $z(P) = z_0$, we may use $(z - z_0)^{1/k}$, $1 \leq k \leq n$, as a uniformizing parameter and expand f in a series of powers of $(z - z_0)^{1/k}$. This gives us a function element (z, f), where f can be developed in powers of $(z - z_0)^{1/k}$ and satisfies an nth-degree irreducible algebraic equation $F_z(u) = 0$. Continuing (z, f) over the z-space gives rise to a Riemann surface of this algebraic function which is an n-sheeted branched covering surface of the z-sphere and hence a compact Riemann surface.

If P_1 and P_2 are different points of S, and $z(P_1) = z_1$, $z(P_2) = z_2$, there are two possibilities:

(1) if $z_1 \neq z_2$, then $(z_1, f_1) \neq (z_2, f_2)$, and
(2) if $z = z_2$, then in a neighborhood of P_1, $f = f_1[(z - z_1)^{1/k}]$, while in a neighborhood of P_2, $f = f_2[(z - z_1)^{1/l}]$, where f_1 and f_2 are distinct function elements of f, and hence $(z_1, f_1) \neq (z_2, f_2)$.

Since there are n points P_i corresponding to each z, and also n function elements (z, f_i) corresponding to each z, the mapping $P \to (z, f)$ is *one-to-one* and *onto* from S to the Riemann surface of the algebraic function. Finally, at P, where $z(P) = z_0$, $(z - z_0)^{1/k}$ is a local parameter on S and it is also a local parameter about the point (z, f) on the Riemann surface of the algebraic function. Thus the mapping $P \to (z, f)$ is conformal. We have therefore proved

THEOREM 10–25. *The mapping $P \to (z, f)$ gives us a one-to-one conformal mapping of the compact Riemann surface S onto the Riemann surface of the algebraic function $f(z)$.*

Thus we realize every abstract Riemann surface (in the compact case) as the Riemann surface of an algebraic function.

The totality of meromorphic functions on the surface S forms a field $K(S)$, for the sum, product, or quotient of two meromorphic functions on S is again a meromorphic function. On the surface S, z and f may be found to satisfy an nth-degree irreducible algebraic equation $F_z(u) = 0$. We now prove

THEOREM 10–26. *Any meromorphic function g on S can be represented as a rational function of z and f, so that the whole field $K(S)$ of meromorphic functions on S is generated by taking rational functions of z and f.*

To prove this theorem, we employ the Lagrange interpolation formula.† Let $u_1, u_2, \ldots, u_n$ be distinct complex numbers and $v_1, v_2, \ldots, v_n$ be another set of complex numbers. Then we set

$$F(u) = (u - u_1)(u - u_2) \ldots (u - u_n)$$

and define $G(u)$ by

$$\frac{G(u)}{F(u)} = \frac{v_1}{u - u_1} + \frac{v_2}{u - u_2} + \cdots + \frac{v_n}{u - u_n}.$$

$G(u)$ is a polynomial of degree $n - 1$ in u. The value which $G(u)$ assumes at u_j is easily computed by multiplying both sides by $F(u)$ and letting $u \to u_j$. This gives

$$G(u_j) = v_j F'(u_j).$$

We now set $u_j = f(P_j)$ and $v_j = g(P_j)$, where $P_1, P_2, \ldots, P_n$ are the n distinct points where z assumes the same value, so that there is no branch point of the covering surface of the z-sphere over the point z. Then

$$\frac{G_z(u)}{F_z(u)} = \frac{g(P_1)}{u - f(P_1)} + \frac{g(P_2)}{u - f(P_2)} + \cdots + \frac{g(P_n)}{u - f(P_n)}.$$

†See Walsh (Ref. 49, p. 50).

The coefficients of u^j in

$$
\begin{aligned}
G_z(u) = \; & g(P_1)[(u - f(P_2))(u - f(P_3)) \ldots (u - f(P_n))] \\
& + g(P_2)[(u - f(P_1))(u - f(P_3)) \ldots (u - f(P_n))] \\
& + \cdots + g(P_n)[(u - f(P_1))(u - f(P_2)) \ldots (u - f(P_{n-1}))]
\end{aligned}
$$

are also symmetric functions of the $P_1, P_2, \ldots, P_n$ and hence determine rational functions of z. We have finally that

$$
g(P_j) = \left. \frac{G_z(u)}{F'_z(u)} \right|_{u=f(P_j)}, \qquad F'_z(u) = \frac{dF_z(u)}{du}.
$$

The nth-degree polynomial $F_z(u)$ is irreducible, so that the $(n-1)$th-degree polynomial $F'_z(u)$ is relatively prime to $F_z(u)$. We may, therefore, apply the euclidean algorithm† to find two polynomials $H_z(u)$ and $J_z(u)$ whose coefficients are rational functions of z such that

$$
H_z(u)F'_z(u) + J_z(u)F_z(u) = 1.
$$

But

$$
F_z(u) \Big|_{u=f(P_j)} = 0,
$$

so that

$$
F'_z(u) = \left. \frac{1}{H_z(u)} \right|_{u=f(P_j)} \qquad \text{and} \qquad g(P_j) = G_z(u)H_z(u) \Big|_{u=f(P_j)}
$$

This identity holds for any point P_j on S which is not a multiple point of z, and since both sides are analytic, it holds at all points of S, proving that g is a rational function of z and f. Since f^n can be expressed as a rational function of z and $f, f^2, \ldots, f^{n-1}$, we may always write

$$
g = R_1(z)f^{n-1} + R_2(z)f^{n-2} + \cdots + R_{n-1}(z)f + R_n(z), \qquad (1)
$$

where the $R_j(z)$ are rational functions of z.

In general, if f satisfies an algebraic equation $F_z(u) = 0$ whose coefficients are rational functions of z, those functions represented in the form (1) form what is called a *field of algebraic functions $K(z, f)$* generated by z and f satisfying $F_z(f) = 0$. We have now established that *the meromorphic functions on S form a field of algebraic functions.*

---

†See Birkhoff and MacLane (Ref. 10, p. 94).

If ζ is any other rational function on S which assumes each value m times, we may take ζ as the independent variable instead of z. Then we can find a function g which satisfies an mth-degree irreducible algebraic equation $G_\zeta(g) = 0$. Each of the other meromorphic functions on S can now be expressed rationally in terms of ζ and g. In particular, z and f can each be expressed rationally in terms of ζ and g, while ζ and g can be expressed rationally in terms of z and f. The mapping $(z, f) \leftrightarrows (\zeta, g)$, where

$$z = R_1(\zeta, g), \qquad f = R_2(\zeta, g)$$

and

$$\zeta = R_3(z, f), \qquad g = R_4(z, f),$$

and the R_ν, $\nu = 1, 2, 3, 4$, are rational functions of their arguments, is called a *birational transformation of the field of algebraic functions*. The algebraic equation $F_z(f) = 0$ is transformed into what must be an irreducible algebraic equation satisfied by (ζ, g) by the birational transformation $(z, f) \leftrightarrows (\zeta, g)$, and hence into $G_\zeta(g) = 0$.

Let S' be a Riemann surface which is conformally equivalent to S and let $P' = \varphi(P)$ be a one-to-one conformal mapping of S onto S'. Then each meromorphic function f on S is transformed into a meromorphic function $f \circ \varphi^{-1}(P')$ on S', and each meromorphic function g on S' is transformed into $g \circ \varphi(P)$, which is meromorphic on S. This correspondence between meromorphic functions on S and on S' defines an isomorphism of the fields of algebraic functions on S and on S'. If S is given by (z, f) satisfying $F_z(f) = 0$, and S' is given by (ζ, g) satisfying $G_\zeta(g) = 0$, then $\zeta \circ \varphi(P)$ and $g \circ \varphi(P)$ are meromorphic functions on S and hence $\zeta \circ \varphi = R_1(z, f)$ and $g \circ \varphi = R_2(z, f)$. Similarly, $z \circ \varphi^{-1}(P')$ and $f \circ \varphi^{-1}(P')$ are meromorphic functions on S' and hence $z \circ \varphi^{-1} = R_3(\zeta, g)$ and $f \circ \varphi^{-1} = R_4(\zeta, g)$. Thus the conformal mapping φ gives rise to a birational transformation of $K(z, f)$ and of $K(\zeta, g)$ which makes $F_z(f) = 0$ go into $G_\zeta(g) = 0$. On the other hand, any such birational transformation of the algebraic function fields of $F_z(f) = 0$ into $G_\zeta(g) = 0$ defines a conformal mapping of the Riemann surface (z, f) onto the Riemann surface (ζ, g).

We have seen earlier that two compact Riemann surfaces are topologically equivalent if and only if they have the same genus. Any Riemann surface of genus zero is conformally equivalent to a sphere, so that in this case topological equivalence implies conformal equivalence. We now see that in order to have conformal equivalence, we must have a birational transformation defining an isomorphism of the algebraic function fields on the two surfaces. In the case $g > 0$, topological equivalence is not sufficient to guarantee conformal equivalence. In the case of the torus, $g = 1$, two real parameters determine the conformal class of a Riemann surface.

In the case $g > 1$, $6g - 6$ real parameters determine the conformal class of a surface. These parameters are called *moduli* of the surface. We shall not pursue the question of moduli any further here, but rather turn to an example of the above theory.

10–10 The hyperelliptic case. If there is on S a meromorphic function z which assumes each value once, z maps S one-to-one and conformally onto the complex number sphere, so that S must have genus zero. In this case $F_z(u)$ has degree 1 and every meromorphic function on S can be expressed as a rational function of z alone; we call the field of algebraic functions on S the *rational field*.

If S has no function which assumes each value once but does have one which assumes each value twice, then we can find a function u on S which satisfies an equation of the form

$$u^2 + R_1(z)u + R_2(z) = 0,$$

where the $R_\nu(z)$ are rational functions of z. If we replace u by the function

$$v = u + \frac{R_1(z)}{2},$$

we get another meromorphic function v on S which satisfies

$$v^2 = -R_2(z) + \frac{R_1^2(z)}{4} = \frac{(z - a_1)(z - a_2) \ldots (z - a_n)}{(z - b_1)(z - b_2) \ldots (z - b_n)}.$$

We now replace v by the function

$$w = v(z - b_1)(z - b_2) \ldots (z - b_n)$$

to get a meromorphic function w on S which satisfies

$$w^2 = (z - a_1)(z - a_2) \ldots (z - a_n)(z - b_1)(z - b_2) \ldots (z - b_n).$$

Finally, if any of the roots of the polynomial on the right are equal, say $a_1 = a_2$, we let $y = w/(z - a_1)$ and get

$$y^2 = (z - a_3)(z - a_4) \ldots (z - a_n)(z - b_1)(z - b_2) \ldots (z - b_n).$$

In this way, we may remove all pairs of equal roots until the polynomial on the right has distinct roots. Then we have found a meromorphic function f on S which satisfies the irreducible equation

$$f^2 = (z - e_1)(z - e_2) \ldots (z - e_k),$$

where the $e_1, e_2, \ldots, e_k$ are distinct.

The k points $e_1, e_2, \ldots, e_k$ are branch points of the Riemann surface (z, f) covering the z-sphere, and if k is odd, $z = \infty$ is also a branch point. We may compute k in terms of the genus of S using the formula $V = 2(n + g - 1)$ [see (2) of Section 10–6]; when $n = 2$, $g = (k - 2)/2$ if k is even and $g = (k - 1)/2$ if k is odd. If $k = 1$ or 2, $g = 0$ and we again get the rational field. If $k = 2$ or 3, $g = 1$ and the algebraic function field is called an *elliptic function field*. Finally, if $k > 4$, we get the *hyperelliptic function field*.

We may always select the functions z and f in such a way that the polynomial on the right has odd degree $k = 2m + 1$. For if k is even, $k = 2m + 2$, we need only take e_k to ∞ by an inversion $\zeta = 1/(z - e_k)$ and replace f by

$$h = \frac{\zeta^{m+1} f}{\sqrt{\prod_{j=1}^{k-1} (e_j - e_k)}}.$$

Then h will satisfy an equation

$$h^2 = (\zeta - c_1)(\zeta - c_2) \ldots (\zeta - c_{k-1}),$$

where $k - 1 = 2m + 1$ is odd, and the $c_1, c_2, \ldots, c_{k-1}$ are distinct roots. We therefore consider the case when z and f satisfy

$$f^2 = (z - e_1)(z - e_2) \ldots (z - e_{2m+1}).$$

Now $g = m$ and there are m linearly independent differentials of the first kind on S which are given by

$$\frac{dz}{f}, \quad \frac{z\,dz}{f}, \quad \frac{z^2\,dz}{f}, \quad \ldots, \quad \frac{z^{m-1}\,dz}{f}. \tag{1}$$

To verify that these are everywhere regular differentials on S, we observe first that at any point P on S, other than the poles or multiple points of z, we can select $\zeta = z - z_0$, $z_0 = z(P)$, as the local parameter, and $z^\lambda dz/f$, $\lambda = 0, 1, 2, \ldots, m - 1$, is regular about $\zeta = 0$. At a point P where $z(P) = e_j$, we can take $\zeta = \sqrt{z - e_j}$ as the local uniformizing parameter; then $\zeta^2 = z - e_j$ or $2\zeta\,d\zeta = dz$. In the neighborhood of $\zeta = 0$,

$$\frac{z^\lambda\,dz}{f} = \frac{2(\zeta^2 + e_j)^\lambda\,d\zeta}{\sqrt{\prod_{\nu=1, \nu \neq j}^{2m+1} [\zeta^2 - (e_\nu - e_j)]}},$$

which is regular at $\zeta = 0$. Finally, if $z(P) = \infty$, $\zeta = 1/\sqrt{z}$ is a local uniformizing parameter and $z = 1/\zeta^2$ or $dz = -2/\zeta^3 \, d\zeta$. Then

$$f^2 = \left(\frac{1}{\zeta^2} - e_1\right)\left(\frac{1}{\zeta^2} - e_2\right) \cdots \left(\frac{1}{\zeta^2} - e_{2m+1}\right)$$

$$= \frac{1}{\zeta^{2(2m+1)}} (1 - e_1\zeta^2)(1 - e_2\zeta^2) \cdots (1 - e_{2m+1}\zeta^2)$$

and

$$\frac{z^\lambda \, dz}{f} = \frac{-2\zeta^{2m+1} \, d\zeta}{\zeta^{2\lambda+3}\sqrt{\prod_{\nu=1}^{2m+1} (1 - e_\nu\zeta^2)}}.$$

Since $\lambda \leq m - 1$, we see that $2\lambda + 3 \leq 2m + 1$, so that $z^\lambda dz/f$ is regular about $\zeta = 0$. This proves our assertion.

If $g = 1$, the Riemann-Roch theorem tells us that for any point P on the surface, $r[P^{-1}] = 1$ and $r[P^{-2}] = 2$, so that we can always find a function z on S which has a pole of order 2 at P and no other singularity on S. Thus every surface of genus 1 has an elliptic function field. If $g = 2$, each differential φ of the first kind has $2g - 2 = 2$ zeros. Let P_1 and P_2 be the zeros of φ. Then $i[P_1 P_2] = 1$ and $r[1/P_1 P_2] = 2$. Since $r[1/P_1] = 1$ and $r[1/P_2] = 1$, there is a function z on S which has simple poles at P_1 and P_2 and is otherwise regular. Thus every surface of genus 2 has a hyperelliptic function field.

This is as far as we can go making such general statements, for there are surfaces of genus 3 which are not hyperelliptic. An example of an algebraic function field of genus 3 which is not hyperelliptic is the field in which z and f satisfy the equation

$$f^4 = z^4 - 1.$$

To see that the field is of genus 3, we note that the Riemann surface (z, f) over the z-sphere covers each point four times, so $n = 4$. Furthermore, $V = 12$, since there is a branch point of order 3 at the four points $1, i, -1, -i$. Then from $V = 2(n + g - 1)$, we get $g = 3$.

The differentials of the first kind for this surface are dz/f^3, $z\,dz/f^3$, and $f\,dz/f^3$. To verify this, we need only investigate the branch points $z = 1$, $-1, i, -i$ and the point $z = \infty$. At $z = 1$, we may take as uniformizing parameter $\zeta = \sqrt[4]{z - 1}$, so that $\zeta^4 = z - 1$ or $4\zeta^3 \, d\zeta = dz$. Then

$$f^4 = \zeta^4(\zeta^4 + 2)(\zeta^4 + 1 + i)(\zeta^4 + 1 - i),$$

and

$$\frac{dz}{f^3} = \frac{4\, d\zeta}{[(\zeta^4 + 2)(\zeta^4 + 1 + i)(\zeta^4 + 1 - i)]^{3/4}},$$

$$\frac{z\, dz}{f^3} = \frac{4(\zeta^4 + 1)\, d\zeta}{[(\zeta^4 + 2)(\zeta^4 + 1 + i)(\zeta^4 + 1 - i)]^{3/4}},$$

$$\frac{f\, dz}{f^3} = \frac{4\zeta\, d\zeta}{[(\zeta^4 + 2)(\zeta^4 + 1 + i)(\zeta^4 + 1 - i)]^{1/2}},$$

which are all regular about $\zeta = 0$. The same argument holds at $z = -1$, i, $-i$, leaving only $z = \infty$ to be investigated. At $z = \infty$, we take $\zeta = 1/z$ as local parameter, so that $dz = (-1/\zeta^2)\, d\zeta$ and $f^4 = \zeta^{-4}(1 - \zeta^4)$. We have

$$\frac{dz}{f^3} = \frac{-\zeta\, d\zeta}{(1 - \zeta^4)^{3/4}},$$

$$\frac{z\, dz}{f^3} = \frac{-d\zeta}{(1 - \zeta^4)^{3/4}},$$

$$\frac{f\, dz}{f^3} = \frac{-d\zeta}{(1 - \zeta^4)^{1/2}},$$

which are all regular at $\zeta = 0$. These three differentials are linearly independent, since no linear relation exists between 1, z, and f, so that

$$\frac{dz}{f^3}, \quad \frac{z\, dz}{f^3}, \quad \frac{f\, dz}{f^3}$$

form a basis for the differentials of the first kind. We now observe that the ratio of the first and third is just f and the ratio of the first and second is just z, so that the ratios of the differentials of the first kind generate the *whole* field of algebraic functions.

In the case of the hyperelliptic field, a basis for differentials of the first kind is given by $z^\lambda dz/f$, $\lambda = 0, 1, \ldots, g - 1$, and the ratios of the differentials of the first kind generate a *proper subfield* of the field of algebraic functions; namely, the powers of z. This difference between the field $f^4 = z^4 - 1$ and the hyperelliptic field proves that $f^4 = z^4 - 1$ is not hyperelliptic.

Let S be an arbitrary compact Riemann surface on which z and f are a pair of meromorphic functions satisfying the irreducible equation $F_z(f) = 0$. Let ω be an arbitrary abelian differential on S. Then ω/dz is a meromorphic function on S and hence

$$\frac{\omega}{dz} = R(z, f),$$

where R is a rational function of its arguments. We then have that the most general abelian differential on S is $R(z, f)\, dz$. We call the integral

$$\int_{z_0}^{z} R(z, f)\, dz$$

an *abelian integral*. According to (1) of Section 10–2,

$$R(z, f)\, dz = \omega_2 + \sum_{j=1}^{n} c_j \omega_{j,0} + \sum_{k=1}^{g} A_k \varphi_k,$$

where ω_2 is a normalized differential of the second kind, c_j is the residue of $R\, dz$ at P_j, $\omega_{j,0}$ is a normal differential of the third kind, and the φ_k form a basis for the differentials of the first kind. Therefore

$$\int_{z_0}^{z} R(z, f)\, dz = \int_{z_0}^{z} \omega_2 + \sum_{j=1}^{n} c_j \int_{z_0}^{z} \omega_{j,0} + \sum_{k=1}^{g} A_k \int_{z_0}^{z} \varphi_k.$$

We call

$$\int_{z_0}^{z} \omega_2, \qquad \int_{z_0}^{z} \omega_{j,0}, \qquad \text{and} \qquad \int_{z_0}^{z} \varphi_k$$

normalized abelian integrals of the second, third, and first kind, respectively.

When $F_z(f) = 0$ has a hyperelliptic field, then $\int_{z_0}^{z} R(z, f)\, dz$ is called a *hyperelliptic integral* and if $F_z(f) = 0$ is elliptic, then $\int_{z_0}^{z} R(z, f)\, dz$ is called an *elliptic integral*. We shall now look at the normalized hyperelliptic and elliptic integrals of the first, second, and third kinds.

We first construct a differential of the second kind in the hyperelliptic case

$$f^2 = (z - e_1)(z - e_2) \ldots (z - e_{2g+1}), \quad g \geq 1,$$

which will have a pole of order 2 at a specified point P_0 and will otherwise be regular. If $z(P_0) = a$ is finite and $a \neq e_\nu$, $\nu = 1, 2, \ldots, 2g + 1$, we may use $z - a$ as a local parameter and expand f as

$$f(z) = b_0 + b_1(z - a) + b_2(z - a)^2 + \cdots, \quad b_0 \neq 0.$$

Then

$$\frac{f + b_0 + b_1(z - a)}{(z - a)^2 f}\, dz = \frac{f(z) - f(a) + f'(a)(z - a)}{(z - a)^2 f(z)}\, dz$$

is a differential of the second kind whose only pole is a pole of order 2 at P_0 with zero residue. If $z(P_0) = e_\nu$, then $\zeta = \sqrt{z - e_\nu}$ is a local parameter and

$$\frac{dz}{(z - e_\nu)f}$$

has a pole of order 2 at P_0 with zero residue and is otherwise regular. Finally, if $z(P_0) = \infty$, then $\zeta = 1/\sqrt{z}$ is a local parameter and

$$\frac{z^g \, dz}{f}$$

has a pole of order 2 with zero residue at P_0.

We next construct a differential of the third kind which has residue -1 at P_0 and residue $+1$ at P_1 with simple poles only at these two points. We shall select P_0 to be the point at which $z(P_0) = \infty$ and then let P_1 be any point other than a multiple point of z; then $z(P_1) = a$, $a \neq e_\nu$, $\nu = 1, 2, \ldots, 2g + 1$. In the neighborhood of P_1, $z - a$ serves as a local parameter and f can be expanded as

$$f(z) = b_0 + b_1(z - a) + b_2(z - a)^2 + \cdots .$$

Then

$$\frac{1}{2} \frac{f + b_0}{z - a} \frac{dz}{f} = \frac{1}{2} \frac{f(z) + f(a)}{z - a} \frac{dz}{f(z)}$$

is the desired differential of the third kind. If $z(P_1) = e_\nu$, this expression becomes simply

$$\frac{dz}{z - e_\nu} .$$

In the elliptic case, $g = 1$, let us represent each point on S by (z, f), where $f^2 = (z - e_1)(z - e_2)(z - e_3)$ for three distinct points e_1, e_2, e_3 of the z-plane. Let P_0 be the point where $z(P_0) = \infty$ so $P_0 = (\infty, \infty)$. Suppose that the abelian differential $R(z, f) \, dz$ has poles at the points $P_1 = (a_1, b_1), \ldots, P_n = (a_n, b_n)$ of orders $\alpha_1, \alpha_2, \ldots, \alpha_n$ with residues $c_1, c_2, \ldots, c_n$ (some of which may be zero). The differential

$$\omega = R(z, f) \, dz - \sum_{\nu=1}^{n}{}' c_\nu \frac{f - b_\nu}{z - a_\nu} \frac{dz}{f}$$

(where the prime on Σ indicates that if $a_k = \infty$, $\nu = k$ is omitted from the summation) has zero residues at all points of S. The Riemann-Roch theorem and the fact that any differential of the first kind does not vanish at any point when $g = 1$ tell us that we can construct a function g_ν for each ν with $\alpha_\nu > 1$ which has a simple pole at $P_0 = (\infty, \infty)$ and a pole of order $\alpha_\nu - 1$ at P_ν such that dg_ν has the same principal part as ω at P_ν. If $P_\nu = P_0$ for some ν and $\alpha_\nu > 2$, we can construct a function g_ν with a pole of order $\alpha_\nu - 1$ at P_0 such that dg_ν has the same terms of orders $3, 4, \ldots, \alpha_\nu$ in its principal part as does ω at P_0. Then $g = \sum_{\nu=1}^{n}{}' \, g_\nu$ (where the prime indicates the omission of those ν for which $\alpha_\nu = 1$) is a meromorphic function such that dg has the same singularities on S as ω except for a pole of order 2 at P_0. Furthermore, $\Sigma' \, g_\nu = R_1(z, f)$, where R_1 is a rational function of its arguments. Finally, to cancel off the singularity left at P_0 in $\omega - dg$, we observe that for some constant A, $Az \, dz/f$ has the right behavior. Therefore

$$\omega - dg - \frac{Az \, dz}{f}$$

is a differential of the first kind and is simply a complex constant B times the single basis differential dz/f. This gives us

$$\int_{z_0}^{z} R(z, f) \, dz = R_1(z, f) + B \int_{z_0}^{z} \frac{dz}{f} + A \int_{z_0}^{z} \frac{z \, dz}{f}$$

$$+ \sum_{\nu=1}^{n}{}' \int_{z_0}^{z} c_\nu \frac{f - b_\nu}{z - a_\nu} \frac{dz}{f}$$

as the representation of the most general elliptic integral.

We have now accomplished the connection between the compact Riemann surfaces and the algebraic functions and their integrals. The treatment here has been designed to serve as a springboard from which the reader can begin his study of the many aspects of the theory of Riemann surfaces not touched upon here. There still remain such questions as the moduli for compact Riemann surfaces. For the noncompact (or open) Riemann surfaces, there is the question of the classification of surfaces and the characterization of the functions on the surface. Moreover, the generalization of the notion of Riemann surface to an n-dimensional analytic manifold or an algebraic variety in n variables has produced a very fruitful field. The notions of Riemann surfaces have been applied to problems in applied mathematics in connection with the solutions of elliptic partial differential equations.[†] Thus the reader can turn in many directions to continue his study of Riemann surfaces.

[†] See, for example, Bergman, Ref. 8.

Problems

1. Show that on the hyperelliptic Riemann surface

$$w^2 = (z - e_1)(z - e_2) \ldots (z - e_{2g+1})$$

the function $F = 1/(z - e_i)$ has a double pole at $z = e_i$, $w = 0$, and is otherwise regular. Prove that the points $z = e_i$, $w = 0$, for $i = 1, 2, \ldots, 2g+1$ are Weierstrass points of the surface.

2. If ω is any abelian differential and $\mathfrak{a}$ any divisor, prove that

$$2\left(i[\mathfrak{a}] - i\left[\frac{(w)}{\mathfrak{a}} \right] \right) = d\left[\frac{(w)}{\mathfrak{a}} \right] - d[\mathfrak{a}].$$

(Brill-Nöther reciprocity theorem.)

3. Prove that the number of fixed points of a conformal self-transformation f (not the identity mapping) of a compact Riemann surface S of genus g is at most $2g + 2$. [Consider the function h that has a pole of order $n \leq g + 1$ at a single point P_0, not a fixed point of f. Then study the number of zeros and poles of $h(P) - h(f(P))$.]

4. Prove that any one-to-one conformal self-mapping of a compact Riemann surface takes Weierstrass points into Weierstrass points. With the fact that there is a finite positive number of Weierstrass points, conclude that any compact Riemann surface of genus $g \geq 2$ has only a finite number of one-to-one conformal self-mappings.

5. When the $V = 2(n + g - 1)$ ramification points are arbitrarily prescribed on the w-sphere, show that there is a finite, positive number of distinct n-sheeted compact Riemann surfaces having their branch points of the prescribed orders over the prescribed points.

6. Show that the Riemann-Roch theorem implies that if $n > 2g - 2$ on a compact Riemann surface S of genus g, there exists a $2n + 1 - g$ complex parameter family of conformal mappings of S on n-sheeted coverings of the sphere. (Note that the positions of the n poles are arbitrary too!)

7. Using the fact that the surface S has a ρ real parameter group of self-transformations (problem 3, Chapter 9), show that a $2n + 1 - g - (\rho/2)$ complex parameter family of n-sheeted covering surfaces of genus g are conformally equivalent.

8. From problems 5 and 7 conclude that there is a $3g - 3 + (\rho/2)$ complex parameter family of conformally distinct Riemann surfaces of genus g. These parameters are called the *moduli* of the compact surface.

REFERENCES

1. AHLFORS, L. V., *Complex Analysis*. New York: McGraw-Hill, 1953.
2. ——, "Zur Uniformisierung," *Neuvième Congress des Mathematiciens Scandinaves, Helsingfors*, 1938, pp. 235–248.
3. ALEXANDROFF, P., and HOPF, H., *Topologie*. Berlin: Springer-Verlag, 1935. (Ann Arbor: Edwards Brothers, 1945.)
4. APPEL, P., and GOURSAT, E., *Théorie des Fonctions Algebraiques*. Paris: Gauthier-Villars, Vol. 1 (1929), Vol. 2 (1930).
5. ARONSZAJN, N., *Introduction to the Theory of Hilbert Spaces*. Stillwater, Oklahoma, Research Foundation, 1950.
6. BEHNKE, H., and SOMMER, F., *Theorie der analytischen Funktionen einer komplexen Veränderlichen*. Berlin: Springer-Verlag, 1955.
7. BEHNKE, H., and STEIN, K., "Entwicklung analytischer Funktionen auf Riemannschen Flächen," *Math. Ann.* **120**, 430–461 (1949).
8. BERGMAN, S., *The Kernel Function and Conformal Mapping*, A.M.S. Survey No. 5, N. Y., 1950.
9. ——, "On Solutions of Algebraic Character of Linear Partial Differential Equations," *Trans. A.M.S.* **68**, 461–507 (1950).
10. BIRKHOFF, G., and MACLANE, S., *A Survey of Modern Algebra*. New York: Macmillan, 1951.
11. CALABI, E., and ROSENLICHT, M., "Complex Analytic Manifolds without Countable Base," *Proc. A.M.S.* **4**, 335–340 (1953).
12. CARATHEODORY, C., *Conformal Representation*, Cambridge Tract No. 28. New York: Cambridge University Press, 1932.
13. ——, *Theory of Functions of a Complex Variable*, Vols. I and II. New York: Chelsea, 1954.
14. CARTAN, E., *Les systèmes différentiels extérieur et leurs applications géométriques*. Paris: Hermann, 1945.
15. COURANT, R., *Dirichlet Principle, Conformal Mapping, and Minimal Surfaces*. New York: Interscience, 1950.
16. ——, and HURWITZ, A., *Geometrische Funktionentheorie*. Berlin: Springer-Verlag, 1929.
17. FORD, L., *Automorphic Functions*. New York: McGraw-Hill, 1929.
18. FRICKE, R., and KLEIN, F., *Theorie der automorphen Funktionen*. Leipzig: Teubner, Vol. I (1897), Vol. II (1912).
19. HALL, D. W., and SPENCER, G. L., *Elementary Topology*. New York: Wiley, 1955.
20. HALMOS, P. R., *Introduction to Hilbert Space*. New York: Chelsea, 1951.
21. HEINS, M., "The Conformal Mapping of Simply Connected Riemann Surfaces," *Ann. Math.* **50**, 686–690 (1949).

22. ——, "Interior Mappings of an Orientable Surface onto S^2," *Proc. A.M.S.* **2** (6), 951–952 (1951).

23. HODGE, W. V. D., *Harmonic Integrals*, 2nd ed. New York: Cambridge University Press, 1952.

24. HURWITZ, A., "Algebraische Gebilde mit eindeutigen Transformationen in sich," *Math. Ann.* **41**, 1893.

25. KLEIN, F., *On Riemann's Theory of Algebraic Functions and Their Integrals.* Cambridge: Macmillan and Bowes, 1893.

26. ——, *Riemannschen Flächen*, Vols. I and II. Göttingen, 1894.

27. KNOPP, K., *Theory of Functions*, Vol. II. New York: Dover, 1947.

28. KODAIRA, K., "Harmonic Fields in Riemannian Manifolds," *Ann. Math.* **50**, 587–665 (1949).

29. KOEBE, P., "Über die Uniformisierung beliebigen analytischer Kurven," *J. fur reine u. angew. Math.*, Heft 3, Bd. 138, 192–253 (1910).

30. LEFSCHETZ, S., *Algebraic Topology*, A.M.S. Colloquium Publication No. 27, N. Y., 1942.

31. ——, *Introduction to Topology.* Princeton: Princeton University Press, 1949.

32. MUNROE, R. E., *Introduction to Measure and Integration.* Reading, Mass.: Addison-Wesley, 1953.

33. NEHARI, Z., *Conformal Mapping.* New York: McGraw-Hill, 1952.

34. NEUMANN, C., *Vorlesungen über Riemanns Theorie der Abelschen Integrale*, 2nd ed. Leipzig: Teubner, 1884.

35. NEVANLINNA, R., *Uniformisierung.* Berlin: Springer-Verlag, 1953.

36. PERRON, O., "Über die Behandlung der ersten Randwertaufgabe für $\nabla^2 u = 0$," *Math. Zeit.* **18**, 42–54 (1923).

37. POINCARE, H., *Oevres.* Paris: Gauthier-Villars, Vol. II (1916), Vol. IV (1950), Vol. IX (1954).

38. PONTRJAGEN, L. S., *Topological Groups.* Princeton: Princeton University Press, 1939.

39. RADÓ, T., "Über den Begriff der Riemannschen Flächen," Acta Szeged **2**, 101–121, 1925.

40. DERHAM, G., "Sur l'analysis situs des variétés à n dimensions," *J. Math. Pures Appl.* **9** (10), 115–200, 1931.

41. RIEMANN, B., *Gesammelte Mathematische Werke*, 2nd ed. Leipzig: Teubner, 1892.

42. SCHIFFER, M., and SPENCER, D. C., *Functionals of Finite Riemann Surfaces.* Princeton: Princeton University Press, 1954.

43. SCHWARZ, H. A., *Gesammelte Mathematische Abhandlungen.* Berlin: Springer-Verlag, Vols. I and II (1890).

44. SEIFERT, H., and THRELFALL, W., *Lehrbuch der Topologie.* Leipzig: Teubner, 1934. (New York: Chelsea, 1945.)

45. STEENROD, N., *Topology of Fibre Bundles.* Princeton: Princeton University Press, 1951.

46. STOILOW, S., *Leçons sur les principes topologique de la théorie des fonctions analytiques.* Paris: Gauthier-Villars, 1938.

47. STRUIK, D. J., *Differential Geometry.* Reading, Mass.: Addison-Wesley, 1950.

48. VAN DER WAERDEN, B. L., "Topologie und Uniformisierung der Riemannschen Flächen," *Bericht über die Verhandlungen der Kgl. Sächsischen Akademie der Wissenschaften zu Leipzig, Math.-Naturwiss. Klasse,* **93,** 147–160 (1941).

49. WALSH, J. L., *Interpolation and Approximation by Rational Functions in the Complex Domain,* A.M.S. Colloquium Publication No. 20, N. Y., 1935.

50. WEYL, H., *Die Idee der Riemannschen Flächen,* 2nd ed. Leipzig: Teubner, 1923. (New York: Chelsea, 1951.) 3rd ed. Stuttgart: Teubner, 1955.

51. ——, "Method of Orthogonal Projections in Potential Theory," *Duke Math. J.* **7,** 411–444 (1940).

52. WILDER, R. L., *Topology of Manifolds,* A.M.S. Colloquium Publication No. 32, N. Y., 1949.

INDEX

Abelian differential of the first kind, 252

Abelian differential of the second kind, 256

Abelian differential of the third kind, 256

Abelian integral, 296

Abelianized fundamental group, 130

Abel's theorem, 277

Adherent, 45

Algebraic branch point, 74

Algebraic function, 1

Analytic configuration, 71

Analytic continuation, direct, 63
along a chain of disks, 64
along a curve, 64

Analytic curve, 114

Analytic manifold of regular function elements, 68

Analytic structure, 59

Angle function, 108

Arcwise connected, 53

Automorphic functions, 228

Barycentric coordinates, 101

Barycentric mapping, 101

Barycentric subdivision, 102

Base for open sets, 49

Basis for regular potentials, 28

Beltrami equations, 20

Behnke, H., 209, 269

Bergman, S., 214, 298

Bergman kernel function, 214

Betti number, 127

Bicontinuous function, 52

Bilinear relations of Riemann for abelian differentials, of the first kind, 245
of the first and second kinds, 260
of the first and third kinds, 257

Birational transformation, 291

Birkhoff, G., 124, 290

Boundary, 45
simplicial n-, 125

Boundary operator, 125

Boundary-value problem, 214

Branch point of order $(n - 1)$, 76

Canonical basis, for abelian differentials of the first kind, 255
for harmonic differentials, 252

Carathéodory, C., 217, 231

Carrier, of a curve, 53
of a differential, 158

Cartan, E., 163

Cauchy sequence, 50

Cauchy theorem, 172

Chain, of disks, 63
simplicial n-, 124
singular 1-, 139

Chevalley, C., 160

Circulation, 13

Class C^n, 58

Closed differential, 154

Closed domain, 49

Closed set, 45

Closed surface, 97

Closure, 45

Cluster point, 46

Co-closed, 166

Coexact, 166

Coherently oriented triangles, 107

Commutator, 130

Compact carrier, 196

Compact space, 46

Complete analytic function, 65

Complete metric space, 50

Complex conjugation operator, 172

Complex potential function, in the plane, 13
on a surface, 20

Component, 49

Conformal mapping, 22

Conformally equivalent Riemann surfaces, 61

Congruence modulo periods, 281

Conjugate flow, 172

Conjugate harmonic differential, 172